Fiona Mapp

ESSENTIALS

KS3

Maths Coursebook

covers all three years

How to Use this Coursebook

How to Use this Coursebook

A Note to the Teacher

This coursebook provides full coverage of the programme for study for Key Stage 3 maths. It brings together all the relevant information in a single book to provide a flexible resource that can be used to support any model for delivering the curriculum.

The coursebook includes lots of questions and tasks. These provide opportunities for skills practice relevant to the Assessing Pupils Progress (APP) assessment criteria and focuses, as well as helping to reinforce students' learning and improve their confidence.

The content is divided into three study areas to correspond with the programme of study:
- Number and algebra
- Geometry and measures
- Statistics.

The topics within each study area are ordered and levelled to support progression. They are colour-coded by level for ease of reference:
- Levels 4–6 (green)
- Levels 5–7 (red)
- Levels 6–8 (blue).

Each topic has the following features:
- Content that students need to learn.
- Key words picked out in colour in the text and listed at the end of the section.

- A Quick Test to assess students' understanding through a combination of theory-based questions, multiple choice questions and true / false questions.
- Skills Practice questions to provide students with the opportunity to apply and practise what they have learned.

The answers to all the Quick Test and practice questions are included at the back of the coursebook.

This coursebook is supported by three workbooks for Years 7, 8 and 9, which feature levelled questions to support development and progression.

The workbooks provide further skills practice relevant to the APP assessment criteria and focuses, and help to consolidate students' learning.

To make cross-referencing between the coursebook and workbooks easy, details of the relevant workbook pages are given on the last page of practice questions in each topic of the coursebook.

Together, the coursebook and workbooks can be used to...
- help identify relative strengths and weaknesses for curricular target setting
- generate evidence of attainment as part of day-to-day assessment
- build evidence of student achievement for periodic, level-related assessment.

A Note to the Student

We're sure you will enjoy using this coursebook. Follow these helpful hints to make the most of it:
- Try to learn what all the key words mean.
- Use the tick boxes on the contents page to track your progress: put a tick in the box next to each topic when you're confident you know it.
- Try to write your answers in good English, using correct spelling and good sentence construction. Read what you have written to be sure it makes sense.

- Think carefully when drawing graphs. Always make sure you have labelled your axes, given your graph a title and plotted points accurately.
- Where questions require you to make calculations, remember to show your workings.

🖩 You might need to use a calculator to answer questions that carry this symbol. All other questions should be attempted without using a calculator and you should show your workings.

Contents

Contents

Numbers

Place Value

Our number system was invented in India by mathematicians about 1400 years ago.

The value of a **digit** depends on its place in a number.

In this place value diagram, the digit 6 means...

1000 Thousands	100 Hundreds	10 Tens	1 Units	
2	7	1	⑥	6 units
Two thousand, seven hundred and sixteen				
8	3	⑥	5	6 tens
Eight thousand, three hundred and sixty-five				
3	⑥	2	2	6 hundreds
Three thousand, six hundred and twenty-two				
⑥	9	1	0	6 thousands
Six thousand, nine hundred and ten				

A place value diagram can help you to read large numbers:

10 000 Ten thousands	1000 Thousands	100 Hundreds	10 Tens	1 Units
7	5	6	3	9
Seventy-five thousand, six hundred and thirty-nine				

The largest UK National Lottery jackpot was £42 008 610, that's forty-two million, eight thousand, six hundred and ten pounds.

Ordering Large Numbers

When sorting large numbers, firstly sort them by the highest-value digits.

For example, 3-digit numbers should first be sorted by the **hundreds** digits, then the **tens** digits, and then the **units**.

Example

Put these numbers in order of size, smallest first:
719, 642, 711, 317, 306, 207, 159

Sort by the 100s digits: 159, 207, 317, 306, 642, 719, 711

Sort by the 10s digits: 159, 207, 306, 317, 642, 719, 711

Sort by the units: 159, 207, 306, 317, 642, 711, 719

Rounding to the Nearest Ten

To round a number to the nearest ten, look at the digit in the units column:
- If it is less than 5, round down
- If it is 5 or more, round up.

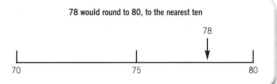

78 would round to 80, to the nearest ten

Rounding to the Nearest Hundred

Rounding a number to the nearest hundred is similar to rounding to the nearest ten, except you look at the digit in the tens column:
- If it is less than 5, round down
- If it is 5 or more, round up.

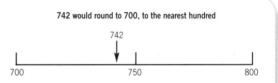

742 would round to 700, to the nearest hundred

Rounding to the Nearest Thousand

To round a number to the nearest thousand, look at the digit in the hundreds column:
- If it is less than 5, round down
- If it is 5 or more, round up.

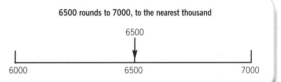

6500 rounds to 7000, to the nearest thousand

Estimating

Rounding numbers can help when estimating the answers to calculations.

Estimating can be useful when shopping so that you have a rough idea of how much your shopping bill should be.

It's also a good way of checking calculations.

When estimating...
- round the numbers to easy numbers, usually to the nearest ten, hundred or thousand
- use these easy numbers to work out the estimate
- when multiplying or dividing, never round a number to zero.

Examples
1. $9 + 21$ is approximately $10 + 20 = 30$
2. 12×402 is approximately $10 \times 400 = 4000$

Numbers

Addition

When adding numbers using a written method, it's important to line up the place values.

Example
Work out 276 + 5291

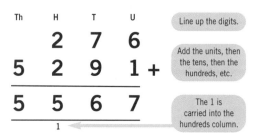

Th	H	T	U	
	2	7	6	
5	2	9	1	+
5	5	6	7	
	1			

Line up the digits.

Add the units, then the tens, then the hundreds, etc.

The 1 is carried into the hundreds column.

This addition can be checked mentally by using **partitioning** and an empty number line:

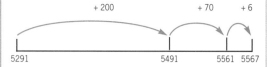

+ 200   + 70   + 6

5291   5491   5561 5567

Estimating to check gives
300 + 5300 = 5600 approximately.

Market traders often calculate the costs of goods by mental methods.

Subtraction

When subtracting numbers, place values must line up one on top of the other. Subtracting is also known as 'finding the **difference**'.

Example
Work out 642 – 129

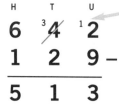

H	T	U	
6	³4̸	¹2	
1	2	9	–
5	1	3	

In the units column, 2 – 9 won't work. Borrow 10 from the next column, so the 4 becomes a 3 and the 2 becomes 12.

This subtraction can be checked by subtracting too much and then **compensating** by adding on the extra.

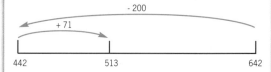

- 200

+ 71

442   513   642

Quick Test

1. Write the following number in words: 9832
2. To sort large numbers in order of size, do you look at the digit with the highest place value or the lowest place value first?
3. Amy is told to round the number 636 to the nearest ten.
   a) What is the place value of the digit that she needs to work with?
   b) Should she round the digit up or down? Explain your answer.

KEY WORDS
Make sure you understand these words before moving on!
- Digit
- Units
- Tens
- Hundreds
- Thousands
- Partitioning
- Difference
- Compensation

Skills Practice

1 What does the 6 mean in each of these numbers?
- **a)** 629
- **b)** 4276
- **c)** 3006
- **d)** 2651
- **e)** 267

2 What does the 3 mean in each of these numbers?
- **a)** 3157
- **b)** 2369
- **c)** 52 032
- **d)** 143
- **e)** 49 385

3 Write the following numbers in digits:
- **a)** Four thousand, six hundred and thirty-eight.
- **b)** Six hundred and five thousand, two hundred and nine.
- **c)** Eighty-three thousand and thirty-nine.
- **d)** Nine thousand, seven hundred and five.
- **e)** Two hundred thousand and seventy-three.

4 Put these numbers in order of size, starting with the smallest:
- **a)** 62, 7, 93, 127, 156
- **b)** 201, 1169, 37, 58, 291
- **c)** 5, 37, 18, 26, 52, 41
- **d)** 583, 1271, 162, 837, 26

5 Round the following numbers to the nearest 10:
- **a)** 65
- **b)** 71
- **c)** 279
- **d)** 1374

6 Round the following numbers to the nearest 100:
- **a)** 727
- **b)** 1493
- **c)** 6281
- **d)** 3079

7 Round the following numbers to the nearest 1000:
- **a)** 5216
- **b)** 12 931
- **c)** 18 500
- **d)** 79 657

8 Describe one method that can be used for estimating the answer to an addition.

9 Is the following subtraction set out correctly? Explain your answer.
549
23 –

10 Estimate the answers to these calculations:
- **a)** 33 + 28
- **b)** 615 + 893
- **c)** 76 – 18
- **d)** 1032 – 564

11 Charlie is in the supermarket and wants to buy the groceries on her list, but she only has £10. Estimate how much the shopping will come to. Does Charlie have enough money?

Shopping list

Jam tarts	
White loaf	69p
Pizza	75p
Caster sugar	89p
Bread roll	73p
Biscuits	44p
Mushrooms	49p
Yoghurt	31p
Yoghurt	64p
Baking potatoes	64p
Rump steak	£1.34
	£1.87

12 Work out...
- **a)** 529 + 14
- **b)** 603 + 27
- **c)** 8291 + 842
- **d)** 629 – 143
- **e)** 725 – 361
- **f)** 1752 – 169

13 The answer to an addition sum is 693. Give one example of what the question could be.

Numbers

Multiplying a 3-Digit Number By a 2-Digit Number

There are two different methods that can be used.

Method 1: Grid Method

524×63

	500	20	4
60	30000	1200	240
3	1500	60	12

$31\,440$ ⟵ 30 000 + 1200 + 240
$\underline{1\,572\,+}$ ⟵ 1500 + 60 + 12
$33\,012$

Method 2: Long Multiplication

$$524$$
$$\underline{63\,\times}$$
$$1\,57_12 \quad ⟵ \quad 524 \times 3$$
$$\underline{31_14_240} \quad ⟵ \quad 524 \times 60$$
$$33\,012$$

Either method can be used but be careful when carrying numbers.

Dividing a 3-Digit Number By a 2-Digit Number

Example

Divide 882 by 49

Method 1

$$\begin{array}{r} 18 \\ 49\overline{)882} \\ 49 \quad- \\ \overline{392} \\ 392 \quad- \\ \overline{0} \end{array}$$

Step 1: 49 goes into 88 once
Step 2: Subtract 49 from 88
Step 3: Bring down the 2
Step 4: 49 goes into 392 8 times, with no remainder

Method 2

$$\begin{array}{r} 18 \\ 49\overline{)882} \\ 490 \quad- \\ \overline{392} \\ 245 \quad- \\ \overline{147} \end{array}$$

Step 1: 490 (10 × 49) is less than 882, so 49 goes into 882 at least 10 times.
Step 2: Subtract 490 from 882
Step 3: 5 × 49 = 245, so 49 goes into 392, 5 times.
Step 4: Subtract 245 from 392 (= 147)
Step 5: 3 × 49 = 147
Step 6: add the 10, 5 and 3 together, so 49 goes into 882 18 times

Indices

An **index** is sometimes known as a **power**.

Examples

7^5 is read as '7 to the power of 5'.
This means $7 \times 7 \times 7 \times 7 \times 7$
4^9 is read as '4 to the power of 9'.
This means $4 \times 4 \times 4 \times 4 \times 4 \times 4 \times 4 \times 4 \times 4$

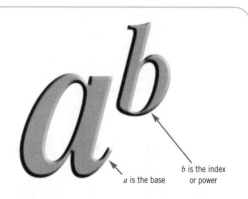

a is the base
b is the index or power

BIDMAS is a word that helps you to remember the order for calculations.

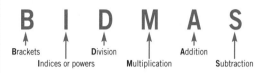

B — Brackets
I — Indices or powers
D — Division
M — Multiplication
A — Addition
S — Subtraction

The brackets are worked out first then division and multiplication are done before addition and subtraction.

Examples

Work out...

1. $7 \times (5 - 3)$
   $= 7 \times 2$
   $= 14$

2. $(27 - 5^2) \times 2$
   $= (27 - 25) \times 2$
   $= 2 \times 2$
   $= 4$

3. $(15 \times 2) \div (2 \times 3)$
   $= 30 \div 6$
   $= 5$

4. $20 \div (7 - 3)$
   $= 20 \div 4$
   $= 5$

Calculating Powers

y^x or x^y are used for calculating powers such as 5^4.

Bell Punch Co.

At the end of 1961, the Bell Punch Company brought out the 'Anita MKVII' and 'Anita MK 8' as the world's first electronic desktop calculators.

Using a Calculator

This calculator shows the important calculator keys. It's important that you know how your calculator works.

Shift or *2nd* or *Inv* allows second functions to be carried out.

– or **+/–** changes positive numbers to negative ones.

Example

$5^2 + (2 \times 72) = 169$. Key in:

5 x^y 2 + (2 × 7 2) =

Square root
Square button
Works out powers
Memory keys
Cancels only the last key you pressed

Numbers

Types of Numbers

Factors are whole numbers that divide exactly into other numbers.

Example
Factors of 20 = 1, 2, 4, 5, 10, 20

Multiples are numbers that are in the multiplication tables.

Example
Six multiples of 10 are 10, 20, 30, 40, 80 and 210

Prime numbers have only two factors, 1 and itself. The prime numbers up to 20 are 2, 3, 5, 7, 11, 13, 17 and 19.

Square numbers are whole numbers raised to the power of 2. Examples of square numbers are 1, 4, 9, 16, 25, 36, 49, 64, 81 and 100.

Cube numbers are whole numbers raised to the power of 3. Examples of cubed numbers are 1, 8, 27, 64, 125, 216 and 343.

$\sqrt{}$ is the **square root** sign. Taking the square root is the opposite of squaring. $\sqrt{25} = {}^{\pm}5$, since $(5)^2 = 25$ and $(-5)^2 = 25$.

$\sqrt[3]{}$ is the **cube root** sign. Taking the cube root is the opposite of cubing. $\sqrt[3]{64} = 4$.

ICT can be used to find an approximate square and cube root by using Excel or a similar spreadsheet package.

The **reciprocal** of a number $\frac{a}{x}$ is $\frac{x}{a}$.

The reciprocal of $\frac{5}{9}$ is $\frac{9}{5}$.

Multiplying a number by its reciprocal always gives 1. Zero has no reciprocal.

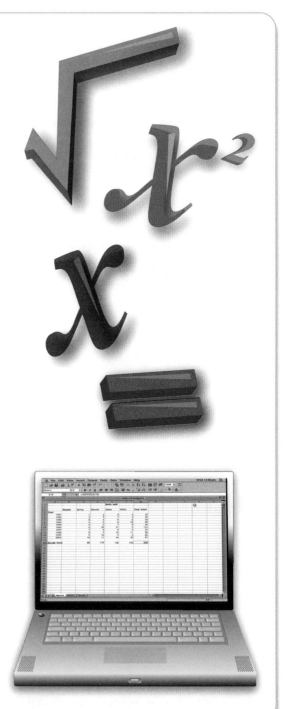

Prime Factors

Prime factors are factors that are prime numbers. Some numbers can be written as the product of their prime factors.

Example

The diagram shows prime factors of 30:
- Divide 30 by its first prime factor, 2.
- Divide 15 by its first prime factor, 3.
- Keep on until the final number is prime.

As a product of its prime factors, 30 may be written as: $2 \times 3 \times 5 = 30$

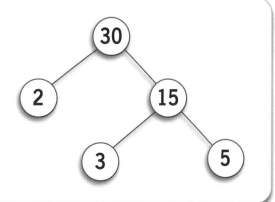

Highest Common Factor

The highest factor that two numbers have in common is called the Highest Common Factor (**HCF**).

Example

Find the HCF of 60 and 84.

Write the numbers as a product of their prime factors:

$60 = 2 \times 2 \times 3 \times 5$
$84 = 2 \times 2 \times 3 \times 7$

> The prime factors of 60 could be written as $2^2 \times 3 \times 5$ in index notation

Now ring the common factors.

These give the HCF as $2 \times 2 \times 3$
$= 12$

Lowest Common Multiple

The Lowest Common Multiple (**LCM**) is the lowest number that is a multiple of two or more numbers.

Example

Find the LCM of 12 and 20.

Write the numbers as a product of their prime factors and ring the common factors:

$12 = 2 \times 2 \times 3$
$20 = 2 \times 2 \times 5$

Line up the columns carefully. 12 and 20 have common prime factors of 2×2, these are only counted once.

The LCM of 12 and 20 is $2 \times 2 \times 3 \times 5 = 60$.

Quick Test

1. Work out the answer to 246×83.
2. Work out the answer to $390 \div 26$.
3. $5 \times 5 \times 5 \times 5$ is read as '4 to the power of 5'. True or false?
4. Work out:
   $9^2 - (4^2 + 2^3)$
5.  is the fraction button. True or false?
6. What are the prime factors of 36?
7. Work out the answer to 234×56

Numbers

Skills Practice

1. 362 pupils are going on a trip. A coach can seat 48 people. Work out how many coaches are needed and how many seats are empty in the final coach.

2. A garden centre buys 248 trees costing £68 per tree. How much did they spend?

3. Write the following in index notation:

   a) $6 \times 6 \times 6 \times 6 \times 6$

   b) $2 \times 2 \times 2 \times 2 \times 2 \times 2$

   c) $8 \times 8 \times 8 \times 8$

4. Write the following out fully:

   a) 5^9 b) 10^7 c) $2^3 \times 3^5$

5. Work out the following:

   a) $5 + (2 \times 6)$

   b) $16 - (3^2 + 1)$

   c) $5^2 \times (2 \times 3^2)$

   d) $81 - 2 \times 7$

   e) $(81 - 2) \times 7$

6 Use your calculator to work out the following:

a) $5 + (2 - 9)^2$

b) $6 + (3 \times 2)$

c) $\dfrac{15 + 9}{2 \times 6}$

7 Work out the following:

a) $\sqrt{64}$

b) $\sqrt{81}$

c) $\sqrt{169}$

d) 5^2

e) 4^3

f) $\sqrt[3]{729}$

8 Write the following as prime factors:

a) 25

b) 32

c) 18

d) 100

9 Find the HCF and the LCM of:

a) 42 and 20

b) 16 and 36

10 A gardener buys 174 bags of bulbs at 79p per bag. How much was the total cost of the bulbs?

Numbers

Rounding Numbers

Numbers are rounded frequently as this makes them easier to work with. They can be rounded to the nearest 10, 100, 1000, etc. Decimals can be rounded to a particular number of decimal places (d.p.).

17.639 = 17.64 (2 d.p.)

1.5983 = 1.598 (3 d.p.)

263.55 = 263.6 (1 d.p.)

Significant Figures

To find the 1st **significant figure** (s.f. or sig. fig.) look for the the first digit which is not zero. The 2nd, 3rd, 4th... significant figures may or may not be zero.

After rounding the last digit you must fill in the end zeros. For example, 525 = 530 to 2 s.f.

Examples

Number	to 3 s.f.	to 2 s.f.	to 1 s.f.
2.715	2.72	2.7	3
5273	5270	5300	5000
0.06883	0.0688	0.069	0.07

Estimating and Approximating

Estimating can be used to check your answers. For example, it's useful when decorating to estimate the number of tins of paint needed.

When estimating...
- round the numbers to easy numbers, 1 or 2 s.f.
- use 0.1, 0.01, etc. when multiplying or dividing, not zero
- use the symbol ≈ as this means 'approximately equal to'
- small numbers can be approximated to zero when adding or subtracting.

Examples

$$9.7 \times 4.1 \approx 10 \times 4 = 40$$

$$0.073 \times 51 \approx 0.1 \times 50 = 5$$

$$\frac{795 + 106}{2.7 \times 3.1} \approx \frac{800 + 100}{3 \times 3} = \frac{900}{9} = 100$$

$$299.9 + 0.001 \approx 300 + 0 = 300$$

Upper and Lower Bounds

When a number has been rounded to a given number of significant figures you might need to know the largest and smallest values the number may have been. These are called the **upper** and **lower bounds** of the number.

Examples

① 62 000 (2 s.f.) people watched Liverpool's football game this weekend. What are the lower and upper bounds of the numbers of supporters?

People or items can only take a whole number value. You can't have a fraction of a person.

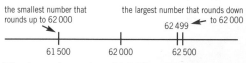

the smallest number that rounds up to 62 000

the largest number that rounds down to 62 000

62 499

61 500   62 000   62 500

The lower bound = 61 500 supporters
The upper bound = 62 499 supporters

② A piece of string is 6.3cm correct to the nearest centimetre. Write down the lower and upper bounds of the piece of string.

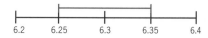

6.2   6.25   6.3   6.35   6.4

The lower bound = 6.25cm
The upper bound = 6.35cm

The piece of string can be any length up to 6.35cm.

Laws of Indices

5^7 means $5 \times 5 \times 5 \times 5 \times 5 \times 5 \times 5$.

5 is the **base** and 7 is the **power** of the **index**.

When multiplying the powers of the same numbers you add the indices.

Example
$5^4 \times 5^3 = (5 \times 5 \times 5 \times 5) \times (5 \times 5 \times 5)$
$= 5^{4+3}$
$= 5^7$

When dividing powers of the same number you subtract the indices.

Example
$5^6 \div 5^4 = \dfrac{\cancel{5} \times \cancel{5} \times \cancel{5} \times \cancel{5} \times 5 \times 5}{\cancel{5} \times \cancel{5} \times \cancel{5} \times \cancel{5}}$

$= 5^{6-4}$

$= 5^2$

> You need to know how to use the power key on your calculator.

Any number (other than zero) raised to the power of zero equals 1.

Example
$5^0 = 1$
$6^0 = 1$
$100^0 = 1$

Prime Factors

Some numbers can be written as the **product** of their **prime factors**.

Example
The prime factors of 36 can be shown on a prime factor tree.

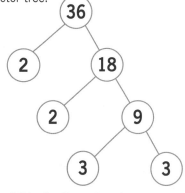

36

2   18

2   9

3   3

- Divide 36 by its first prime factor, 2.
- Divide 18 by its first prime factor, 2.
- Keep on until the final number is prime.

As a product of its prime factors, 36 may be written as:

$36 = 2 \times 2 \times 3 \times 3$
$= 2^2 \times 3^2$

Numbers

Highest Common Factor

You need to know the highest common factor (**HCF**) when you're factorising.

Example

Find the HCF of 80 and 56.

1 Write the numbers as a product of their prime factors.

$80 = 2 \times 2 \times 2 \times 2 \times 5$
$56 = 2 \times 2 \times 2 \qquad \times 7$

2 Circle the common factors.

These give the HCF as $2 \times 2 \times 2 = 8$.

The HCF of 80 and 56 is 8.

Lowest Common Multiple

You need to know the lowest common multiple (**LCM**) when you're adding and subtracting fractions.

Example

Find the LCM of 80 and 56.

1 Write the numbers as a product of their prime factors.

$80 = 2 \times 2 \times 2 \times 2 \times 5$

$56 = 2 \times 2 \times 2 \qquad \times 7$

Line the columns up carefully. Take one number from each column.

2 The LCM of 80 and 56 is:
$2 \times 2 \times 2 \times 2 \times 5 \times 7 = 560$

Quick Test

1 Work out an estimate to $\dfrac{29.2 \times 41.6}{6.1}$

2 Round the following to 2 s.f.
   a) 2735
   b) 9.647
   c) 2.075

3 The LCM of 12 and 20 is 60. True or false?

4 $5° = 5$. True or false?

KEY WORDS

Make sure you understand these words before moving on!
- Significant figure
- Estimation
- Upper bound
- Lower bound
- Base
- Power
- Index
- Product
- Prime factor
- HCF
- LCM

Skills Practice

1 True or false?

a) 492 = 490 to 2 s.f.

b) 1057 = 106 to 3 s.f.

c) 4476 = 5000 to 1 s.f.

d) 279 = 300 to 1 s.f.

e) 1955 = 2000 to 2 s.f.

f) 476 = 48 to 2 s.f.

g) 10 071 = 10 070 to 5 s.f.

h) 605 = 610 to 2 s.f.

2 By rounding each number to 1 s.f. find an approximate answer to...

a) 921×407

b) 36×19

c) 204×1599

d) $\dfrac{8576 - 10.2}{10.1}$

3 Simplify...

a) $4^5 \times 4^2$

b) $3^6 \times 3^2$

c) $4^2 \times 4^5$

d) $6^3 \times 6^2$

e) $10^7 \div 10^3$

f) $6^9 \div 6^2$

g) $7^4 \div 7^1$

h) $8^6 \div 8^3$

4 Work out the index missing from each box.

a) $2^4 \times 2^{\square} = 2^{10}$

b) $12^{\square} \div 12^2 = 12^{20}$

c) $3^{\square} \div 3^5 = 3^3$

d) $6^{\square} \times 6^2 = 6^7$

5 Find the prime factors of...

a) 25

b) 42

c) 72

6 Find the HCF and LCF of...

a) 20 and 45

b) 16 and 28

c) 32 and 60

7 For each of these statements, write the upper and lower bound.

a) There are 620 people in a hall, to 2 s.f.

b) There are 5600 supporters at a second division football club, to 2 s.f.

c) The population of Cardiff is 157 000, to 3 s.f.

d) The height of a tree is 2.7 metres, to 1 d.p.

e) There are 3550 ants in an ant colony, to 3 s.f.

Multiplication and Division

Multiplication Tables

You need to know the multiplication tables up to 10×10.

For example, you can see from the table that:

$7 \times 4 = 28$
$4 \times 7 = 28$
$28 \div 7 = 4$
$28 \div 4 = 7$

×	1	2	3	4	5	6	7	8	9	10
1	1	2	3	4	5	6	7	8	9	10
2	2	4	6	8	10	12	14	16	18	20
3	3	6	9	12	15	18	21	24	27	30
4	4	8	12	16	20	24	28	32	36	40
5	5	10	15	20	25	30	35	40	45	50
6	6	12	18	24	30	36	42	48	54	60
7	7	14	21	28	35	42	49	56	63	70
8	8	16	24	32	40	48	56	64	72	80
9	9	18	27	36	45	54	63	72	81	90
10	10	20	30	40	50	60	70	80	90	100

Multiplying and Dividing by 10, 100 and 1000

When multiplying a number by 10, you move each digit one place to the left and put a zero on the end.

e.g. $72 \times 10 = 720$

Th	H	T	U
		7	2
	7	2	0

When multiplying a number by 100, you move each digit two places to the left and put two zeros on the end.

e.g. $63 \times 100 = 6300$

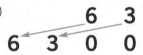

When multiplying a number by 1000, you move each digit three places to the left and put three zeros on the end.

e.g. $9 \times 1000 = 9000$

When dividing a number by 10, you move each digit one place to the right. If the original number ends in zero, it's lost from the end.

e.g. $750 \div 10 = 75$

Multiplying and Dividing by 10, 100 and 1000 (cont.)

A similar process applies when dividing a number by 100 or 1000.

Examples

① $6300 \div 100 = 63$

② $2700 \div 1000 = 2.7$

Multiplication

Multiplying two or more numbers together is called finding the **product**.

Multiplication is usually used to solve problems.

Example

A school shop orders 9 boxes of rulers.
Each box contains 25 rulers.
How many rulers did the school shop order?

$$
\begin{array}{r}
25 \\
9 \times \\
\hline
225 \\
\hline
{}_{4}
\end{array}
$$

$9 \times 25 = 225$ rulers

Multiplying a 3-Digit Number by a 2-Digit Number

There are two different methods that you can use to multiply large numbers together:

- the grid method
- long multiplication.

Example

Sarah works in a stationary store.
She earns £272 per week.
How much does Sarah earn in a 52-week year?

Method 1 – the grid method:

×	200	70	2
50	10 000	3500	100
2	400	140	4

$$
\begin{array}{r}
13\,600 \\
544 + \\
\hline
14\,144 \\
\hline
{}_{1}
\end{array}
$$

10 000 + 3500 + 100

400 + 140 + 4

Method 2 – long multiplication:

$$
\begin{array}{r}
272 \\
52 \times \\
\hline
544 \\
13\,600 + \\
\hline
14\,144 \\
\hline
{}_{1}
\end{array}
$$

272×2

272×50

Sarah earns £14 144 per year

Division

Dividing quite often produces a remainder and you will need to decide what is a sensible answer.

$$
\begin{array}{r}
7 \\
6\overline{)46}
\end{array}
$$
remainder 4

Example

A baker is packing cakes in a box.
Each box can hold 6 cakes.
How many full boxes will the baker pack if he has 46 cakes?
How many cakes will be left over?

The baker will pack 7 full boxes and have 4 cakes left over.

Multiplication and Division

Dividing a 3-Digit Number by a 2-Digit Number

Example

A bar of chocolate costs 63p. Jonathan has £9.57 to spend. What is the maximum number of chocolate bars that Jonathan can buy? How much change will he have left?

Method 2:

```
    15
63)957
   630 –
   327
   315 –
    12
```

Step 1: 630 (10 × 63) is less than 957, so 63 goes into 957 at least ten times

Step 2: Subtract 630 from 957 (= 327)

Step 3: 5 × 63 = 315, so 63 goes into 327 five times

Step 4: Subtract 315 from 327 (= 12)

Step 5: Add the 10 and 5 together, so 63 goes into 957 15 times, with a remainder of 12.

Method 1:

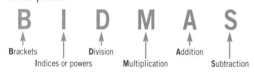

```
    15
63)957
   63 –
  327
  315 –
   12
```

Step 1: 63 goes into 95 once, write down 1

Step 2: Subtract 63 from 95 (= 32)

Step 3: Bring down the 7 (= 327)

Step 4: 63 goes into 327 five times, write down 5

Step 5: 63 x 5 = 315

Step 6: 327 – 315 = 12. This is the remainder.

Jonathan can buy 15 chocolate bars and has 12p left over.

BIDMAS

BIDMAS is a made-up word that helps you to remember the order in which calculations take place.

B Brackets
I Indices or powers
D Division
M Multiplication
A Addition
S Subtraction

This means that brackets are worked out first, then division and multiplication are done before addition and subtraction.

Examples

Work out...

❶ $(5 + 3) \times 6$ ← Carry out the addition first.

= 8×6

= 48

❷ $5 + 3 \times 6$ ← Carry out the multiplication first.

= $5 + 18$

= 23

Multiples

Multiples are numbers that are in the multiplication tables.

Example

What are the multiples of 4?

Multiples of 4 are 4, 8, 12, 16, 20, ...

Factors

If one number can be divided exactly by another number, the second number is a **factor** of the first.

Example

What are the factors of 18?

The factors of 18 are: 1×18

2×9

3×6

i.e. 1, 2, 3, 6, 9, 18

Prime Numbers

A **prime number** has only two factors, 1 and itself.

The prime numbers up to 20 are 2, 3, 5, 7, 11, 13, 17 and 19.

Note that...
- 1 isn't a prime number
- 2 is the only even prime number.

Eratosthenes and Euclid

Eratosthenes was a Greek mathematician (276BC–194BC).

He's famous for devising a method for finding primes called the 'Sieve of Eratosthenes'.

Euclid, another Greek mathematician (c.330BC–260BC), proved that there are infinitely many prime numbers.

Square Numbers

Square numbers are whole numbers raised to the power 2.

For example...
$4^2 = 4 \times 4 = 16$ ('four squared')

The first 12 square numbers are:

1	**4**	**9**	**16**	**25**	**36**
(1 × 1)	(2 × 2)	(3 × 3)	(4 × 4)	(5 × 5)	(6 × 6)

49	**64**	**81**	**100**	**121**	**144**
(7 × 7)	(8 × 8)	(9 × 9)	(10 × 10)	(11 × 11)	(12 × 12)

Square numbers can be illustrated by drawing squares:

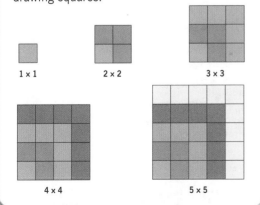

1 x 1   2 x 2   3 x 3

4 x 4   5 x 5

Cube Numbers

Cube numbers are whole numbers raised to the power 3.

For example...
$4^3 = 4 \times 4 \times 4 = 64$ ('four cubed')

This could be illustrated by drawing a cube:

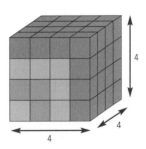

Some other cube numbers include:

1	**8**	**27**	**64**	**125**
(1 × 1 × 1)	(2 × 2 × 2)	(3 × 3 × 3)	(4 × 4 × 4)	(5 × 5 × 5)

Multiplication and Division

Triangular Numbers

The sequence of triangular numbers is
1, 3, 6, 10, 15, ...

With each step in the sequence, the
difference goes up by 1.

Triangular numbers can be illustrated
by drawing triangles.

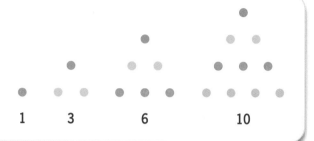

1   3   6   10

Square Roots

$\sqrt{}$ is the square root sign.

Taking the square root is the opposite
of squaring.

For example, $\sqrt{36} = 6$ or -6

since $6^2 = 36$ and $(-6)^2 = 36$

Cube Roots

$\sqrt[3]{}$ is the cube root sign.

Taking the cube root is the opposite
of cubing.

For example, $\sqrt[3]{27} = 3$

since $3^3 = 3 \times 3 \times 3 = 27$

Quick Test

1. Describe how you would multiply a
   number by 100.
2. Describe how you would divide a
   number by 1000.
3. What does the word 'product' mean?
4. Is the following multiplication true or false?
   $675 \times 23 = 15\,525$
5. The 'I' in BIDMAS stands for 'Indices'
   or 'Powers'? True or false?
6. How many factors does 24 have?
   A 10   **B** 6   **C** 8   **D** 4
7. What is a cube number?
8. The square root of 49 is 7 or -7.
   True or false?

KEY WORDS
Make sure you understand
these words before moving on!
- Product
- BIDMAS
- Multiple
- Factor
- Prime number
- Square number
- Cube number
- Triangular number
- Square root
- Cube root

1 Work out the answers to the following:

a) 63×10 **c)** $270 \div 10$ **e)** 16×100

b) 27×1000 **d)** $5900 \div 100$

2 A gymnast practises for 3 hours every day.
For how many hours does she practise in a year?

3 A fruit grower has 110 apples to put into packets. Each packet holds 4 apples.

a) How many packets can the fruit grower fill?

b) How many apples are left over?

4 From the cloud of numbers, write down the...

a) factors of 20   **c)** cube numbers   **e)** prime numbers.

b) square numbers   **d)** multiples of 6

27   24   6   81   4
17   12   5   49   3
25   1   13   20

5 Work out...

a) $7 + 2 \times 4$ **c)** $\sqrt[3]{125}$ **e)** 4^3

b) $12 - (3 + 4)$ **d)** 6^2 **f)** $\sqrt{144}$

6 In a conference hall, there are 43 chairs per row.
How many chairs in total are needed for 289 rows?

7 A train carriage can hold 126 people.
If a train has 13 carriages, how many people can it hold?

8 Paperclips come in boxes of 54.
An office needs 900 paperclips.
How many boxes should be bought?

9 Cans of cola cost 64p each.
Mark needs to buy as many cans as possible.
He has £17.

a) How many cans of cola can Mark buy?

b) How much change will he get back?

Activity

The Sieve of Eratosthenes

- On a 100 square, cross out the number 1, since it isn't a prime number.
- Circle 2 and then cross out all other multiples of 2. The next number not crossed out is 3.
- Circle 3 and then cross out all other multiples of 3. The next number not crossed out is 5.
- Circle 5 and then cross out all other multiples of 5. The next number not crossed out is 7.
- Continue the process until no more numbers can be circled.

The circled numbers are all the prime numbers less than 100.

Fractions

Fractions

A **fraction** is a whole unit divided into equal parts.

For example, $\frac{7}{9}$ means 7 parts out of 9:

Fractions are used every day. An example is shown below:

The top number is the **numerator**.

The bottom number is the **denominator**.

$$\frac{1}{2}$$

If the numerator is smaller than the denominator, it's called a **proper fraction**, for example, $\frac{7}{11}$.

If the numerator is bigger than the denominator, it's called an **improper fraction**, for example, $\frac{12}{7}$.

A fraction that has a whole number and a fraction is called a **mixed number**, for example, $3\frac{1}{2}$.

Equivalent Fractions

Equivalent fractions are fractions that have the same value.

Fractions can be changed into their equivalent by either multiplying or dividing the numerator and denominator by the same number.

From the diagram, it can be seen that $\frac{2}{3} = \frac{4}{6}$.

Examples
Complete the equivalent fractions:

① $\frac{3}{11} = \frac{?}{44}$

$$\frac{3}{11} = \frac{12}{44}$$

> Multiply the numerator and denominator by 4.

② $\frac{50}{60} = \frac{5}{?}$

÷ 10

$$\frac{50}{60} = \frac{5}{6}$$

> Divide the numerator and denominator by 10.

÷ 10

Simplifying Fractions

Fractions can be **simplified** if the numerator and denominator have a common factor. This process is called **cancelling**.

÷10

$$\frac{20}{30} = \frac{2}{3}$$

> 10 is the highest common factor of 20 and 30, so dividing the numerator and denominator by 10 gives $\frac{2}{3}$.

÷10

Adding and Subtracting Fractions

Only fractions with the same denominator can be added or subtracted.

Examples

1. Work out $\frac{2}{3} + \frac{5}{6}$

   The lowest common denominator (i.e. lowest common multiple of 3 and 6) is 6.

   Therefore, change $\frac{2}{3}$ into an equivalent fraction with a denominator of 6.

   $$\frac{2}{3} = \frac{4}{6}$$

   $\times 2$

Now, rewrite the sum:

$$\frac{2}{3} + \frac{5}{6} = \frac{4}{6} + \frac{5}{6} = \frac{4+5}{6} = \frac{9}{6}$$

$$\frac{9}{6} = 1\frac{3}{6} = 1\frac{1}{2} \quad \longleftarrow \text{Simplify the fraction.}$$

$$\begin{array}{ccccc} \square & + & \square & = & \square \\ \frac{2}{3} & + & \frac{5}{6} & = & 1 \quad \frac{1}{2} \end{array}$$

2. Work out $\frac{9}{10} - \frac{3}{5}$

$$\frac{9}{10} - \frac{3}{5} = \frac{9}{10} - \frac{6}{10} = \frac{3}{10} \quad \boxed{\text{10 is the lowest common denominator of 5 and 10.}}$$

Fractions of Quantities

To find a fraction of a quantity, you multiply the fraction with the quantity.

Examples

1. Find $\frac{3}{8}$ of £24

   Rewrite the question as $\frac{3}{8} \times 24$

   $24 \div 8 = 3$
   $3 \times 3 = 9$ $\boxed{\text{Divide 24 by 8; multiply by 3.}}$

   So, $\frac{3}{8}$ of £24 is £9

2. In a town of 12 000 households, $\frac{5}{6}$ recycle their rubbish.
   Work out the number of households that recycle.

   $\frac{5}{6}$ of 12 000 is:

   $\frac{5}{6} \times 12\,000 = 10\,000$ households

Quick Test

1. The top number in a fraction is called the denominator. True or false?
2. What is $\frac{21}{6}$ written as a mixed number?
   A $3\frac{1}{3}$ **B** $6\frac{2}{3}$ **C** $2\frac{1}{2}$ **D** $3\frac{1}{2}$
3. How would you work out $\frac{1}{4}$ of £16?
4. What is $\frac{3}{5} + \frac{4}{10}$?
   A $\frac{7}{15}$ **B** $\frac{7}{10}$ **C** 1   **D** $\frac{4}{10}$
5. The answer to $\frac{3}{5}$ of £20 is £12. True or false?

KEY WORDS

Make sure you understand these words before moving on!

- Fraction
- Numerator
- Denominator
- Proper fraction
- Improper fraction
- Mixed number
- Equivalent fraction
- Simplify
- Cancel
- Highest common factor

Fractions

Skills Practice

1. For each shape, write down...
   i) the fraction that's shaded
   ii) the fraction that's not shaded.

   a)    b) 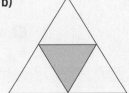   c)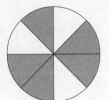

2. Copy this shape and shade in $\frac{5}{6}$.

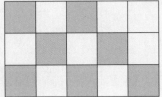

3. Copy and complete these fractions:
   a) $\frac{2}{3} = \frac{?}{12}$ b) $\frac{25}{30} = \frac{5}{?}$ c) $\frac{9}{12} = \frac{27}{?}$ d) $\frac{20}{36} = \frac{10}{?}$

4. The following cards show some fractions.

   | $\frac{2}{3}$ | $\frac{4}{5}$ | $\frac{5}{9}$ | $\frac{12}{15}$ | $\frac{10}{15}$ |

   | $\frac{9}{10}$ | $\frac{21}{27}$ | $\frac{11}{32}$ | $\frac{25}{45}$ | $\frac{20}{40}$ | $\frac{7}{9}$ |

   Write down the fractions that are equivalent.

5. Work out...
   a) $\frac{2}{3} + \frac{1}{3}$ c) $\frac{2}{5} - \frac{3}{10}$ e) $\frac{12}{17} - \frac{3}{34}$

   b) $\frac{7}{9} - \frac{2}{9}$ d) $\frac{3}{8} + \frac{1}{16}$ f) $\frac{3}{10} + \frac{1}{2}$

6 Richard is designing his garden.
$\frac{2}{3}$ of the garden is grass and $\frac{1}{6}$ of the garden is a vegetable plot.
The rest of the garden is a flower bed.
What fraction of the garden is the flower bed?

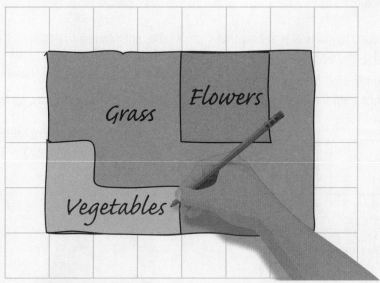

7 An architect is designing a play area.
$\frac{1}{5}$ of the area will be a children's playground.
$\frac{3}{10}$ of the area will be a swimming pool.
How much of the area has the architect used and how much is left?

8 Find...
a) $\frac{2}{3}$ of 30ml
b) $\frac{5}{7}$ of 49kg
c) $\frac{3}{8}$ of £40

9 Find...
a) $\frac{7}{12}$ of 1200kg
b) $\frac{8}{9}$ of £81
c) $\frac{7}{10}$ of £640

10 Rupinder gets £10 pocket money per week.
She spends $\frac{3}{5}$ of her pocket money on magazines.
How much does Rupinder spend on magazines each week?

11 John's mobile phone package includes 500 minutes
and 350 text messages per month.
In February, he used $\frac{4}{5}$ of his inclusive minutes
and $\frac{3}{7}$ of his text message allowance.
a) How many of his inclusive minutes did John
not use in February?
b) How many text messages did John send?

12 Jessica wrote down the following sum:

$\frac{2}{3} + \frac{4}{6} = \frac{6}{8}$

Show whether or not Jessica is correct.

Decimals

Decimals

Decimals are used for parts of numbers that are less than 1.

A **decimal point** is used to separate whole number columns from fractional columns. For example...

Thousands	Hundreds	Tens	Units	Decimal Point	Tenths	Hundredths	Thousandths
9	5	4	3	•	8	7	2

- The column headings tell us the place value of each figure.
- The 7 has a value of $\frac{7}{100}$ (seven hundredths).

Decimals are used every day, for example...
- digital thermometers
- height restrictions (e.g. a bridge with a height restriction of 4.2m)
- swimming pools.

Max Depth 1.1m

Recurring Decimals

A decimal that **recurs** is shown by placing a dot over the number that repeats.

If more than one number is repeated, place a dot over the first and last number in the recurring sequence.

Example
Write 0.474747... as a recurring decimal.

$$0.474747... = 0.4\dot{7}$$

Converting between Decimals and Fractions

When converting decimals into fractions, use the place values of the figures.

Example
Write 0.35 as a fraction.

$$0.35 = \frac{3}{10} + \frac{5}{100} = \frac{30}{100} + \frac{5}{100} = \frac{35}{100}$$

When converting fractions into decimals, divide the numerator by the denominator.

Example
Convert $\frac{3}{5}$ into a decimal.

$$\frac{3}{5} = 3 \div 5 = 0.6$$

Multiplying Decimals by 10, 100 and 1000

- To multiply a decimal number by 10, move each digit one place to the left.
- To multiply a decimal number by 100, move each digit two places to the left.
- To multiply a decimal number by 1000, move each digit three places to the left.

Examples
1. $16.93 \times 10 = 169.3$
2. $273.61 \times 100 = 27\,361$
3. $0.294 \times 1000 = 294$

Dividing Decimals by 10, 100 and 1000

- To divide a decimal number by 10, move each digit one place to the right.
- To divide a decimal number by 100, move each digit two places to the right.
- To divide a decimal number by 1000, move each digit three places to the right.

Examples
1. $25.62 \div 10 = 2.562$
2. $71.3 \div 100 = 0.713$
3. $493.7 \div 1000 = 0.4937$

Adding, Subtracting, Multiplying and Dividing Decimals

The methods used to add, subtract, multiply and divide whole numbers can also be used for decimals.

Examples
Work out...

1. $27.93 + 14.62$

$$\begin{array}{r} 27.93 \\ 14.62\ + \\ \hline 42.55 \\ \tiny{11} \end{array}$$

It's important that you line up the digits carefully.

So, $27.93 + 14.62 = 42.55$

2. $89.6 - 41.37$

$$\begin{array}{r} 89.\overset{5}{6}\overset{1}{0} \\ 41.37\ - \\ \hline 48.23 \end{array}$$

Fill in the zero after the 6 tenths.

So, $89.6 - 41.37 = 48.23$

3. 7.39×5

$$\begin{array}{r} 7.39 \\ 5\ \times \\ \hline 36.95 \\ \tiny{1\ \ 4} \end{array}$$

Multiply each of the digits 7, 3 and 9 by 5, starting from the right and moving to the left.

So, $7.39 \times 5 = 36.95$

4. 2.63×45

This requires long multiplication. It's made easier if you first multiply 2.63 by 100 to remove the decimal point:

$$\begin{array}{r} 263 \\ 45\ \times \\ \hline 1315 \\ 10520\ + \\ \hline 11835 \end{array}$$

263 x 5
263 x 40

The answer now needs to be divided by 100, because you multiplied by 100 originally:

$11\,835 \div 100 = 118.35$

5. $25.5 \div 5$

$$\begin{array}{r} 5.1 \\ 5\overline{)25.5} \end{array}$$

Make sure that the decimal points are lined up.

So, $25.5 \div 5 = 5.1$

6. $47.4 \div 0.2$

$47.4 \div 0.2$ is equivalent to $474 \div 2$ (multiplying both numbers by 10):

$$\begin{array}{r} 237 \\ 2\overline{)47^{1}4} \end{array}$$

So, $47.4 \div 0.2 = 237$

Decimals

Rounding Decimals

It's sometimes useful to round decimals to the nearest whole number, or to a given number of decimal places.

To round to the nearest whole number, look at the number in the first decimal place:
- If it is 5 or more, round the units up to the next whole number.
- If it is less than 5, the units stay the same.

Examples
1. 6.3 = 6 (to the nearest whole number)
2. 12.5mm = 13mm (to the nearest whole number)

To round to the nearest tenth (one decimal place), look at the number in the second decimal place and follow the same rules as above.

Examples
1. 12.35 is 12.4 (to 1 d.p.)
2. 14.23 is 14.2 (to 1 d.p.)

A similar method can be used when rounding any number to a particular number of decimal places.

Examples
1. 15.675 = 15.68 (to 2 d.p.)
2. 9.363 = 9.36 (to 2 d.p.)

Measurements are rounded to different degrees of accuracy depending on the circumstance.

In a school sports event, the time taken to run the 100m is likely to be rounded to one decimal place, whereas at International Level it's rounded to two decimal places.

Rounding can have a big impact. This article shows how important rounding is:

100 METRE WORLD RECORD BLUNDER

American sprinter Justin Gatlin's hopes of being named the world's fastest man have been dashed following news that his record-breaking time of 9.76 seconds will not count.

GUTTED
Gatlin was told that he'd beaten Asafa Powell's 9.77 second record by one one-hundredth of a second in Qatar. However, the sport's officials have now announced that he actually clocked 9.766 seconds, not 9.760 as first announced.

According to the rules of the IAAF, the world governing body for track and field, Gatlin's time should've been rounded up to 9.77 seconds, only equalling – not beating – the record already set by Powell.

Quick Test

1. In the number 639.465 what is the place value of the digit 5?
2. The decimal 0.27 written as a fraction is $\frac{27}{100}$. True or false?
3. What is 83.62 – 14.79?
   A 67.83 **B** 68.83 **C** 71.17 **D** 69.37
4. What is 25.6 × 31?
5. When rounding a number to the nearest tenth, which number do you look at?

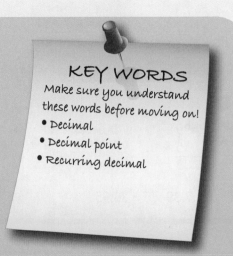

KEY WORDS
Make sure you understand these words before moving on!
- Decimal
- Decimal point
- Recurring decimal

1 Write down the value of the underlined digit in each decimal number.
   a) 62.3   **b)** 4.07   **c)** 156.231   **d)** 27.264

2 Work out...
   a) 27.6 × 10   **c)** 96.3 × 100   **e)** 16.2 × 1000
   b) 493.2 ÷ 100   **d)** 294.3 ÷ 1000   **f)** 2.9 ÷ 10

3 Work out...
   a) 27.6 + 491.3   **c)** 28.6 × 4   **e)** 14.3 × 12
   b) 273.69 – 12.7   **d)** 211.5 ÷ 5   **f)** 13.5 ÷ 0.3

4 Work out...
   a) 271.6 + 45.3   **c)** 37.4 × 9   **e)** 18.6 × 17
   b) 279.4 – 102.6   **d)** 515.65 ÷ 5   **f)** 48.8 ÷ 0.4

5 Rebecca took part in a triathlon.
   She ran 1.8km, swam 0.24km and cycled 2.241km.
   How far in total did Rebecca travel?

6 Mohammed sawed 0.38 metres off a one-metre long piece of wood.
   Work out the length of wood left over.

7 Find the total cost, in pounds (£), of four loaves of bread costing £0.92 each and
   seven cans of cola at £0.55 each.

8 Find the total cost, in pounds (£), of 26 train tickets costing £9.62 each.

9 A piece of rope is 4.72m long.
   If Mr Percy cuts off 2.31m from the rope, how much will be left?

10 Round these numbers to one decimal place:
   a) 6.49   **b)** 7.43   **c)** 5.65   **d)** 4.27

11 Round these numbers to two decimal places:
   a) 3.527   **d)** 4.692   **g)** 38.471
   b) 16.653   **e)** 12.685   **h)** 38.528
   c) 127.425   **f)** 37.255   **i)** 37.725

12 Charlotte jumped 1.4 metres (correct to one decimal place) in a long jump competition.
   What's the minimum possible distance that Charlotte could have jumped?

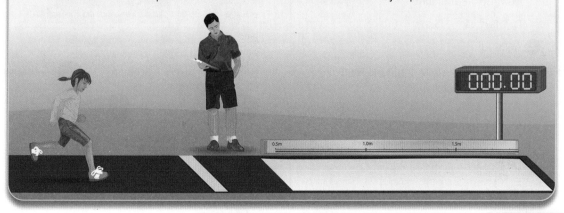

Fractions, Decimals & Estimating

Fractions – A Quick Reminder

A **fraction** is a whole unit divided into equal parts.

$\dfrac{5}{7}$ ← the **numerator**
← the **denominator**

$\frac{5}{7}$ is a **proper fraction**.

$\frac{7}{5}$ is called an **improper fraction**.

A fraction that has a whole number and a fraction is called a **mixed number**, for example, $5\frac{1}{3}$.

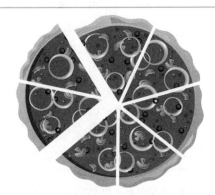

Adding & Subtracting Fractions

Only fractions with the same denominator can be added or subtracted.

Example

1 Work out $\frac{3}{5} + \frac{2}{3}$

- Find the lowest common denominator of 5 and 3. In this case it's 15.
- Change the fractions into their equivalent with a denominator of 15.

$$\overset{\times 3}{\frac{3}{5}} = \underset{\times 3}{\frac{9}{15}} \qquad \overset{\times 5}{\frac{2}{3}} = \underset{\times 5}{\frac{10}{15}}$$

Now rewrite the sum:
$\frac{9}{15} + \frac{10}{15} = \frac{19}{15} = 1\frac{4}{15}$

2 Work out $3\frac{4}{5} - 1\frac{2}{7}$

Rewrite as improper fractions then continue as normal:

$$\frac{19}{5} - \frac{9}{7}$$
$$= \frac{133}{35} - \frac{45}{35}$$
$$= \frac{88}{35}$$
$$= 2\frac{18}{35}$$

Multiplying & Dividing Fractions

When multiplying and dividing fractions, write out whole or mixed numbers as improper fractions.

Example

$\frac{5}{7} \times \frac{4}{9} = \frac{20}{63}$ ← Multiply the numerators together
← Multiply the denominators together

For division, turn the second fraction upside down (taking the reciprocal) and multiply the fractions together.

Example

$$3\frac{1}{2} \div \frac{4}{5}$$
$$= \frac{7}{2} \div \frac{4}{5}$$
$$= \frac{7}{2} \times \frac{5}{4}$$ ← Turn the second fraction upside down and multiply with $\frac{7}{2}$
$$= \frac{35}{8} = 4\frac{3}{8}$$ ← Give the answer as a mixed number

The Fraction Key on the Calculator

[a%] is the fraction key.

Example

$\frac{5}{7}$ is keyed in as [5] [a%] [7]

This is displayed as [5⌐7] or [7⌐5]

The calculator will automatically cancel down fractions when the [=] is pressed.

A display of [3⌐5⌐9] means $3\frac{5}{9}$.

If you press [Shift] [a%] it converts to an improper fraction: $\frac{32}{9}$.

Fractions of a Quantity

To find a fraction of a quantity, you multiply the fraction with the quantity.

Example

Out of 6000 people surveyed only $\frac{2}{5}$ of them eat five helpings of fruit or vegetables per day.

$\frac{2}{5}$ of 6000 is:

$\frac{2}{5} \times 6000 = 2400$ people

$6000 \div 5 = 1200$
$1200 \times 2 = 2400$

Egyptian Fractions

The Egyptians of 3000BC had an interesting way to represent fractions. They could write unit fractions like $\frac{1}{2}$, $\frac{1}{4}$ and $\frac{1}{3}$ but they couldn't write fractions like $\frac{2}{3}$, or $\frac{3}{4}$ as we can. Instead they would write any fraction as a sum of unit fractions, where all the unit fractions were different.

Example

$\frac{3}{4} = \frac{1}{2} + \frac{1}{4}$

$\frac{6}{7} = \frac{1}{2} + \frac{1}{3} + \frac{1}{42}$

A fraction written as a sum of a distinct unit fraction is called an Egyptian fraction.

Fractions, Decimals & Estimating

Decimals

Decimals are used for parts of numbers that are less than 1. A **decimal point** is used to separate whole number columns from fractional columns.

72.4 has 7 tens, 2 units and 4 tenths.

A **terminating decimal** is a decimal that ends, for example 6.42.

All terminating decimals can be converted to a fraction using place value:

$0.3 = \frac{3}{10}$ $0.47 = \frac{4}{10} + \frac{7}{100} = \frac{47}{100}$

A **recurring decimal** is a decimal in which one or more figures repeat.

To show that a figure recurs, place a dot above the figure:

0.3333 is written as $0.\dot{3}$

0.252525 is written as $0.\dot{2}\dot{5}$

Ordering Decimals

When ordering decimals...
1. firstly write them with the same number of digits after the decimal point
2. then compare whole numbers, digits in the tenths place, digits in the hundredths place, and so on.

Example

Arrange these numbers in order of size, smallest first:

5.63, 5.621, 5.029, 5.03, 5.14, 5.137

First rewrite them: 5.630, 5.621, 5.029, 5.030, 5.140, 5.137

Then reorder them: 5.029, 5.030, 5.137, 5.140, 5.621, 5.630

the 2 is worth less than the 3.

Multiplying & Dividing Decimals

When multiplying decimals, use the same method as you would use for multiplying ordinary numbers. Then find the position of the decimal point.

Examples

① 4.62×3.5

This requires long multiplication. It is made easier if you multiply 4.62 by 100 and 3.5 by 10 to remove the decimal point.

$$
\begin{array}{r}
462 \\
35 \times \\
\hline
23_31_10 \\
13_1860 + \\
\hline
16170
\end{array}
$$

$\leftarrow$ 462×5

$\leftarrow$ 462×30

Now divide the answer by 100 and then 10:

$16170 \div 100 = 161.70$

$161.70 \div 10 = 16.17$

② $58.6 \div 0.4$

$58.6 \div 0.4$ is equivalent to $58.6 \div 4$ (multiplying both numbers by 10).

$$
\begin{array}{r}
1\,4\,6.\,5 \\
4\overline{)\,5^18^26.^20}
\end{array}
$$

so $58.6 \div 0.4 = 146.5$

When multiplying by numbers between 0 and 1, the result is smaller than the starting value.

Example

$5 \times 0.1 = 0.5$

$5 \times 0.01 = 0.05$

$5 \times 0.001 = 0.005$

When dividing numbers between 0 and 1, the result is bigger than the starting value.

Example

$3 \div 0.1 = 30$

$3 \div 0.01 = 300$

$3 \div 0.001 = 3000$

Rounding Decimals

Decimals can be rounded to the nearest whole number or a given number of decimal places. Rounding decimals is useful in calculations and also when measuring.

When rounding to a specified number of decimal places:

① Look at the digit in the last required place, for example to round to the nearest tenth (one decimal place), look at the number in the second decimal place.

② If the number that is not needed is 5 or more, round up the last required digit. If it is less than 5 the last required digit remains the same.

Examples

$7.29 = 7.3$ (to 1dp)

$15.235 = 15.24$ (to 2dp)

$6.381 = 6.38$ (to 2dp)

$142.3645 = 142.365$ (to 3dp)

Fractions, Decimals & Estimating

Significant Figures

The first **significant figure** (*sf* or *sig fig*) is the first digit that is not zero. The second, third, fourth... significant figures follow on after the first digit. They may or may not be zeros.

Examples

2.7305 has 5 *sf*

1st 2nd 3rd 4th 5th

0.00239 has 3 *sf*

1st 2nd 3rd

To round a number to a given number of significant places, apply the same rules as with decimal places. If the next digit is 5 or more, round up.

Number	to 3 *sf*	to 2 *sf*	to 1 *sf*
5.306	5.31	5.3	5
4268	4270	4300	4000
0.720	0.720	0.72	0.7

After rounding the last digit you must fill in the end zeros, for example 275 = 280 to 2 *sf*.

Estimating and Approximates

Estimating is a good way of checking your answer. It is useful when shopping to estimate the cost of your purchases.

When estimating...
- round the numbers to easy numbers, usually ones with 1 or 2 significant figures
- use the symbol ≈ this means 'approximately equal to'
- when multiplying and dividing, don't approximate a number to zero, use 0.1, 0.01, etc.

Examples

$9.21 \times 10.98 \approx 9 \times 11 = 99$

$0.082 \times 42 \approx 0.1 \times 40 = 4$

$$\frac{398 \times 53.1}{19.6 \times 0.097} \approx \frac{400 \times 50}{20 \times 0.1}$$

$$= \frac{20\,000}{2}$$

$$= 10\,000$$

When adding or subtracting, very small numbers can be approximated to zero.

$200.1 + 0.0037 \approx 200 + 0 = 200$

Checking Calculations

To check a calculation, the calculation can be reversed.

Example

$526 \times 9 = 4734$

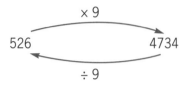

Check with $4734 \div 9 = 526$

$729 + 637 = 1366$

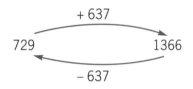

Check with $1366 - 637 = 729$

Quick Test

1. In the number 82.631 what is the place value of the digit 3?

2. Write $\frac{37}{5}$ as a mixed number.

3. What is $2\frac{1}{3} + 1\frac{1}{2}$?
   a) $3\frac{2}{5}$ b) $3\frac{5}{6}$ c) $3\frac{1}{6}$ d) $3\frac{2}{3}$

4. The answer to $\frac{4}{7}$ of 21kg is 12 kg. True or false?

5. Arrange these numbers in order of size, smallest first:
   3.26, 0.72, 0.719, 3.21, 3.255, 0.76

Fractions, Decimals & Estimating

Skills Practice

1 Work out...

a) $\frac{5}{7} + \frac{1}{3}$　　　c) $\frac{4}{5} - \frac{1}{2}$　　　e) $2\frac{1}{3} - 1\frac{4}{9}$

b) $\frac{6}{11} - \frac{1}{3}$　　　d) $\frac{7}{10} + \frac{2}{15}$　　　f) $5\frac{6}{13} + 2\frac{3}{26}$

2 Work out...

a) $\frac{2}{7} \times \frac{3}{11}$　　　c) $\frac{5}{8} \times \frac{1}{2}$　　　e) $\frac{4}{7} \times 1\frac{1}{2}$

b) $\frac{5}{9} \times \frac{4}{5}$　　　d) $\frac{8}{15} \times \frac{2}{3}$　　　f) $3\frac{2}{3} \times 1\frac{1}{4}$

3 Work out...

a) $\frac{5}{7} \div \frac{10}{11}$　　　c) $\frac{8}{9} \div \frac{3}{5}$　　　e) $3\frac{1}{2} \div 2\frac{1}{3}$

b) $\frac{6}{11} \div \frac{2}{3}$　　　d) $\frac{4}{7} \div \frac{2}{9}$　　　f) $5\frac{1}{4} \div 2\frac{1}{8}$

4 Raj earns £35000 per year. $\frac{2}{5}$ of his salary is used to pay his mortgage. How much does Raj pay towards his mortgage each year?

5 There are 1200 students in a school. $\frac{2}{5}$ of those students eat school lunches. How many eat school lunches?

6 Place each of these sets of decimals in order of size, smallest first:

a) 4.26, 4.31, 4.09, 4.29, 4.293, 4.02
b) 8.73, 8.48, 8.429, 8.475, 8.481, 8.427
c) 6.92, 6.915, 6.902, 6.926, 6.925, 6.931

7 Work out...

a) 41.6×25 c) 19.31×4.1 e) $98.35 \div 3.5$
b) 27.3×2.8 d) $84.76 \div 5.2$ f) $82.8 \div 6.9$

8 Round these numbers to two decimal places:

a) 16.425   c) 12.869   e) 8.712
b) 9.371   d) 3.425   f) 146.925

9 Round these numbers to the number of significant figures shown in brackets.

a) 572 (2)   c) 0.6305 (3)   e) 0.027059 (2)
b) 1375 (3)   d) 2.7916 (3)   f) 15736 (3)

10 Estimate the answers to the following by rounding the numbers to 1 significant figure.

a) 7.6×4.1 b) 9.9×3.8 c) $(6.1)^2$ d) $\dfrac{18.2 \times 41.7}{9.93}$

Ratio

Ratio

This flag is divided into three equal parts:

Two of the parts are coloured red and one part is coloured green:
- The **ratio** of red to green is 2 : 1
- The ratio of green to red is 1 : 2

The colon means 'compared to'.

A ratio is a way of comparing two or more related quantities.

Example
In a maths class, 17 students are girls and 13 students are boys.
a) What is the ratio of boys to girls?

The ratio of boys to girls is 13 : 17

b) What is the ratio of girls to boys?

The ratio of girls to boys is 17 : 13

c) What fraction of the class is girls?

There are 30 students altogether.

$\frac{17}{30}$ of the students are girls.

Equivalent Ratios

Ratios are **equivalent** when they represent the same relationship. The units must be the same.

Example
Dermot is making some fruit punch for a party. He mixes 200ml of orange juice with 800ml of cranberry juice.
Write this as a ratio in its simplest form.

The ratio is:

$$\text{Orange} : \text{Cranberry}$$
$$200 : 800$$
$$1 : 4$$

÷ 200 ÷ 200

Simplifying Ratios

A ratio in its **simplest form** is also said to be in its **lowest terms**.

For example, the ratio 200 : 800 is equivalent to the ratio 1 : 4.

Calculating with Ratios

A common way to solve ratio problems is to reduce one of the ratios to one, and then find what one quantity is worth.

Examples

① A box of 8 pens costs £2.24.
How much will 12 pens cost?

8 pens = £2.24

1 pen = £2.24 ÷ 8
= £0.28   In other words, one pen costs 28p

12 pens = 12 × 28p
= £3.36

② It costs £1.50 to travel 3 miles on a bus.
How much would a 7 mile journey cost?

3 miles = £1.50

1 mile = £1.50 ÷ 3
= £0.50

7 miles = 7 × £0.50
= £3.50

③ A bottle of blackcurrant squash carries the following mixing instructions:

Just mix 1 part of juice with 6 parts of water for a refreshing drink

a) How much water should Ray add to five centilitres of juice?

There needs to be six times as much water as juice:

6 × 5 = 30 centilitres of water

b) What quantity of juice should Ray add to one litre of water?

1 litre = 100 centilitres of water

There should be one-sixth as much juice as water:

100 ÷ 6 = 16.7 centilitres of juice

Quick Test

① What is a ratio?
② The ratio 20 : 15 fully simplified is 4 : 3.
True or false?
③ What is the ratio 48 : 24 when fully simplified?
   A 12 : 6   B 6 : 12   C 1 : 2   D 2 : 1
④ 7 pencils cost 98p.
What is the cost of 18 pencils?
   A 14p   B £2.52   C £1.40   D £2.60
⑤ When are ratios equivalent?

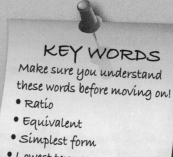

KEY WORDS
Make sure you understand these words before moving on!
• Ratio
• Equivalent
• Simplest form
• Lowest terms

Ratio

Skills Practice

1 For each of these shapes, what is the ratio of red parts to green parts?

a) 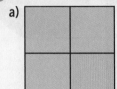   b) 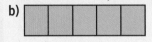   c)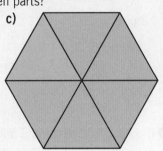

2 Write each of these ratios in their simplest form:

a) 3 : 6   e) 75 : 35   i) 25 : 55
b) 5 : 10   f) 50 : 55   j) 75 : 30
c) 200 : 500   g) 24 : 18   k) 64 : 4
d) 200 : 100   h) 16 : 22   l) 27 : 81

3 Write these ratios in their lowest terms:

a) 20cm : 10mm   d) £5 : 200p   g) £6 : 30p
b) 40cm : 2m   e) 5km : 100cm   h) 50cm : 2m
c) 1 hour : 30 minutes   f) 3 hours : 45 minutes   i) 5000g : 1kg

4 Pewter contains lead and tin in the ratio 20 : 80.
Write this ratio in its simplest form.

5 A mega-chip cookie contains milk, plain and white chocolate chips in the ratio 5 : 10 : 25.
Write this ratio in its simplest form.

6 In one month, there were 14 sunny days and 16 wet days.
Find the ratio of wet days to sunny days.

7 In a bag of counters, there are 7 blue counters and 28 red counters.
Find the ratio of blue to red counters.

8 In a survey of cars, 250 cars were silver, 80 were red and 50 were blue.
Find the ratio of silver to red to blue cars.

9 In a wood, there are 65 beech trees, 45 conifers and 75 oak trees.
Find the ratio of beech trees to conifers to oak trees.

10 Sara buys six packets of seeds for £12.
How much would Sara pay for nine packets of seeds?

11 Three packs of A4 paper cost £6.51.
How much does 13 packs of A4 paper cost?

12 12 sheets of paper are photocopied at a cost of £1.08.
How much would it cost to photocopy 75 sheets of paper?

13 Molly is decorating three rooms.
The areas of the rooms are $30m^2$, $15m^2$ and $45m^2$.
Molly knows that a tin of paint covers $32m^2$.
How many tins of paint does Molly need to buy if she is painting each room with two coats?

14 70 maths books cost £805.
Work out the cost of buying...
a) 45 maths books   **b)** 123 maths books.

15 At a bank, Bobby changes £60 into 114 American dollars.
a) How many American dollars would Bobby get for changing £85 at this rate?
b) How many American dollars would Bobby get for changing £205 at this rate?

16 Rashna earns £142.80 for working 17 hours.
How much will Rashna earn if she works...
a) 15 hours?   **b)** 27 hours?   **c)** 36 hours?

17 A car drives steadily for 8 hours covering 304 miles.
a) How far has the car travelled after 6 hours?
b) How far has the car travelled after 11 hours?

Ratio

What is a Ratio?

A **ratio** is used to compare two or more quantities. The symbol for 'compared to' is two dots (:).

For example, 12 red apples compared to 20 green apples is written as 12 : 20.

To put ratios in their **simplest form**, divide both parts of the ratio by the highest common factor.

For example 12 : 20 (divide both parts by 4)
$$= 3 : 5$$

To express the ratio 3 : 5 in the ratio $1 : n$, divide both sides by 3

$$3 : 5$$
$$= \frac{3}{3} : \frac{5}{3}$$
$$= 1 : 1\frac{2}{3}$$

Or $1 : 1.\dot{6}$

Using Ratios as Scales

Scale diagrams are often used in building plans and maps to represent distance on the ground. Each length in the scale diagram represents a real length in the building or map.

On the diagram above 2cm represents 1m.

A distance of 8cm on the diagram represents 4m.

A distance of 3m in real life would be 6cm on the diagram.

Sharing a Quantity in a Given Ratio

Fiona won £85000 in the lottery and decided to share it between Samuel and Thomas in the ratio 2 : 3.

Work out how much Thomas and Samuel receive:

$2 + 3 = 5$ parts   (add up the parts)

5 parts = £85000

1 part $= \dfrac{£85000}{5}$

$= £17000$

Thomas receives 3 x 17000 = £51000

Samuel receives 2 x 17000 = £34000

Calculating with Ratio

When solving ratio problems remember to reduce one of the ratios to one.

Examples

① 40 maths books cost £760. Work out the cost of buying 27 maths books.

40 books = £760

1 book $= \dfrac{£760}{40}$

$= £19$

27 books $= 27 \times 19$

$= £513$

② At a bank, Rashna changes £80 into US$156.80. How many US dollars would Rashna get for changing £230?

£80 $= \$156.80$

£1 $= \dfrac{156.80}{80}$

£1 $= \$1.96$

£230 $= 230 \times 1.96$

$= \$450.80$

③ This is a recipe for 8 biscuits:

80g of butter
100g of sugar
2 eggs
120g of flour

How much flour is needed for 12 biscuits?

8 biscuits = 120g of flour

1 biscuit $= \dfrac{120}{8} = 15g$

12 biscuits $= 12 \times 15$

$= 180g$

④ It takes 8 builders 6 days to build a playground. At the same rate how long would it take 3 builders?

8 builders = 6 days

1 builder = 8 × 6

= 48 days

3 builders = 48 ÷ 3

= 16 days ← 3 builders will take a third of the time taken by 1 person

The Golden Ratio

The Golden Ratio is a measurement of about 1.618. The painter Leonardo da Vinci used this to explore the human body, involving the ratio of lengths of various body parts. He called this ratio the 'divine proportion' and featured it in many of his paintings.

Ratio

Best Buys

Many products are sold in different sized boxes. For example, a supermarket may have different sized boxes of cornflakes. It's important to be able to work out which is the best value for money.

Example

The same brand of cornflakes is sold in three different sized packages. Which packet represents the best value for money?

500g costs £1.69	1g costs $169 \div 500 = 0.338p$
750g costs £2.13	1g costs $213 \div 750 = 0.284p$
1kg costs £2.59	1g costs $259 \div 1000 = 0.259p$

Since the 1kg packet costs less per gram it is the best value for money.

(An alternative method for this example would be to work out the cost of 250g.)

500g

750g

1kg

Quick Test

1. The ratio 15 : 30 fully simplified is 2 : 1. True or false?
2. What is the ratio 16 : 24 fully simplified?
   a) 8 : 12   **b)** 16 : 24   **c)** 2 : 3   **d)** 3 : 2
3. £36 000 is divided in the ratio 1 : 5. Work out the size of the larger share.
4. 5 pens cost £1.40. How much do 7 pens cost?
5. The ratio 7 : 2 expressed in the form n : 1 is 3.5 : 1. True or false?

KEY WORDS
Make sure you understand these words before moving on!
- Ratio
- Simplest form

Skills Practice

1 Write each ratio in its simplest form:
- **a)** 12 : 15
- **c)** 6 : 2
- **e)** 250 : 450
- **b)** 25 : 50
- **d)** 12 : 28
- **f)** 125 : 75

2 In a car park there are 50 silver cars, 36 blue cars and 20 black cars. Write down the ratio of the number of silver cars to black cars to blue cars.

3 In a class, the ratio of left-handed students to right-handed students is 1 : 6. What fraction of the class are left handed?

4 The scale of a map is 1:100 000. Work out the real distance that 7.2cm on the map represents.

5 The ratio of the number of yellow beads to the number of blue beads in a bag is 1 : 4. Work out the number of blue beads if there are 8 yellow beads.

6 £45 is shared in the ratio of 2 : 7. Work out the size of the largest share.

7 William and Edward share 28 marbles in the ratio 2 : 5. Work out how many marbles Edward gets.

8 Ian went on holiday to Spain. The exchange rate was £1 = €1.58.
He changed £250 into Euros.
- **a)** Work out the amount of Euros that Ian got.

When Ian came home he had €88 left. The new exchange rate was £1 = €1.60.
- **b)** Work out how much Ian got in Pounds Sterling for his €88.

9 Here is a list of ingredients to make potato soup for four people:
200g potatoes, 2 onions, 40g butter and 200ml stock
Work out how much stock is needed to make potato soup for 14 people.

Fractions, Decimals & Ratio

Adding and Subtracting Fractions

You should already know that only **fractions** with the same denominators can be added or subtracted.

Examples

1 $\dfrac{2}{7} + \dfrac{7}{10}$

Change the fractions to their equivalents with a denominator of 70 and rewrite the sum.

$$\frac{20}{70} + \frac{49}{70} = \frac{69}{70}$$

2 $3\frac{1}{4} - 2\frac{5}{12}$

Rewrite as an **improper fraction**.

$$\frac{13}{4} - \frac{29}{12}$$
$$= \frac{39}{12} - \frac{29}{12}$$
$$= \frac{10}{12} = \frac{5}{6}$$

Multiplying and Dividing Fractions

When you're asked to multiply and divide fractions, you should remember to write whole or mixed numbers as improper fractions.

Example
Multiply...
$$1\frac{2}{3} \times 2\frac{4}{5}$$
$$= \frac{\overset{1}{5}}{3} \times \frac{14}{\underset{1}{5}}$$

Multiply the numerators together
Multiply the denominators together

Cancel any fractions first. Give the answer as a mixed number.
$$= \frac{14}{3} = 4\frac{2}{3}$$

For division, take the reciprocal of the second fraction (i.e. turn it upside down) and multiply the fractions together.

Example
$$4\frac{2}{3} \div \frac{2}{9}$$
$$= \frac{14}{3} \div \frac{2}{9}$$
$$= \frac{14}{\underset{1}{3}} \times \frac{\overset{3}{9}}{2}$$
$$= \frac{14}{3} = 21$$

The Fraction Key on a Calculator

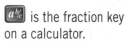 is the fraction key on a calculator.

$2\frac{1}{3}$ is keyed in as

Decimals

A **terminating decimal** is a decimal that ends.

Example
$$0.637 = \frac{6}{10} + \frac{3}{100} + \frac{7}{1000} = \frac{637}{1000}$$

A **recurring decimal** is a decimal where one or more figures repeat.

Example
$0.6666...$ is written as $0.\dot{6}$
$0.373737...$ is written as $0.\dot{3}\dot{7}$

Multiplying and Dividing Numbers Between 0 and 1

When multiplying numbers between 0 and 1, the result is smaller than the starting value.

Examples

$72 \times 0.1 = 7.2$

$72 \times 0.01 = 0.72$

$72 \times 0.001 = 0.072$

When dividing numbers between 0 and 1, the result is bigger than the starting value.

Examples

$63 \div 0.1 = 630$ — Since $63 \div 0.1 = 63 \div \frac{1}{10} = 63 \times 10$

$63 \div 0.01 = 6300$ or $\frac{63}{0.01} = \frac{6300}{1} = 6300$

$63 \div 0.001 = 63\,000$

Ordering Decimals

Remember when ordering decimals to use the same number of digits after the decimal point, and then compare the whole numbers, followed by the digits in the correct order.

Example

Arrange these numbers in order of size, smallest first.

52.06, 51.72, 50.769, 51.715, 51.296, 52.073, 52.172

Rewrite them...

52.060, 51.720, 50.769, 51.715, 51.296, 52.073, 52.172

> The 1 tenth is worth less than the 2 tenths

Then order them...

50.769, 51.296, 51.714, 51.720, 52.060, 52.073, 52.172

Powers of 10

The powers of 10 are...

$10^0 = 1$

$10^1 = 10$

$10^2 = 100$

$10^3 = 1000$, etc.

When the power of 10 is smaller than zero, we use a negative power...

$10^{-1} = 0.1$

$10^{-2} = 0.01$

$10^{-3} = 0.001$

$10^{-4} = 0.0001$

Which means...

$\frac{1}{10} = 0.1 = 10^{-1} = 10\%$

Ratio

When you see this symbol **:** you are dealing with **ratio**.

To simplify ratios divide both parts of the ratio by their highest common factor.

$30 : 50$ ◄ Divide both parts by 10

$= \quad 3 : 5$

Fractions, Decimals & Ratio

Calculations Involving Ratio

You'll need to be able to recognise questions in which ratio is needed as you might not be told to use it.

Examples

① At a bank Sukhvinder changes £400 into 2560 Dirhams. How many Dirhams would Sukhvinder get for changing £270?

£400 = 2560 Dirhams

£1 = $\frac{2560}{400}$ = 6.4

£270 = 270 × 64
      = 1728 Dirhams

② The same type of washing powder is sold in three different sized packs (see alongside). Which pack represents the best value for money?

Change kilograms into grams.

780g = £1.92	1g costs	192 ÷ 780 = 0.246
2.4kg = £4.32	1g costs	432 ÷ 2400 = 0.18
3kg = £6.73	1g costs	673 ÷ 3000 = 0.224

Since the 2.4kg pack costs less per gram it is the best value for money.

Quick Test

① The ratio 6 : 18 fully simplified is 1 : 3. True or false?

② £27 000 is divided in the ratio 4 : 5. How much is the smaller share?

③ 657 × 0.02 = 13.14. True or False?

④ Arrange these decimals in order of size...
6.37, 6.49, 6.04, 6.371, 6.27

KEY WORDS
Make sure you understand these words before moving on!
- Fraction
- Improper fraction
- Terminating decimal
- Recurring decimal
- Ratio

Skills Practice

1 Work out...

a) $\frac{2}{7} + \frac{6}{11}$

c) $2\frac{1}{5} + 3\frac{2}{3}$

b) $\frac{4}{5} - \frac{1}{3}$

d) $6\frac{1}{9} - 4\frac{1}{3}$

2 Work out...

a) $\frac{2}{5} \times \frac{3}{7}$

c) $4\frac{1}{5} \times \frac{7}{8}$

b) $2\frac{1}{2} \times 3\frac{1}{3}$

d) $\frac{7}{15} \times 2\frac{1}{3}$

3 Work out...

a) $\frac{4}{7} \div \frac{1}{3}$

c) $2\frac{1}{3} \div 4\frac{1}{7}$

b) $\frac{2}{3} \div \frac{1}{4}$

d) $3\frac{1}{8} \div 2\frac{1}{3}$

4 Round these numbers to 2 decimal places.
a) 6.479
c) 25.416
b) 17.235
d) 9.384

5 Estimate, by rounding the numbers to 1 significant figure, the answer to: $\dfrac{61.5 \times 2.9}{(3.1)^2}$

6 The following distances were thrown in a javelin competition. Arrange the distances in order of size, smallest first.
7.37m, 12.63m, 12.06m, 12.39m, 12.41m, 12.04m

7 If $62 \times 0.02 = 1.24$, what is the answer to 6.2×0.002?

8 7 water bottles cost £10.64. How much do 11 water bottles cost?

9 There are 320 daffodils and iris plants in a garden in the ratio 5 : 3. How many daffodils are there?

Negative Numbers

Negative Numbers

Integers are whole numbers. They can be positive or negative:
- **Positive numbers** are above zero.
- **Negative numbers** are below zero.

Negative numbers are written with the minus sign in front of the digits, for example, -13.

Temperatures often use positive and negative numbers.

The weather map opposite shows the forecast for one day in December. Edinburgh has a temperature of -3°C and London has a temperature of 2°C.

It's predicted that the average temperature is set to rise by between 1 and 4 degrees by the end of the century, due to global warming.

Edinburgh (-3°C)

London (2°C)

Ordering Positive and Negative Numbers

This is a number line:

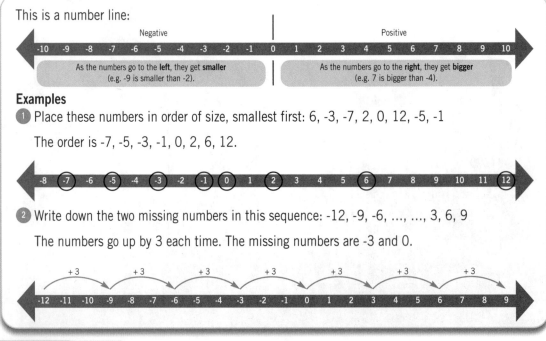

Negative | Positive

-10 -9 -8 -7 -6 -5 -4 -3 -2 -1 0 1 2 3 4 5 6 7 8 9 10

As the numbers go to the **left**, they get **smaller** (e.g. -9 is smaller than -2).

As the numbers go to the **right**, they get **bigger** (e.g. 7 is bigger than -4).

Examples

1 Place these numbers in order of size, smallest first: 6, -3, -7, 2, 0, 12, -5, -1

The order is -7, -5, -3, -1, 0, 2, 6, 12.

2 Write down the two missing numbers in this sequence: -12, -9, -6, ..., ..., 3, 6, 9

The numbers go up by 3 each time. The missing numbers are -3 and 0.

Adding and Subtracting Positive and Negative Numbers

Example

The temperature at 4am was -3°C. By 11am it had risen by 9°C.
What is the new temperature?

-3 + 9 = 6°C

A number line can be used to help when adding and subtracting positive and negative numbers.

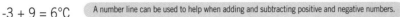
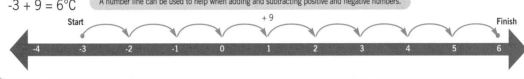

Adding and Subtracting Negative Numbers

When two negative numbers are added together, the result is a negative number.

For example, -6 + -2 is the same as -6 – 2 = -8

When you subtract numbers, you find the difference between them.

For example, 3 – -5 = 8

The difference between 3 and -5 is 8.

Hence, subtracting a negative number has the same effect as adding a positive number.
For example, -3 – -4 becomes -3 + 4 = 1

Quick Test

1. -6 is smaller than -5. True or false?
2. -8 is smaller than -10. True or false?
3. The temperature at 9am is 3°C. By 9pm it has
   fallen by 7°C. What is the temperature at 9pm?
   A -3°C **B** -4°C **C** -5°C **D** 4°C
4. When subtracting a negative number, it has
   the same effect as adding a negative number.
   True or false?
5. What is 6 – -3?
   A 3   **B** -3   **C** 9   **D** -9
6. What is the missing number in the sequence
   -7, -5, ..., -1, 1, 3, 5, 7?
   A -4   **B** -3   **C** -2   **D** 0

Negative Numbers

Skills Practice

1 For each list, write down...
- **i)** the highest temperature
- **ii)** the lowest temperature.
- **a)** 6°C, -5°C, 4°C, 7°C, -3°C, 0°C
- **b)** -5°C, -4°C, 2°C, -6°C, 1°C, -3°C
- **c)** -9°C, 4°C, 7°C, 0°C, -6°C, -2°C
- **d)** -12°C, 6°C, 7°C, -3°C, 14°C, -1°C
- **e)** 13°C, -4°C, -7°C, 6°C, 5°C, -8°C
- **f)** -9°C, 9°C, 0°C, 6°C, -7°C, 10°C

2 Write each set of temperatures in order of size, starting with the lowest.
- **a)** 5°C, -3°C, 6°C, -2°C, 0°C, 4°C
- **b)** -7°C, -2°C, 3°C, -9°C, 5°C
- **c)** 2°C, -5°C, 12°C, -10°C, 9°C, 4°C
- **d)** 7°C, -4°C, 9°C, 0°C, -6°C, -1°C
- **e)** -12°C, 7°C, 14°C, 9°C, -5°C, -2°C
- **f)** -8°C, 6°C, 12°C, -1°C, 9°C, -3°C

3 The table shows the temperature at midnight and midday on one day in five cities.

City	Midnight Temperature (°C)	Midday Temperature (°C)
Dublin	-3	6
Glasgow	-5	7
London	2	8
Manchester	-2	7
Cardiff	1	12

- **a)** Which city had the lowest midnight temperature?
- **b)** At midnight, how many degrees higher was the temperature in London than in Glasgow?
- **c)** Which city had the smallest rise in temperature from midnight to midday?
- **d)** Which city had the largest rise in temperature from midnight to midday?

4 The temperature at midnight is -6°C.
By midday it has risen by 8°C.
What is the temperature at midday?

5 Find the value of each of the following:
- **a)** 6 – 9
- **b)** -7 + 2
- **c)** -3 + 4
- **d)** -7 – 2
- **e)** 5 – 12
- **f)** 16 – 26
- **g)** 3 – 4
- **h)** -4 + 8
- **i)** -127 + 200
- **j)** -7 + 2
- **k)** -6 – 10
- **l)** 5 –12

6 Write down the next two numbers in each of these patterns:
   a) 7, 4, 1, -2, ..., ...
   b) -7, -5, -3, -1, ..., ...
   c) -2, -4, -6, -8, ..., ...

7 Work out...
   a) 2 – -5   **f)** -12 + -4   **k)** -5 + -2
   b) 3 – -4   **g)** 6 + -10   **l)** 9 + -3
   c) -2 – -3   **h)** -10 – -5   **m)** 5 – -1
   d) 5 + -2   **i)** 2 – -7   **n)** -3 – ⁺2
   e) -7 – -6   **j)** 7 – -2   **o)** -7 – -5

8 A number pyramid is completed by adding two cells to give the number in the cells above. For example:

-2 + 5 = 3

Copy and complete the number pyramids below.

a)
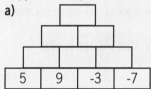

c)
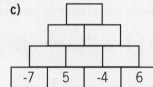

e)
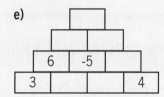

b)
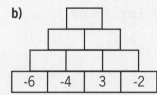

d)
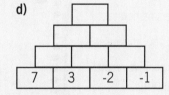

f)
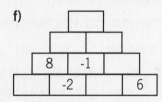

9 Copy and complete these arithmagons.
On each side of the arithmagon, the total of the numbers in the circles goes in the squares between them.

a)
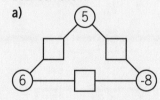

c)
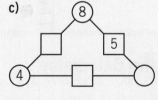

e)
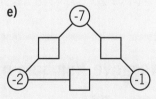

b)
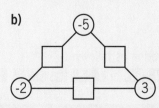

d)
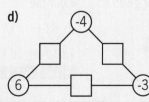

f)
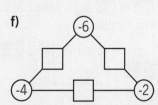

Negative Numbers

Adding and Subtracting Positive and Negative Numbers

Positive numbers are above zero and negative numbers are below zero.

Example

The temperature at 2am was -3°C.
By 2pm it had risen 10°C.
What is the new temperature?
-3 + 10 = 7°C

Adding a negative number is the same as subtracting a positive number.
6 + -4 is the same as 6 – 4 = 2

Subtracting a negative number is the same as adding a positive number.
6 – -5 becomes 6 + 5 = 11

Multiplying and Dividing Positive and Negative Numbers

When multiplying or dividing two numbers you need to check the signs.

Firstly multiply and divide the numbers as normal.

Use these rules to find the sign for the answer:

- Two like signs (both + or -) give a positive result.
- Two unlike signs (one + and the other -) give a negative result.

Examples

-5 × (+3) = -15	-12 ÷ (-2) = 6
-10 × (-2) = 20	15 ÷ (-3) = -5

You should know...

$(+) \times (+) = +$ $(+) \div (+) = +$

$(–) \times (–) = +$ $(–) \div (–) = +$

$(+) \times (–) = –$ $(+) \div (–) = –$

$(–) \times (+) = –$ $(–) \div (+) = –$

Negative Numbers on the Calculator

The **+/-** or **(-)** key on the calculator gives a negative number.

For example, to get -5, press **5** **+/-**
or **(-)** **5**
↙ this represents the sign.

Example

-5 + (-2) = -7

This may be keyed in as follows:

5 **+/-** **+** **2** **+/-** **=**, or **(-)** **5** **+** **(-)** **2** **=**.

Skills Practice

1 What number is four less than two?

2 Write each set of numbers in order of size, starting with the lowest.
- **a)** -6, 4, -10, 3, 7, -2, 0, -4, -5
- **b)** -9, -36, -12, -7, 4, -5, -4, 6
- **c)** -3, 7, -26, -41, -10, -11, -13, -8

3 Find the value of each of the following:
- **a)** -6 – 3
- **b)** -5 + 2
- **c)** 4 – 9
- **d)** -6 + 10
- **e)** -1 + 10
- **f)** 9 – 11
- **g)** -65 + 100
- **h)** -28 – 10
- **i)** 47 – 100
- **j)** 5 – 6
- **k)** -9 + 10
- **l)** 17 – 27

4 Work out...
- **a)** 5 – -3
- **b)** 6 + -2
- **c)** -5 + -7
- **d)** 2 – -5
- **e)** 4 + -3
- **f)** -7 – 2
- **g)** 6 – -5
- **h)** -7 + -2
- **i)** -7 – -4
- **j)** -6 + -3
- **k)** -9 – -2
- **l)** 8 + -6

5 Work out...
- **a)** 7 × -3
- **b)** 6 × -2
- **c)** -5 × -4
- **d)** -7 × -3
- **e)** -10 ÷ -2
- **f)** -20 ÷ 4
- **g)** 100 ÷ -2
- **h)** -25 ÷ -5
- **i)** 7 × -6
- **j)** $(-8)^2$
- **k)** 100 ÷ -5
- **l)** -50 ÷ -2

6 Use your calculator to work out the following:
- **a)** -9 + 2 – 6
- **b)** -10 – -5 + -3
- **c)** 6 – 4 – -7
- **d)** -10 × -3 x -2
- **e)** -50 ÷ (-2)
- **f)** -8 – (-2)
- **g)** 12 + (-6)
- **h)** -9 × -7 × -1

Percentages

Percentages

A **percentage** is a **fraction** with a **denominator** of 100.

The symbol % is the percentage sign.

For example, 12% means $\frac{12}{100}$:

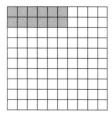

In the above diagram, 12 squares out of 100 are shaded (12%).

Example
A flag has two colours: red and green. If 30% of the flag is red, what percentage is green?

Percentage green = 100 – 30
              = 70%

Percentages are often seen in everyday life, as in the examples opposite.

SAVINGS BANK
Watch your money grow with our new rate of
5.7%

SALE NOW ON
up to 50% off

Lonsdale News
Olympic Games: Report Claims **70%** Overspend

Percentages, Fractions and Decimals

Percentages, fractions and **decimals** are related. You should learn these simple **equivalents**.

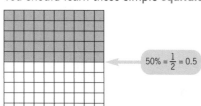

$50\% = \frac{1}{2} = 0.5$

Percentages	Fractions	Decimals
75%	$\frac{3}{4}$	0.75
50%	$\frac{1}{2}$	0.5
25%	$\frac{1}{4}$	0.25
10%	$\frac{1}{10}$	0.1
1%	$\frac{1}{100}$	0.01

Percentages of a Quantity (1)

Using a non-calculator method

When finding a percentage of a quantity without using a calculator, 10% is the easiest percentage to work out. This is because 10% is the same as one tenth.

Finding one tenth is the same as dividing by 10.

Examples
Find...

1 10% of £220

$$10\% = 220 \div 10$$
$$= £22$$

2 20% of £44

$$10\% = 44 \div 10$$
$$= £4.40$$

$$20\% = 4.40 \times 2$$
$$= £8.80$$

> Once you know 10%, you can find 20% by multiplying by 2.

3 5% of £60

$$10\% = 60 \div 10$$
$$= £6$$

$$5\% = 6 \div 2$$
$$= £3$$

> 5% is one half of 10%

Example

VAT (Value Added Tax) is a tax you pay on the cost of items bought.
VAT is charged at 17.5%.
Find the VAT on a coat that costs £80.

$$17.5\% = 10\% + 5\% + 2.5\%$$

$$10\% = 80 \div 10$$
$$= £8$$

$$5\% = 8 \div 2$$
$$= £4$$

$$2.5\% = 4 \div 2$$
$$= £2$$

So, VAT charged on a coat costing £80 is
£8 + £4 + £2 = £14

The actual price of the coat including VAT is
£80 + £14 = £94

Percentages of a Quantity (2)

Using a calculator

When finding a percentage of a quantity using a calculator, multiply the quantity by the percentage and divide by 100.

Example
Find 23% of £60

Key in:

2 3 × 6 0 ÷ 1 0 0 =

$$\frac{23}{100} \times 60 = £13.80$$

Percentages of a Quantity (3)

Problems

Problems can be solved using percentages of a quantity.

Example
A school raises £12 000 in a gala event.
30% of the money is given to charity.
How much is given to charity?

You need to find 30% of £12 000:

$$\frac{30}{100} \times £12\,000 = £3600$$

£3600 is given to charity.

Percentages

Percentage Increase and Decrease

Increases and decreases are often given in percentages.

Examples

1 In a sale, all prices are reduced by 15%. Find the sale price of a jacket that originally cost £80.

$$10\% = 80 \div 10$$
$$= £8$$

$$5\% = 8 \div 2$$
$$= £4$$

$$15\% = 8 + 4$$
$$= £12$$

Jacket costs £80 − £12 = £68

2 Tracey earns £45 000 per year. She gets a 2% pay rise. How much does Tracey earn after her pay rise?

First, you need to find 2% of £45 000:

$$\frac{2}{100} \times £45\,000 = £900$$

So, salary after pay rise = £45 000 + £900
= £45 900

Quick Test

1 What is the percentage sign?

2 Explain how you would find 10% of a quantity.

3 What is 30% of £60?

   A £9   **B** £18   **C** £24   **D** £6

4 Explain how you would work out 37% of £70 using a calculator.

5 Katie earns £35 000 per year. She pays 22% tax on her earnings. How much tax does Katie pay in a year?

   A £7700   **C** £7000

   B £27 300   **D** £28 000

6 A television costs £500. In a sale it's reduced by 15%. How much does the television cost now?

   A £50   **B** £75   **C** £450   **D** £425

KEY WORDS

Make sure you understand these words before moving on!

- Percentage
- Fraction
- Denominator
- Decimal
- Equivalent

1. What percentage of each shape is shaded?

   a)

   b)

   c)

2. A class of students is made up of 54% girls.
   What percentage of the class is male?

3. In a class of students, 27% are left-handed whilst the rest are right-handed.
   What percentage of the students are right-handed?

4. From the money raised by a fun run, 65% is given to a local hospice and the rest is used to buy a school minibus.
   What percentage of the money is used to buy the minibus?

5. Find...
a) 10% of 70kg	**c)** 30% of 50mm	**e)** 40% of £80	**g)** 65% of £120
b) 20% of £140	**d)** 60% of £240	**f)** 30% of £90	**h)** 35% of £150

6. Using a calculator, find...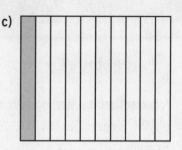
a) 12% of 850km	**c)** 13% of 48kg	**e)** 15% of £650	**g)** 36% of £82
b) 72% of £800	**d)** 6% of £12.50	**f)** 28% of 270m	**h)** 64% of 350kg

7. The 60 girls in Year 8 were asked to choose their favourite sport.
   70% of the girls chose netball.
   Work out how many girls chose netball.

8. 35% of students walk to school.
   If there are 1200 students at a school,
   how many walk to get there?

9. Robert had £560 in his savings account.
   He left the money in the account for one year.
   Interest was paid at 6% per year.
   a) Calculate the interest paid to Robert at the end of the year.
   b) At the end of the year, how much did Robert have altogether?

10. Perlita bought a CD in a sale.
    The original price of the CD was £12.
    In the sale, the price of the CD was reduced by 20%.
    How much did Perlita pay for the CD?

Percentages

Percentages

A **percentage** is a fraction with a denominator of 100, for example $13\% = \frac{13}{100}$.

Percentages are often seen in everyday life, for example bank interest rates and discounts in summer and winter sales.

Using a Calculator

When finding a percentage of a quantity using a calculator, multiply the quantity by the percentage and divide by 100.

Example
Find 47% of 257m

Key in

`4` `7` `×` `2` `5` `7` `÷` `1` `0` `0` `=`

$\frac{47}{100} \times 257 = 120.79\text{m}$

Percentages of a Quantity

When finding a percentage of a quantity without a calculator, 10% is the easiest to work out. This is because 10% is the same as one tenth.

Examples
Find:

1. 10% of £240

   $10\% = 240 \div 10$
   $= £24$

2. 40% of £60

   $10\% = 60 \div 10$
   $= £6$
   $40\% = 6 \times 4$
   $= £24$

Value added tax (VAT) is a tax you pay on the cost of items bought. VAT is currently charged at 15%

Example
Find the VAT on a jumper that costs £30.

$15\% = 10\% + 5\%$
$10\% = 30 \div 10 \quad 5\% = 3 \div 2$
$\quad\;\; = 3 \qquad\qquad\;\;\; = 1.50$

So VAT charged on a jumper costing £30 is:

£3 + £1.50
= £4.50

The actual price of the jumper including VAT is £30 + £4.50 = £34.50.

Increasing and Decreasing by a Percentage

You will often have to find a value when an amount is increased or decreased by a percentage.

Examples

1 In a sale, all the prices are reduced by 30%. Find the sale price of a TV which originally cost £699.

Method 1

Work out 30% of £699

$30 \div 100 \times 699 = £209.70$

Subtract this from the original amount
$699 - 209.70 = £489.30$

Method 2

Use a **multiplier**. A 30% decrease is a multiplier of $100 - 30 = 70\%$

$70\% = 0.7$ (just divide 70 by 100)

$£699 \times 0.7 = £489.30$

2 The cost of a train ticket increases by 5%. If the original price of the train ticket is £47, using a multiplier method what is the new cost of the ticket?

An increase of 5% is a multiplier of $100 + 5 = 105\%$

$105\% = 1.05$ (just divide by 100)

$1.05 \times 47 = £49.35$

One Quantity as a Percentage of Another

Sometimes you need to write one quantity as a percentage of another.

Example

Write 25cm as a percentage of 3m.

Firstly check that the units are the same, then change if necessary: 3m = 300cm.

Now write as a **fraction**: $\frac{25}{300}$

Now multiply by 100%: $\frac{25}{300} \times 100 = 8.\dot{3}\%$

Inflation

Inflation is a general rise in prices across the economy. The rate of inflation is given as a percentage. The inflation rate is the measure of the average change in prices across the economy over a specified period – usually 12 months.

This is called the annual rate of inflation.

The target rate of inflation is 2%. But, in June 2008 the inflation rate rose to 3.8%, the highest rate in 16 years. Soaring fuel costs and energy bills were blamed for the rise.

Percentages

Profit and Loss

If you buy a product, the price you pay is the **cost price**. If you sell the product, the price you sell it for is the **selling price**.

Profit (or loss) is the difference between the cost price and the selling price.

You can write profit or loss as the percentage of the original price:

Percentage profit (or loss) $= \dfrac{\text{Profit (or loss)}}{\text{Original}} \times 100\%$

Examples

❶ Charlotte bought a flat for £137 000. She sold it four years later for £185 000. Calculate her percentage profit.

Profit $= £185\,000 - £137\,000$
$\qquad = £48\,000$
Percentage profit $= \dfrac{48000}{137000} \times 100\% \approx 35\%$

❷ Reece bought a new car for £8500. He sold it two years later for £4300. Work out his percentage loss.

Loss $= £8500 - £4300$
$\qquad = £4200$
Percentage loss $= \dfrac{4200}{8500} \times 100$
$\qquad\qquad\qquad \approx 49\%$

Repeated Percentage Change

When a quantity is increasing or decreasing over a period of time, we usually use multipliers to work out the percentage change.

Example

A boat was bought for £13 700. During the first year it depreciated in value by 15%, the second year by 10% and the third year by 8%. Work out the value of the boat at the end of the third year.

A decrease of 15% is a multiplier of 0.85%
A decrease of 10% is a multiplier of 0.9%
A decrease of 8% is a multiplier of 0.92%

Value of the boat $= 13\,700 \times 0.85 \times 0.9 \times 0.92$

year 1   year 2   year 3

$\qquad = £9642.06$

Fractions, Decimals & Percentages

Fractions, **decimals** and percentages are all related:

Divide the numerator by the denominator to change to a decimal → $\frac{1}{2} = 0.5$

Multiply the decimal by 100 → $0.5 \times 100 = 50\%$

The table shows some of the common fractions and their equivalents that you need to learn:

Fraction	Decimal	Percentage
$\frac{1}{2}$	0.5	50%
$\frac{1}{3}$	$0.\dot{3}$	$33.\dot{3}\%$
$\frac{2}{3}$	$0.\dot{6}$	$66.\dot{6}\%$
$\frac{1}{4}$	0.25	25%
$\frac{3}{4}$ $\xrightarrow{3 \div 4}$	0.75 $\xrightarrow{\times 100\%}$	75%
$\frac{1}{5}$	0.2	20%
$\frac{1}{8}$	0.125	12.5%
$\frac{3}{8}$	0.375	37.5%
$\frac{1}{10}$	0.1	10%
$\frac{1}{100}$	0.01	1%

The Daily News

BANK OF ENGLAND CUTS BASE RATE BY HALF A PERCENT

In October 2008, when the global financial markets were in freefall, the Bank of England and other European banks cut their base rates by 0.5 percent in order to kick start the economy and avoid an economic downturn.

Percentage

Ordering Different Numbers

When putting fractions, decimals and percentages into order of size, it is best to change them all to decimals first.

Example

Place these numbers in order of size, smallest first...

$\frac{1}{3}$, 0.362, 34%, 29.1%, $\frac{2}{9}$, 0.271

Put into decimals:

$0.\dot{3}$, 0.362, 0.34, 0.291, $0.\dot{2}$, 0.271

Now order:

$0.\dot{2}$, 0.271, 0.291, $0.\dot{3}$, 0.34, 0.362

Rewrite in their original form:

$\frac{2}{9}$, 0.271, 29.1%, $\frac{1}{3}$, 34%, 0.362

0.271
0.291
0.34
0.362

Quick Test

1. Explain how you would find 5% of a quantity.
2. What is 60% of £80?
   a) £8   b) £32   c) £4.80   d) £48
3. An increase of 20% is the same as which multiplier?
   a) 0.2   b) 1.2   c) 0.8   d) 1.8
4. Write 62kg as a percentage of 80kg.
5. A laptop computer costs £450. It is sold two years later for £320. The percentage loss is 41%. True or false?

Skills Practice

1 There are 140 people on a train. 25% have a newspaper.
How many of them have a newspaper?

2 Use a calculator to find: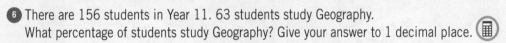
   a) 12% of 420 miles   **b)** 76% of £640   **c)** 37% of 8200g   **d)** 28% of 92cm

3 Sarah earns £328 per week. She is given a 3% pay rise.
Work out Sarah's new weekly wage.

4 Write 62kg as a percentage of 125kg.

5 Molly got 16 out of 30 in a Science test. What percentage did she get in the Science test?

6 There are 156 students in Year 11. 63 students study Geography.
What percentage of students study Geography? Give your answer to 1 decimal place.

7 For each of the following, work out the percentage profit:

Garden furniture	Bought: £199	Sold: £320
Bay tree	Bought: £24	Sold: £40
Plant pot	Bought: £9	Sold: £34

8 A lorry was bought for £9500. A year later it was sold for £7100.
Work out the percentage loss.

9 A block of company shares was bought for £200000. During the first year the value
increased by 8% and then in the second year by 4%. What is the value of the block
of shares after two years?

10 Place in order of size, smallest first:

   41%, $\frac{2}{5}$, 0.369, 37%, $\frac{2}{3}$, 0.409

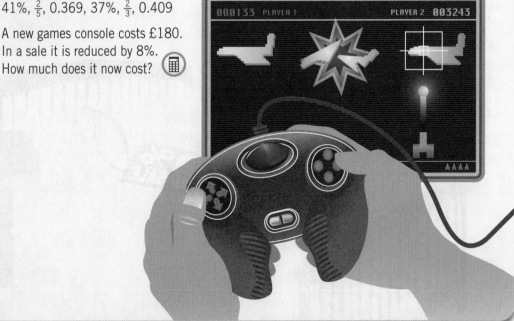

11 A new games console costs £180.
In a sale it is reduced by 8%.
How much does it now cost?

Percentages

Percentages

We see percentages all the time in everyday life. A percentage is a fraction with a denominator of 100.

Increasing and Decreasing by a Percentage

You can choose to use either of the following methods to solve increases and decreases by a percentage.

Example
In a sale a bed is reduced by 20%. Find the sale price if the bed originally cost £499.

Method 1
20% of £499

$$\frac{20}{100} \times 499 = 99.80$$

£499 – £99.80 = £399.20

(For a non-calculator method, work out 10% by dividing by 10 then multiply by 2 to find 20%.)

Method 2
This time we use a multiplier method.

A 20% decrease is a multiplier of 100 – 20 = 80% = 0.8

£499 × 0.8 = £399.20

> If you had a 20% increase this would have been added to 100.
> 100 + 20 = 120% = 1.2
> The multiplier would be 1.2

One Quantity as a Percentage of Another

There are many situations where you may need to find a quantity as a percentage of another quantity.

Example

Charlotte got 64 out of 82 in a Science test. What percentage did Charlotte get (to the nearest percentage)?

① Check that the units are the same and then write as a fraction.

$$\frac{64}{82}$$

② Then multiply by 100

$$\frac{64}{82} \times 100 = 78\%$$

Profit and Loss

Profit and loss calculations are used in everyday life.

Percentage **profit** (or **loss**)

$$= \frac{\text{Profit (or loss)}}{\text{Original}} \times 100$$

Examples

① Jonathan bought a motorbike for £8500. Four years later he sold it for £5150. Work out his percentage loss.

cost price – selling price = 8500 – 5150
$$= £3350$$
percentage loss $\frac{3350}{8500} \times 100 = 39.4\%$
(1 d.p.)

② Rupinder bought a time-share for £89 000. Six years later she sold it for £137 000. Work our her percentage profit.

profit = 137 000 – 89 000
$$= £48\,000$$
percentage profit $\frac{48\,000}{89\,000} \times 100 = 53.9\%$
(1 d.p.)

Effect of the Recession

When there's a 'credit crunch' money is more difficult to borrow on mortgages. After 10 years of growth in the housing market, in 2007 / 2008 the price of properties started to fall. Negative equity is when the value of a property is less than the mortgage owed on it.

The UK housing market experienced one of the largest 'unexplained' increases in property prices over the past decade. Prices were 20-30% higher in 2008 than could be justified by 'fundamentals' such as rising population or higher incomes. Due to the recession, housing markets turned down across western Europe and houses subsequently lost much of their increased value.

Percentages

Repeated Percentage Change

Use multipliers to find the increase or decrease of a quantity over a period of time.

Example

A block of shares was bought for £156 000 in 2006. Each year the value of the shares fell by 8%. Work out the value of the shares after three years.

Decrease of 8% is a multiplier of...

$(100 - 8) = 92\% = 0.92$

Value of shares = $156\,000 \times 0.92 \times 0.92 \times 0.92$

$= £121\,457.33$

Alternatively write the equation as

$156\,000 \times 0.92^3 = £121\,475.33$

Simple Interest

Simple interest is the interest that is sometimes paid on money in banks and building societies. The interest is paid each year (per annum or p.a.) and is the same amount each year.

Example

Asif has £1500 in his savings account. Simple interest is paid at 4.5% p.a. How much does Asif have in his account at the end of the year?

Increasing by 4.5% is the same as multiplying by 104.5%. The multiplier is 1.045.

$1500 \times 1.045 = £1567.50$
  Interest paid = £67.50

If Asif kept his money in the account for three years he would get...
$3 \times 67.50 = £202.50$

So, at the end of the year, Asif has £1702.50 in his account.

Compound Interest

Compound interest is the type of interest where the bank pays interest on interest earned as well as on the original money.

Example

Asif has £1500 in his savings account. Compound interest is earned at 4.5% p.a. How much will Asif have in his account after three years?

Increasing by 4.5% is the same as multiplying by 104.5%. The multiplier is 1.045.

Value of savings...
After 1 year = 1500×1.045 = £1567.50
After 2 years = 1567.50×1.045 = £1638.04
After 3 years = 1638.04×1.045 = £1711.75

A quicker way is to write...
      $1500 \times 1.045 \times 1.045 \times 1.045$
  = 1500×1.045^3
  = £1711.75

Reverse Percentage Problems

In reverse percentage problems the original quantity is calculated.

Examples

1 The price of a bottle of perfume is reduced by 10%. If it now costs £34.20, what was the original price?

The sale price is...
100% – 10% = 90% of the pre-sale price.

$0.9 \times$ (original price) = 34.20

original price = $\dfrac{34.20}{0.9}$

= £38

original price ⟶ ×0.9 ⟶ sale price
original price ⟵ ÷0.9 ⟵ sale price

2 The price of a computer is £499 including VAT at 15%. Work out the price of the computer excluding VAT.

The price including VAT...
100% – 15% of the original price.

$1.15 \times$ (original price before tax) = the price including VAT

$1.15 \times$ (original price before tax) = 499

original price before tax = $\dfrac{499}{1.15}$

= £433.91

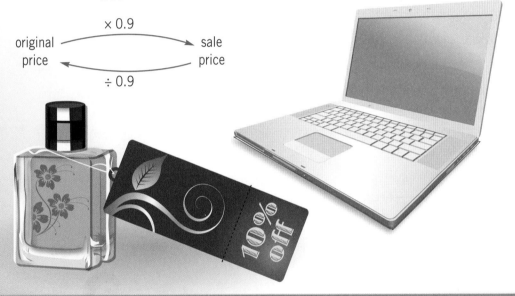

Quick Test

1 20% of £60 = 12. True or false?
2 An increase of 45% is represented by which multiplier?
   a) 0.45   **b)** 1.45   **c)** 1.045   **d)** 0.045
3 The simple interest earned per year on £10 000 with an interest rate of 5% is £10 500. True or false?
4 Calculate 25m as a percentage of 2km.

Percentages

Skills Practice

1. Find the new amount when...
   a) £60 is increased by 8%.
   b) £430 is decreased by 9%.
   c) 2.7kg is decreased by 16%.
   d) 33kg is increased by 35%.

2. Erin earns £428 per week working in an office. She is given a pay rise of 2.45%. 🖩
   Work out Erin's new weekly wage.

3. Amelie gained 56 out of 75 in a German test. What percentage did she get? 🖩

4. Colin spends £48 out of £136 on rent. What percentage does he spend on rent? 🖩

5. In a class of 28 students, 3 students are left-handed. What percentage are left-handed? 🖩

6. The cost of a train ticket is £34. The train fares increase by 6% in April. 🖩
   How much is the train ticket in April?

7. In 2001 Lucy bought a flat for £126 000. She sold it for £212 000 in 2008. 🖩
   What is her percentage profit?

8. Sarah bought an ipod for £175. She sold it for £86. What is her percentage loss? 🖩

9. A car costs £16 500 when new. Two years later it is sold for £12 150. 🖩
   What is the percentage loss?

10. In a survey of 240 people, 37.5% use the gym. How many people use the gym? 🖩

11. A new power saw costs £78. With depreciation its value falls by 12% each year. Work out the value of the power saw after two years.

12. An investment of £7000 is made for three years at 4% p.a. compound interest. What is the total interest earned?

13. If £4500 is invested for two years at 5.5% p.a compound interest, what is the total interest earned?

14. A painting costs £870. Each year it increases in value by 7%. How much is the painting worth after two years?

15. Audrey bought a train ticket using a senior railcard and was given a reduction of 32%. She paid £19.04 for her ticket. Calculate the full price of the ticket, before the discount.

16. The cost of a theatre ticket rises by 7% to £23.54. What was the original price of the ticket?

17. The cost of a washing machine is £424.15 after a 15% reduction. What was the original cost of the washing machine?

15% off

Standard Index Form

Standard Index Form

Standard index form is used as a simpler way to write very large or very small numbers.

A number written in standard form is written as...

$$a \times 10^n$$

Where $1 \leq a < 10$ and n is the power of 10 (index) by which you multiply or divide.

In general...
- the front number (a) must always be at least 1 but less than 10
- the power of 10, n:
  - if the number is large, n is positive
  - if the number is small, n is negative.

Examples

1. The planet Venus is 108 000 000km from the sun. In standard form this is 1.08×10^8km since you move decimal place by eight places.

2. A red corpuscle (blood cell) in a typical adult weighs about 0.000 000 0001 gram. In standard form this is 1×10^{-10} gram.

Large Numbers

Use the method below to simplify very large numbers.

Examples

1. Write 7 210 000 in standard index form.
   - Write the number so it lies between 1 and 10. In this case it is 7.21.

- Work out how many times you multiply by 10 to restore the number (the power of 10).
  7.21×10^6

In standard index form $7\,210\,000 = 7.21 \times 10^6$

2. Write 64 000 in standard index form...
   $64\,000 = 6.4 \times 10^4$

Small Numbers

Use the method below to simplify very small numbers.

Examples

① Write 0.000 546 in standard index form.

- Write the number so that it lies between 1 and 10. In this case it is 5.46.
- Work out how many times you divide the number by 10.
  5.46×10^{-4}

  In standard index form
  $0.000\,546 = 5.46 \times 10^{-4}$

② Write 0.000 000 714 in standard index form...
$0.000\,000\,714 = 7.14 \times 10^{-7}$

Standard Form and the Calculator

To key a number in standard index form into the calculator, use the EXP key. Some calculators have a EE key – check your calculator.

Examples

① 7.9×10^4 is keyed in as

[7] [.] [9] [EXP] [4]

② 5.73×10^{-6} is keyed in as

[5] [.] [7] [3] [EXP] [−] [6]

The display panel of some calculators doesn't show standard form correctly.

4.92^{-07} means 4.92×10^{-7}

③ Work out $(7 \times 10^{29}) \times (6 \times 10^{-12})$.
Leave your answer in standard index form.

Check you get the answer 4.2×10^{18}

④ Work out $\sqrt{\dfrac{(7.6 \times 10^{12})^2}{(3.1 \times 10^{-4})}}$

Check you get the answer 4.32×10^{14}.

Standard Index Form

Calculations with Standard Index Form

A calculator can be used to do more complex calculations involving standard index form.

For example...
$(4 \times 10^9) \times (3 \times 10^{-7}) = 1200 = 1.2 \times 10^3$
would be keyed in as...

The laws of indices can also be used when manually multiplying and dividing numbers written in standard form.

Examples

1     $(3 \times 10^7) \times (5 \times 10^6)$
   $= (3 \times 5) \times (10^7 \times 10^6)$ ← Add the powers together, $6 + 7 = 13$
   $= 15 \times 10^{13}$
   $= 1.5 \times 10^{14}$

2     $(6 \times 10^9) \div (2 \times 10^4)$
   $= (6 \div 2) \times (10^9 \div 10^4)$ ← Subtract the powers, $9 - 4 = 5$
   $= 3 \times 10^5$

Quick Test

1. 270 written in standard form is 2.7×10^2. True or false?
2. 0.0046 written in standard form is 46×10^{-4}. True or false?
3. 3×10^6 written as an ordinary number is...
   a) 3000   b) 30 000   c) 0.000 003
   d) 0.000 000 3
4. $(3 \times 10^5) \times (2 \times 10^7) = 6 \times 10^{35}$. True or false?

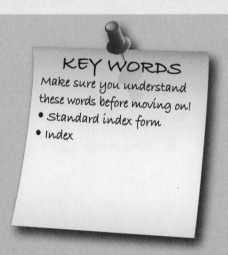

KEY WORDS
Make sure you understand these words before moving on!
- Standard index form
- Index

Skills Practice

1 Write the following in standard form.
- **a)** 7560
- **b)** 3 000 000
- **c)** 520 000
- **d)** 490 000 000
- **e)** 630 000
- **f)** 71 000
- **g)** 5 200 000
- **h)** 41 000
- **i)** 9 800 000

2 Write the following in standard form.
- **a)** 0.0046
- **b)** 0.000 009
- **c)** 0.097
- **d)** 0.84
- **e)** 0.000 009 1
- **f)** 0.000 099
- **g)** 0.476
- **h)** 0.000 000 000 7
- **i)** 0.000 055 5

3 Write the following numbers as ordinary numbers.
- **a)** 3×10^4
- **b)** 6×10^2
- **c)** 3.2×10^5
- **d)** 7.2×10^7
- **e)** 3.6×10^{-5}
- **f)** 2.5×10^{-3}
- **g)** 6×10^{-2}
- **h)** 5×10^{-4}
- **i)** 7.4×10^{-8}

4 Work out the following without using a calculator.
- **a)** $(2 \times 10^6) \times (4 \times 10^5)$
- **b)** $(3 \times 10^9) \times (1 \times 10^2)$
- **c)** $(4 \times 10^5) \times (2 \times 10^3)$
- **d)** $(6 \times 10^7) \div (3 \times 10^4)$
- **e)** $(8 \times 10^{11}) \div (4 \times 10^6)$

5 Work out the following using a calculator.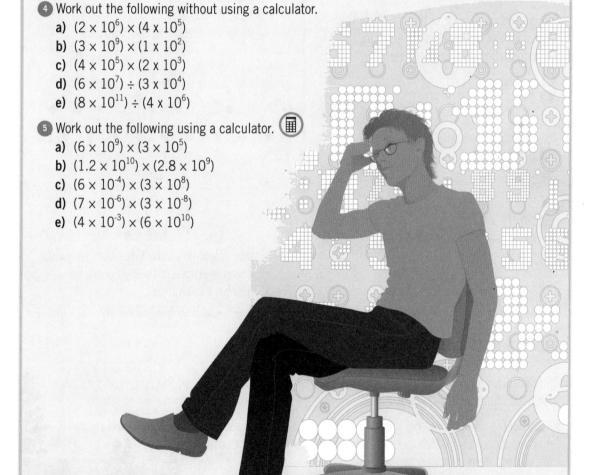
- **a)** $(6 \times 10^9) \times (3 \times 10^5)$
- **b)** $(1.2 \times 10^{10}) \times (2.8 \times 10^9)$
- **c)** $(6 \times 10^{-4}) \times (3 \times 10^8)$
- **d)** $(7 \times 10^{-6}) \times (3 \times 10^{-8})$
- **e)** $(4 \times 10^{-3}) \times (6 \times 10^{10})$

Number Patterns

Number Patterns

A **number pattern** is a list or series of numbers that are connected by a rule.

You need to be able to recognise a number pattern and see how it builds up.

Another name for a number pattern is a **sequence**. Each value in the list of numbers is called a **term**.

When finding a missing term in a number pattern, look to see what's happening in the gap between previous terms.

Examples

1 2, 4, 6, 8, 10, ...
+2 +2 +2 +2

> The rule for this pattern is to add 2 each time.

2 5, 15, 45, 135, ...
×3 ×3 ×3

> The rule for this pattern is to multiply the previous term by 3.

3 20, 17, 14, 11, 8, 5, ...
–3 –3 –3 –3 –3

> The rule for this pattern is to subtract 3 each time.

Special Number Patterns

There are some special number patterns that you need to be able to recognise:
- 1, 4, 9, 16, 25, ...
  these are square numbers
- 1, 8, 27, 64, 125, ...
  these are cube numbers
- 2, 4, 8, 16, 32, ...
  these are the powers of 2
- 1, 3, 6, 10, 15, ...
  these are the triangular numbers

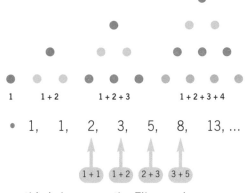

| 1 | 1 + 2 | 1 + 2 + 3 | 1 + 2 + 3 + 4 |

- 1, 1, 2, 3, 5, 8, 13, ...
  1 + 1   1 + 2   2 + 3   3 + 5

this is known as the Fibonacci sequence. The rule is to add the two previous numbers each time.

Who was Fibonacci?

Fibonacci's real name was Leonardo of Pisa. He lived about 1175AD–1250AD.

Fibonacci is often called 'the greatest European mathematician of the Middle Ages' because of his contributions to mathematics.

He was one of the first people to introduce the Hindu-Arabic number system into Europe – the positional system, based on ten digits and the decimal point, used today.

Fibonacci introduced the Fibonacci sequence when looking at the breeding of rabbits.

Many aspects of nature are linked by the Fibonacci sequence.

Number Patterns in Diagrams

Number patterns can be seen in diagrams.

Example

The patterns below are made up of sticks.

4 sticks

7 sticks

10 sticks

13 sticks

Draw the next pattern in the sequence.

First, work out the rule to go from one pattern to the next. The rule is to add on 3 sticks each time.

So, the next pattern looks like this:

16 sticks

Number Machines

Number machines can be used to make number patterns.

When a number pattern is put into a number machine, the output numbers also make a pattern.

Input   **Output**

$3 \longrightarrow \times 4 \longrightarrow 12$

KEY WORDS

Make sure you understand these words before moving on!

- Number pattern
- Sequence
- Term

Number Patterns

Skills Practice

1 For each sequence, write down...
- **i)** the next two numbers
- **ii)** the rule for finding the next number.

- **a)** 2, 4, 6, 8, ...
- **b)** 5, 9, 13, 17, ...
- **c)** 10, 7, 4, 1, ...
- **d)** 64, 32, 16, 8, ...
- **e)** 30, 25, 20, 15, ...
- **f)** 9, 18, 27, 36, ...
- **g)** 70, 60, 50, 40, ...
- **h)** 20, 40, 80, 160, ...

2 For each sequence, fill in the two missing terms and write down the rule that the sequence follows.

- **a)** 3, 6, 9, ..., ..., 18
- **b)** 9, 13, 17, ..., ..., 29
- **c)** 48, 45, 42, ..., ..., 33
- **d)** ..., ..., 26, 21, 16, 11
- **e)** 60, 54, 48, 42, ..., ..., 24
- **f)** 1, 4, 9, ..., ..., 36
- **g)** 1, 2, 4, 7, ..., ..., 22
- **h)** 3, 6, 12, ..., ..., 96

3 Here is a sequence of shapes made up of squares.

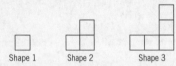

Shape 1   Shape 2   Shape 3

- **a)** Draw the next two shapes in the sequence.
- **b)** Copy and complete the following table:

Shape	1	2	3	4	5
Number of squares	1	3			

- **c)** How many squares will there be in shape 9?
- **d)** How many squares will there be in shape 25?

4 Look at this sequence of shapes made up of matchsticks:

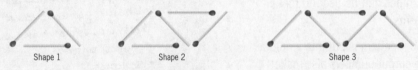

Shape 1   Shape 2   Shape 3

- **a)** Draw the next shape in the sequence.
- **b)** Copy and complete the following table:

Shape	1	2	3	4
Matchsticks				

- **c)** Write down the rule to go from one shape to the next.

5 This sequence is the first seven terms of the Fibonacci sequence:
1, 1, 2, 3, 5, 8, 13, ...
Continue the sequence up to, and including, the 15th term.

6 For each of the function tables below, write down what happens to the input in order to get the output.

a)

Input	Output
3	8
7	12
9	14

c)

Input	Output
2	4
7	14
4	8

e)

Input	Output
16	4
64	16
8	2

b)

Input	Output
7	5
12	10
4	2

d)

Input	Output
12	4
24	8
6	2

f)

Input	Output
2	5
5	11
9	19

7 For each of the number machines below...
i) input the number pattern 2, 4, 6, 8
ii) list the output numbers
iii) describe the pattern it produces.

a)
× 5

c)
× 2   + 3

b)
+ 6

d)
× 3   − 2

8 Begin a sequence by writing the number 8.
Add 4 to give the 2nd term.
Add 4 to the 2nd term to give the 3rd term.
Continue until you have found the first 6 terms in the sequence.

9 Write down the first five terms of four different number patterns that each begin 1, 2, ...

Extension

Find an example of where the Fibonacci sequence occurs in nature.

Number Patterns and Sequences

Number Patterns

A **number pattern** is a list or series of numbers connected by a rule.

Another name for a number pattern is a **sequence**. Each value in the list of numbers is called a **term**.

Example

3,   6,   9,   12,...
  +3 +3 +3

The rule for this pattern is to add 3 each time. This is called a term-to-term rule.

Number patterns can easily be generated by using a spreadsheet.

Number Machines

Number machines can be used to make number patterns. When the number is put into a number machine, the output numbers also make a pattern.

Input   Output
  3   × 2   + 1   7

KEY WORDS
Make sure you understand these words before moving on!
- Number Pattern
- Sequence
- Term
- Common difference

The nth Term

You can find a term in a sequence using a position-to-term rule, if you know the term's position.

Position in Sequence	1	2	3	4	5	n
Term	3	6	9	12	15	$3n$

×3

+3 +3 +3 +3

The term-to-term rule is 'add 3'.

The position-to-term rule is 'multiply by 3'.

The 20th term would be $20 \times 3 = 60$.

The nth term of a sequence is the same as the position-to-term rule, written using algebra.

In the example above, the position-to-term rule is 'multiply by 3'. The nth term would be $3n$.

Example

Position in Sequence	1	2	3	4	5	...	n
Term	7	11	15	19	23	...	$4n+3$

×4
+3

To find the nth term look at the **common difference** between the terms (the term-to-term rule). In this example it is 'add 4'. Since the gap is the same this always multiplies with the nth term, so $4n$.

If you now check: when $n = 1$, $4 \times 1 = 4$. Since the term is 7 we adjust it by adding 3, which gives $4n+3$.

When $n = 2$, $4 \times 2 + 3 = 11$

So here the nth term is $4n+3$

Skills Practice

1 For each sequence, write down:
  i) the next two numbers
  ii) the rule for finding the next number

  a) 3, 5, 7, 9,...   **c)** 10, 20, 30, 40,...   **e)** 3, 6, 12, 24,...
  b) 10, 8, 6, 4,...   **d)** 100, 50, 25, 12.5,...   **f)** 20, 17, 14, 11,...

2 Look at the sequence of shapes made up of matchsticks.

  a) Draw the next two shapes in the sequence.
  b) Copy and complete the following table:

Shape	1	2	3	4	5
Number of Matchsticks					

  c) How many squares will there be in shape 8?
  d) Write down the *n*th term of this sequence.

3 Find the *n*th term of each of these sequences:
  a) 2, 4, 6, 8, 10,...   **c)** 8, 10, 12, 14, 16,...   **e)** 8, 12, 16, 20, 24,..
  b) 3, 5, 7, 9, 11,...   **d)** 5, 7, 9, 11, 13,...   **f)** 4, 7, 10, 13, 16,...

4 For each of the number machines below:
  i) input the number pattern 3, 5, 7...
  ii) list the output numbers.
  iii) describe the pattern it produces.

  a)   × 4

  b)   × 2   − 1

  c)   × 3   + 4

  d)   × 5   − 3

Number Patterns & Sequences

The nth Term of a Linear Sequence

You can find a **term** in a **sequence** using a position-to-term rule if you know its position.

This is called a **linear** sequence because it goes up by a constant amount each time.

Position in Sequence	1	2	3	4	5
Term	6	11	16	21	26

$\times 5 + 1$

$+5$ $+5$ $+5$ $+5$

The term-to-term rule is 'add 5'.

The nth term of a sequence is the same as the position-to-term rule, written using algebra.

For example...

Position in Sequence	1	2	3	4	5	...	n
Term	6	11	16	21	26	...	$5n+1$

$\times 5 + 1$

The position-to-term rule is 'multiply by 5 and add 1'. The nth term would be $5n + 1$.

Position in Sequence	1	2	3	4	5	...	n
Term	4	7	10	13	16	...	$3n+1$

$\times 3 + 1$

$+3$ $+3$ $+3$ $+3$

To find the nth term, look at the gap between the terms. In this example it is 'add 3'. Since the gap is the same it always multiplies with the nth term so $3n$.

Now check: when $n = 1$
$3 \times 1 = 3$, however since the term is 4 we adjust it by adding 1, which gives $3n + 1$.

The *n*th Term of a Quadratic Sequence

For a **quadratic** sequence, the first differences are not constant but the second differences are.

The *n*th term takes the form...
$$an^2 + bn + c$$

Where either *b* and/or *c* may be zero.

Example
Find the *n*th term of 2, 6, 12, 20...

Position in sequence	1	2	3	4	5
Term	2	6	12	20	30
First difference		4	6	8	10
Second difference			2	2	2

a is found by dividing the second difference by 2.
*n*th term is $n^2 + n$ or $n(n + 1)$

The sequence can be represented by a spatial pattern using rectangles. The areas of these rectangles are:

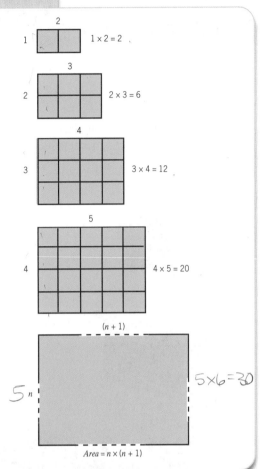

$1 \times 2 = 2$

$2 \times 3 = 6$

$3 \times 4 = 12$

$4 \times 5 = 20$

$5 \times 6 = 30$

Area = $n \times (n + 1)$

Quick Test

1. Find the *n*th term for each of these sequences.

   a) 2, 4, 6, 8, 10,...
   b) 3, 5, 6, 9, 11,...
   c) 4, 6, 8, 10, 12,...
   d) 7, 10, 13, 16, 19,...
   e) 6, 10, 14, 18, 22,...
   f) 9, 8, 7, 6, 5,...
   g) 3, 8, 13, 18, 23,...

2. Find the *n*th term for each of these sequences.
   a) 1, 4, 9, 16, 25,...
   b) 2, 8, 18, 32, 50,...
   c) 0, 3, 8, 15, 24,...
   d) -2, 1, 6, 13, 22,...
   e) 5, 20, 45, 80, 125...

Working with Algebra

Algebra

Algebra is an area of mathematics in which letters are used to represent numbers.

Algebra is used to solve many mathematical problems.

Example

Amy has n sweets.
Bertie has two more sweets than Amy.
Colin has twice as many sweets as Amy.
Davinder has three sweets less than Colin.
Complete the table by filling in the number of sweets each child has.

Child	Sweets
Amy	n
Bertie	$n + 2$
Colin	$2n$
Davinder	$2n - 3$

2 more sweets, i.e. add 2.

Twice as many sweets.

3 sweets fewer, so subtract 3.

Terms and Expressions

A **term** is a number, a letter, or a combination of numbers and letters multiplied together:
- Terms are separated by + or – signs.
- Each + or – sign is joined to the term that follows it.

$$6ab \ - \ 3b \ + \ 5$$

ab term with an invisible plus sign in front of it

b term

Number term

A collection of terms is known as an **expression**.

You should follow these rules when writing expressions:
- A single a is written as a, not $1a$
- $a \times b$ is written as ab
- $a \times 2 \times b$ is written as $2ab$, that is, with the number first and the letters in alphabetical order
- $n \div 3$ is written as $\dfrac{n}{3}$

Collecting Like Terms

Expressions can be simplified by collecting like terms.

Like terms have the same letters and powers.

Examples

1. $5x + 4x = 9x$
2. $3y - y + 7y = 9y$
3. $5xy + 3yx = 8xy$ ← xy and yx mean the same thing.
4. $5a + 4b - a + 6b = 4a + 10b$

The minus is part of the a.

Add the a terms, then the b terms.

Remember to put the sign between the terms, that is, $4a + 10b$, not $4a10b$.

Multiplying Terms Together

Algebraic expressions are often simplified by multiplying terms together.

Examples

1. $3x \times 4y$
   $= 3 \times 4 \times x \times y$
   $= 12xy$

2. $5a \times 2b \times 3c$
   $= 5 \times 2 \times 3 \times a \times b \times c$
   $= 30abc$

Powers in Algebra

x^4 means $x \times x \times x \times x$

This is said as 'x to the power four'.

Similarly, $y^6 = y \times y \times y \times y \times y \times y$

Examples
Simplify these expressions using powers:

1. $2x \times 3y \times x$
   $= 2 \times x \times 3 \times y \times x$
   $= 6x^2y$

2. $b \times 2b \times 3b$
   $= 6b^3$

Multiplying out Single Brackets

Brackets are often used in algebra.

For example, $5 \times (x + y)$ is usually written as $5(x + y)$.

Multiplying out brackets is known as 'expanding the brackets'.

To expand brackets, each term inside the brackets is multiplied by the term outside the brackets.

Examples
Expand...

1. $5(a + b)$
   $= 5 \times a + 5 \times b$
   $= 5a + 5b$

2. $3(a - 4)$
   $= 3 \times a - 3 \times 4$
   $= 3a - 12$

3. $x(2x + 3y)$
   $= x \times 2x + x \times 3y$
   $= 2x^2 + 3xy$

Working with Algebra

Using Word Formulae

A **formula** connects two expressions that contain **variables**.

The value of one variable depends on the values of the others.

A formula must contain an equals sign.

Science uses a lot of formulae. For example, a formula you may use in Physics is...

Force	=	Mass	×	Acceleration

Example
Sukhvinder buys some sweets. She uses this formula:

Cost of sweets	=	Cost of one bag	×	Number bought

If one bag of sweets costs 56p, work out the total cost if Sukhvinder buys eight bags.

Cost of sweets = 56 × 8
= 448
= £4.48

Using Letters in Formulae

Formulae can be shortened by using letters to stand for unknown amounts.

Consider the formula used in science to find the force of an object:

Force	=	Mass	×	Acceleration

This can be written as:

$$F \quad = \quad m \quad \times \quad a$$

Where: F = force
m = mass
a = acceleration

Example
The instructions for cooking a turkey are:

'Allow 40 minutes for each kilogram of turkey, then add a further 35 minutes.'

A turkey has a mass of w kilograms. The total time to cook it is t minutes. Using letters, write a formula connecting w and t.

$t = 40w + 35$ ◀— Add 35 minutes.

↑
Multiply each kilogram by 40.

Substituting into Formulae

Numbers are substituted into formulae to help solve problems.

Examples

❶ The perimeter, P, of a rectangle is given by this formula:

$$P = 2l + 2w$$

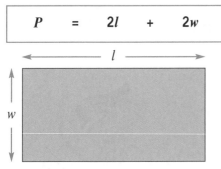

Work out the perimeter of a rectangle with l = 6cm and w = 2cm.

$P = 2l + 2w$
$= 2 \times 6 + 2 \times 2$
$= 12 + 4$
$= 16$cm

❷ The monthly cost, C pence, of making calls from a mobile phone for m minutes is given by the following formula:

$$C = 450 + 8m$$

Work out the cost of the mobile phone bill for a month in which 80 minutes worth of calls were made.

$C = 450 + 8 \times 80$
$= 450 + 640$
$= 1090$
$= £10.90$

Working with Algebra

Skills Practice

1 In a game, Lucy has p marbles.
Write down the number of marbles that each of the following people has in terms of p.
   a) Jake has three times as many marbles as Lucy.
   b) Tia has four fewer marbles than Lucy.
   c) Hannah has six more marbles than Jake.

2 For each of the following, write out the expression that it describes:
   a) 6 less than t **f)** r less than n
   b) 5 more than h **g)** p less than y
   c) 4 more than p **h)** y more than x
   d) 2 less than m **i)** p more than m
   e) 6 more than x **j)** k less than b

3 For each of the following, write out the expression that it describes:
   a) 6 times b **e)** 3 times y
   b) a divided by 2   **f)** 2 times 5 more than x
   c) e divided by 7   **g)** p more than x, divided by y
   d) 5 times x

4 Simplify these expressions by collecting like terms:
   a) $6a + 3a - a$ **h)** $7a + 2a - b + 6b$
   b) $4b + 10b - 7b$ **i)** $3a + 6a - a$
   c) $3p + 4q - 2p + q$ **j)** $7x - 2x + 3y - y$
   d) $5x - 3y + 5y - x$ **k)** $4a - 3p + 2p - 6p + 2a$
   e) $5b + 2b$ **l)** $7b - 2b + 6b + 5b$
   f) $3a + 5b + 2a - b$ **m)** $12a - 3y - 2y - 13a + 9y$
   g) $5a - 3b + 6b$ **n)** $5p - 2p + 3p - 5a - 2a + 3b - 6b$

5 Simplify these expressions:
   a) $3x \times 2x$ **f)** $2a \times 5a$
   b) $4b \times b$ **g)** $3p \times 9p$
   c) $5b \times 3b$ **h)** $a \times 2a \times a$
   d) $4y \times 3y$ **i)** $5a \times 2a \times a$
   e) $6a \times a$ **j)** $5a \times a \times 6a$

6 Multiply out the brackets:

a) $5(x - 1)$

b) $6(x + 5)$

c) $3(2x + 4)$

d) $x(x - 6)$

e) $3(x + 1)$

f) $5(x - 4)$

g) $2(x - 6)$

h) $x(x + 5)$

i) $5(x - 6)$

j) $7(2x + 1)$

k) $x(x - 1)$

l) $3(3x - 6)$

m) $7(5 - 2x)$

n) $3x(x - 2)$

o) $6(2 - 4x)$

p) $5(3 - 6x)$

q) $2x(x - 5)$

7 If $a = 2$, $b = 3$ and $c = 5$, find the value of the following expressions:

a) $2a$

b) $5b$

c) $6c$

d) $a + 3b$

e) $5a - b$

f) $2a + 3b$

g) $6c + a$

h) $2b - 3a$

i) $5c - 2b$

j) b^2

k) $3a + 6c$

l) $10c - 2b - a$

m) $\dfrac{60}{c}$

n) $3a + \dfrac{27}{b}$

8 Billy buys some pens. He uses this formula:

Cost of pens	=	Cost of one pen	×	Number bought

The cost of one pen is 28p.

Billy buys 5 pens.

Find the total price that Billy pays for the pens.

9 The temperature in Dubai is $p°$C.

The temperature in England is $q°$C.

The difference between the temperatures in Dubai and England is $d°$C.

a) Write a formula connecting d, p and q.

b) If the temperature in Dubai is 30°C and in England it's 2°C, use your formula to find the difference, $d°$C.

Working with Algebra

Algebra

Algebra uses letters to represent values.

Algebra is used to solve many problems.

Definitions Used in Algebra

Expression is any arrangement of letters and symbols, e.g. $2z + 3b - 6$.

A **formula** connects two expressions containing variables. The value of one variable depends on the value of another. A formula must have an equals sign. For example:

$F=ma$ is a formula. When the values of m and a are known the value of F can be found.

An **equation** connects two expressions involving definite unknown values. An equation must have an equals sign, e.g. $2x + 1 = 5$.

The **identity** connects expressions involving unspecified numbers. An identity is always true no matter what numerical values replace the letter symbols. It has an $\equiv$ sign, e.g. $4(x - 1) \equiv 4x - 4$.

A **function** is a relationship between two sets of values, so that a value from the first set maps onto a unique value in the second set, e.g. $y = 5x - 1$. For any value of x the value of y can be calculated.

Using Letter Symbols

There are several rules to follow when writing expressions:

$b + b$ is written as $2b$
$b \times c$ is written as bc
$2 \times b \times c$ is written as $2bc$ — Here the number is written first and the letters put in alphabetical order
$b \times b = b^2$
$b \div 2 = \frac{b}{2}$

Example
In a game, John has x counters. Write down the number of counters each person has using x.
a) Imran has three times as many counters as John $= 3x$
b) Sophie has ten less counters than John $= x - 10$
c) Peta has half as many counters as John $= \frac{x}{2}$
d) Rebecca has four less counters than Imran $= 3x - 4$.

Collecting Like Terms

Expressions can be simplified by collecting like **terms**.

Examples

Simplify...

① $3a - a = 2a$

② $2a - b + 6b - 5a = -3a + 5b$ or $5b - 3a$

add the b's together

add the a's together

Powers in Algebra

Powers are used in algebra to help write terms in a shorter form.

$a \times a = a^2$

$a \times a \times a = a^3$

$a \times a \times a \times a = a^4$

a^b is read as 'a to the power of b' where a is the base and b is the **power** or **index**.

Examples

① $2x \times 3x$
$= 2 \times x \times 3 \times x$
$= 6x^2$

② $3a \times 2b$
$= 3 \times a \times 2 \times b$
$= 6ab$

③ $4x \times 3y \times 2x$
$= 4 \times x \times 3 \times y \times 2 \times x$
$= 24x^2y$

④ $12a \times 3a \times a$
$= 12 \times a \times 3 \times a \times a$
$= 36a^3$

To multiply powers of numbers or letters add the powers together.

$$y^2 \times y^4 = (y \times y) \times (y \times y \times y \times y)$$
$$= y^6$$
$$y^2 \times y^4 = y^{2+4} = y^6$$

Examples

① $2a^6 \times a^5 = 2a^{6+5} = 2a^{11}$

② $2a^5 \times 5a^3 = 10a^8$

add the powers together

multiply 2 and 5 together

Multiplying Out Single Brackets

Brackets are often used in algebra, for example $3 \times (x - y)$ is usually written as $3(x - y)$.

Multiplying out brackets is often known as 'expanding brackets'. To expand brackets, each term inside the bracket is multiplied by the term outside the bracket.

Examples

Expand...

① $3(a - b)$
$= 3 \times a - 3 \times b$
$= 3a - 3b$

② $x(2x - 3y)$
$= x \times 2x - x \times 3y$
$= 2x^2 - 3xy$

③ $5(x - 3) + 2(x - 1)$
$= 5x - 15 + 2x - 2$
$= 7x - 17$

Multiply out both brackets

Simplify by collecting like terms

④ $3(2x - 1) - 2(x + 1)$
$= 6x - 3 - 2x - 2$
$= 4x - 5$

Working with Algebra

Factorising Simple Expressions

Factorising is the reverse process to that of removing brackets. An expression is put into brackets by taking out **common factors**.

4 $5x + x^2$

$= x(5 + x)$ ← *x* is the common factor

Examples

Factorise...

1 $8x + 12$

$= 4(2x + 3)$ ← Look for the common factors of $8x$ and 12. 4 is the highest common factor, so this can be put outside the bracket. The expression inside the bracket is what is needed so that when multiplied out it returns to the original.

2 $12x - 3y$

$= 3(4x - y)$

$4(2x + 3)$ —expand→ ←factorise— $8x + 12$

3 $20a + 40b$

$= 20(a + 2b)$

Origins of Algebra

The word 'algebra' comes from the Arabic word *al-jabr*. Al-jabr means 'reunion'. Algebra concerns the study of structure, relation and quantity, and it is one of the main branches of mathematics.

The origins of algebra can be traced to the ancient Babylonians, who developed an advanced arithmetical system which they used to do calculations in an algebraic fashion.

Writing Formulae

A formula can usually be constructed from some information you are given or from a diagram.

Examples

1 Colin buys n bags of sweets at 20p each. He pays with a £5 note. Write down the formula if he receives C pounds change.

$$C = 5 - 0.2n$$

This is the amount of money he spends per bag. Make sure the units are the same: 20p = £0.20.

This represents the amount of money used to buy the sweets.

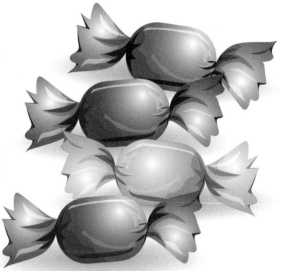

2 Some patterns are made by using grey and white paving slabs.

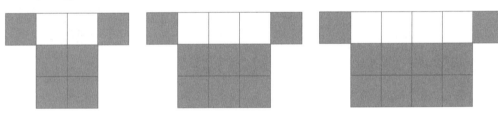

A formula connecting the number of grey paving slabs (g) in a pattern that uses white (w) ones is:

$$g = 2w + 2$$

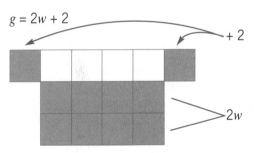

$+ 2$

$2w$

$2w$ represents the two layers

$+ 2$ gives the grey slabs on either side.

When there are 20 white slabs there will be $2 \times 20 + 2 = 42$ grey slabs

Working with Algebra

Substituting into Formulae and Expressions

Lots of formulae are used in science. Numbers are substituted into formulae to help solve problems.

Examples

1 In Science, $v = u + at$ is used to calculate velocity.

a) Calculate the value of v if $u = 20$, $a = 12$ and $t = 7$:

$v = u + at$

$v = 20 + (12 \times 7)$

$v = 20 + 84$

$v = 104$

b) Calculate the value of v if $u = 15$, $a = 13$ and $t = 6$:

$v = u + at$

$v = 15 + (-13 \times 6)$

$v = 15 - 78$

$v = -63$

2 If $a = \dfrac{b^2 c}{\sqrt{d}}$

Find the value of a if $b = 6$, $c = 5.8$ and $d = 49$. Give your answer to 1 decimal place.

$a = \dfrac{b^2 c}{\sqrt{d}}$

$a = \dfrac{6^2 \times 5.8}{\sqrt{49}}$

$a = \dfrac{208.8}{7}$

$a = 29.8$

Gas bills are worked out using formulae. The bill depends on how many units of gas have been used.

Quick Test

1 Explain how you should write the term $5 \times b \times d \times a$?

2 What is the expression $3a - 5b + 6b - a$ fully simplified?

a) $4a + 11b$ **c)** $4a + 1b$

b) $2a + 2b$ **d)** $2a + b$

3 Multiply out the brackets: $3x(x - y)$ gives $3x^2 - 3xy$. True or false?

4 $2a \times 3a \times 2b$ is $8a^2 b$. True or false?

5 $F = ma$. Work out F if $m = 12$ and $a = 3.5$

KEY WORDS

Make sure you understand these words before moving on!

- Algebra
- Expression
- Formula
- Equation
- Identity
- Function
- Term
- Power
- Index
- Factorising
- Common factors

1. Simplify these expressions by collecting like terms:
   a) $3a + 2a - a$
   b) $6a - b + 5a$
   c) $3x + 10y - 2x - y$
   d) $5y - 2y + 10y - y$
   e) $5c - 4d - 3d + 6c$
   f) $3xy + 2xy - xy^2$

2. Simplify these expressions:
   a) $4a \times 2a$
   b) $3a \times 6b$
   c) $5d \times 3e$
   d) $6b \times b$
   e) $7a \times 2a$
   f) $9p \times 6p$
   g) $5a \times 3b \times 2a$
   h) $3a \times 2a \times a$

3. Expand and simplify:
   a) $5(x - 1)$
   b) $3(x + 2y)$
   c) $3(2x - 4)$
   d) $x(x + 3)$
   e) $5(x - 3) + 2(x - 1)$
   f) $12(x - 4) - 3(x - 1)$

4. Factorise the following:
   a) $15x - 5$
   b) $20y + 10$
   c) $3x - 9y$
   d) $x^2 + 2x$
   e) $14y - 2y^2$
   f) $9y + 12$

5. If $a = 3$, $b = 4$ and $c = -4$, work out the following expressions:
   a) $5a + b$
   b) $6a - 2b$
   c) $c^2 + 4$
   d) $3b - a$
   e) $2b^2 + 3$
   f) $5b - 2c$

6. In a garden there are x pink flowers. Write down each of the number of plants in terms of x.
   a) There are three times as many bushes as pink flowers.
   b) There are five fewer white flowers than pink flowers.
   c) There are half the number of hanging baskets as pink flowers.

Working with Algebra

Algebra Terms

Algebra uses letters to represent values.

An **expression** is any arrangement of letters and symbols.

A **formula** connects two expressions containing **variables**. The value of one variable depends on the value of another.

An **equation** connects two expressions, involving definite unknown values. An equation must have an equals sign.

The **identity** connects expressions involving unspecified numbers.

A **function** is a relationship between two sets of variables.

The rules to follow when writing expressions are…

$a + a + a = 3a$

$x \times y \times 3 = 3xy$

> The number is written first and the letters put into alphabetical order

$x \div 4 = \dfrac{x}{4}$

Laws of Indices

There are laws that apply when working with **indices**.

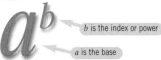

a^b

> b is the index or power

> a is the base

The bases in the equation have to be the same when the laws of indices are applied.

To multiply **powers** of numbers or letters, add the indices together, e.g. $x^a \times x^b = x^{a+b}$.

Example
$$y^5 \times y^2 = (y \times y \times y \times y \times y) \times (y \times y)$$
$$= y^7$$

To divide indices of numbers or letters, subtract the indices, e.g. $x^a \div x^b = x^{a-b}$.

Example
$$y^7 \div y^3 = \frac{y \times y \times y \times y \times y \times y \times y}{y \times y \times y}$$

> Cancel $y \times y \times y$ top and bottom

$$= y \times y \times y \times y$$
$$= y^4$$

To find the power of a power, multiply the indices together, e.g. $(x^a)^b = x^{a \times b}$.

Example
$$(y^2)^3 = y^2 \times y^2 \times y^2 = y^6$$

Any letter raised to the power of zero is equal to 1, e.g. $a^0 = 1$, $x^0 = 1$, $y^0 = 1$.

Examples
Simplify…

1. $2x^5 \times x^4 = 2x^{5+4} = 2x^9$

2. $12x^9 \div 3x^4 = 4x^{9-4} = 4x^5$

> Divide the numbers as usual $12 \div 3 = 4$

3. $(x^6)^4 = x^{6 \times 4} = x^{24}$

4. $x^0 = 1$

5. $\dfrac{x^7 \times 3x^4}{x^5} = \dfrac{3x^{7+4}}{x^5} = \dfrac{3x^{11}}{x^5} = 3x^{11-5} = 3x^6$

Multiplying out Single Brackets

Remember when you're asked to expand an expression that you need to multiply out both **brackets**.

Examples

Expand...

① $5(x - 3)$
$= 5x - 15$

Multiply out both brackets. Simplify by collecting like terms.

② $x(x-6)$
$= x^2 - 6x$

③ $y(2y + 3)$
$= 2y^2 + 3y$

④ $3y(2y - 4)$
$= 6y^2 - 12y$

Expand and **simplify**...

① $3(x - 2) + 2(x + 1)$
$= 3x - 6 + 2x + 2$
$= 5x - 4$

② $5(3x - 1) - 2(x - 3)$
$= 15x - 5 - 2x + 6$
$= 13x + 1$

③ $6(x - 5) - (2x - 1)$
$= 6x - 30 - 2x + 1$
$= 4x - 29$

-(2x – 1) is the same as -1(2x – 1)

④ $2(5x - 1) + 3(x - 6)$
$= 10x - 2 + 3x - 18$
$= 13x - 20$

⑤ $7(3x - 6) - (x - 4)$
$= 21x - 42 - x + 4$
$= 20x - 38$

Factorising Simple Expressions

Factorising is the addition of brackets to an equation by taking out the common factors.

Example

Factorise...

① $5x + 10$
$= 5(x + 2)$

The 5 is the highest common factor. The expression in brackets is the number and letter needed so that when multiplied out it returns to the original.

② $3x - 9$
$= 3(x - 3)$

③ $12x - 4$
$= 4 (3x - 1)$

④ $16 - 8x$
$= 8(2 - x)$

⑤ $7x - 21$
$= 7(x - 3)$

⑥ $15x - 25y$
$= 5(3x - 5y)$

⑦ $20x - 40y$
$= 20(x - 2y)$

⑧ $30a^2 - 60a$
$= 30a(a - 2)$

⑨ $5x^2 + 12x$
$= x(5x + 12)$

⑩ $25a^2 + 15a$
$= 5a(5a + 3)$

Working with Algebra

Multiplying out Two Brackets

There are several methods that can be used to multiply out two brackets.

Expand $(x + 2)(x + 3)$

Method 1

$(x + 2)(x + 3) = x(x + 3) + 2(x + 3)$

$\qquad\qquad\qquad = x^2 + 3x + 2x + 6$

$\qquad\qquad\qquad = x^2 + 5x + 6$

Multiply out in stages

Simplify by collecting like terms

Method 2

$(x + 2)(x + 3) = x^2 + 3x + 2x + 6$

$\qquad\qquad\qquad = x^2 + 5x + 6$

Multiply each term with each other

Method 3

This rectangle has the lengths $(x + 2)$ and $(x + 3)$. The total area of the rectangle is $(x + 2)(x + 3)$.

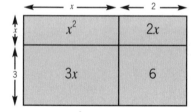

$(x + 2)(x + 3) = x^2 + 3x + 2x + 6$

$\qquad\qquad\qquad = x^2 + 5x + 6$

Examples

Expand...

① $(x + 3)(x + 5)$

$\quad = x^2 + 5x + 3x + 15$

$\quad = x^2 + 8x + 15$

② $(x - 1)(x - 4)$

$\quad = x^2 - 4x - x + 4$

$\quad = x^2 - 5x + 4$

③ $(x - 5)(x + 3)$

$\quad = x^2 + 3x - 5x - 15$

$\quad = x^2 - 2x - 15$

④ $(x + 3)(x - 3)$

$\quad = x^2 - 3x + 3x - 9$

$\quad = x^2 - 9$

⑤ $(x + 3)^2$

$\quad = (x + 3)(x + 3)$

$\quad = x^2 + 3x + 3x + 9$

$\quad = x^2 + 6x + 9$

An expression of the form $ax^2 + bx + c$ is called a **quadratic** expression.

Codes and the Enigma Machine

As long ago as the Ancient Greeks, warring armies have written messages using codes in order to keep their battle plans a secret from their enemies.

Over time the codes and ciphers have become more and more complex and difficult to crack.

During the Second World War, the Germans used the famous Enigma Machine, which they believed to be uncrackable, to encode messages. Polish Mathemeticians worked throughout the pre-war period to try to crack the code. During the war the British worked at Bletchly Park to refine the code breaking and decipher the messages produced using the code.

Factorising Quadratics

You need to be able to factorise a quadratic expression into a pair of linear brackets.

Examples

① Factorise $x^2 + 5x + 6$

> These values multiply to give 6 and add to give 5.

$x^2 + 5x + 6 = (x \pm a)(x \pm b)$
$x^2 + 5x + 6$
$= (x + 2)(x + 3)$

Since $2 \times 3 = 6$ and $2 + 3 = 5$.

② Factorise $x^2 - 6x + 5$

$x^2 - 6x + 5$
$= (x - 1)(x - 5)$

Since $-1 \times -5 = 5$ and $-1 - 5 = -6$.

③ Factorise $x^2 - 3x - 4$

$x^2 - 3x - 4$
$= (x + 1)(x - 4)$

Since $1 \times -4 = -4$ and $1 - 4 = -3$.

④ Factorise $x^2 - 25$

$x^2 - 25$
$= (x - 5)(x + 5)$

> This is known as the difference of two squares

$5 \times -5 = -25$ and $5 - 5 = 0$ as there is no x term.

In general:

$$x^2 - a^2 = (x + a)(x - a)$$

Substituting into Formulae and Expressions

Remember, you will need to substitute numbers into formulae to solve problems.

Examples

① If $a = 3$, $b = -2$ and $c = 0.6$, find the value of the expression:

$a^2 + 2b - 4c$
$= 3^2 + (2 \times -2) - (4 \times 0.6)$
$= 9 - 4 - 2.4$
$= 2.6$

② If $p = 4\frac{1}{2}$, $q = 6.5$ and $r = -2$, find the value of the expression:

$p - 2q^2 + 5r$
$= 4\frac{1}{2} - 2 \times (6.5)^2 + (5 \times -2)$
$= 4\frac{1}{2} - 84.5 + -10$
$= -92$

③ $V = \frac{4}{3}\pi r^3$ is the formula for a sphere.

Find the value of V if $r = 6.4$cm. Give your answer to 4 s.f.

$V = \frac{4}{3} \times \pi \times 6.4^3$
$V = 1098$cm^3 (4 s.f.)

Working with Algebra

Rearranging Formulae

The **subject of a formula** is the letter that appears on its own on one side of the formula. Formula can be rearranged to make one of the other letters the subject.

Examples

1. Make y the subject of this formula:

$$p = 5y - x$$

$$p + x = 5y \qquad \text{Add } x \text{ to both sides}$$

$$\frac{p + x}{5} = y \qquad \text{Divide both sides by 5}$$

2. Make b the subject of this formula:

$$a = \frac{5b^2 - c}{d}$$

$$ad = 5b^2 - c \qquad \text{Multiply both sides by } d$$

$$ad + c = 5b^2 \qquad \text{Add } c \text{ to both sides}$$

$$\frac{ad + c}{5} = b^2 \qquad \text{Divide both sides by 5}$$

$$\sqrt{\frac{ad + c}{5}} = b \qquad \text{Square root both sides}$$

Quick Test

1. $5x^4 \times 3x^6$ simplified is $8x^{10}$. True or false?
2. What does $(x^4)^3$ give?
   a) x^7 b) x^{12} c) x^1 d) x^{16}
3. $5x^2 - 25$ fully factorised is $5(x^2 - 5)$. True or false?
4. Expand and simplify $(x + 2)(x - 6)$
5. $x^2 - 60$ is the difference of two squares. True or false?

KEY WORDS

Make sure you understand these words before moving on!
- Expression
- Formula
- Variable
- Equation
- Identity
- Function
- Indices
- Power
- Brackets
- Expand
- Simplify
- Factorisation
- Quadratic
- Linear
- Difference of two squares

Skills Practice

1 Simplify...

a) $x^7 \times x^2$

b) $4x \times 3x^2$

c) $10x^4 \div 5x$

d) $(x^4)^5$

e) $20x^6 \div 2x$

f) $12x^7 \div 2x^5$

g) $(2x^2)^3$

h) $(xy)^0$

2 Expand...

a) $7(2x - 1)$

b) $3(x + 6)$

c) $x(3x - 5)$

d) $2x(x + 6)$

e) $(x + 3)(x - 1)$

f) $(x - 7)(x - 2)$

g) $(x + 6)(x + 4)$

h) $(x - 5)(x + 2)$

3 Expand and simplify...

a) $5(x - 6) + 2(x - 1)$

b) $3(2x - 1) + 5(x - 6)$

c) $10(x - 3) + 2(2x - 1)$

4 Factorise...

a) $16x - 12$

b) $20x + 10$

c) $3x^2 + 6x$

d) $12x - 24x^2$

e) $x^2 + 8x + 12$

f) $x^2 + 2x + 1$

g) $x^2 - 7x + 10$

h) $x^2 - 3x - 4$

5 Work out these expressions, if $a = 2$, $b = 7.6$ and $c = -\frac{1}{2}$

a) $a^2 + 2b$

b) $3a - b + 5c$

c) $6a - 3b - c^2$

6 Make t the subject of the formula:
$a^2 = t^2 + d$

Equations

Solving Equations

An **equation** has two parts separated by an equals sign.

When solving an equation, a **solution** to the equation is found.

The balance method (doing the same to both sides of the equation) is often used to find the solution.

Examples
Solve the following:

1. $x + 5 = 12$

   $x = 12 - 5$ ← Subtract 5 from both sides.

   $x = 7$

2. $x + 25 = 20$

   $x = 20 - 25$ ← Subtract 25 from both sides.

   $x = -5$

3. $x - 12 = 10$

   $x = 10 + 12$ ← Add 12 to both sides.

   $x = 22$

4. $5x = 20$

   $x = \dfrac{20}{5}$ ← Divide both sides by 5.

   $x = 4$

5. $7x = 15$

   $x = \dfrac{15}{7}$ ← Divide both sides by 7.

   $x = 2\frac{1}{7}$

6. $\dfrac{x}{6} = 3$

   $x = 3 \times 6$ ← Multiply both sides by 6.

   $x = 18$

7. $\dfrac{3x}{2} = 12$

   $3x = 12 \times 2$ ← Multiply both sides by 2.

   $3x = 24$

   $x = \dfrac{24}{3}$ ← Divide both sides by 3.

   $x = 8$

Equations of the Form $ax+b=c$

Some equations are more complicated and are of the form $ax + b = c$

Examples
Solve the following:

1. $5x + 2 = 12$

   $5x = 12 - 2$ ← Subtract 2 from both sides.

   $5x = 10$

   $x = \dfrac{10}{5}$ ← Divide both sides by 5.

   $x = 2$

2. $\dfrac{x}{4} + 3 = 8$

   $\dfrac{x}{4} = 8 - 3$ ← Subtract 3 from both sides.

   $\dfrac{x}{4} = 5$

   $x = 5 \times 4$ ← Multiply both sides by 4.

   $x = 20$

3. $\dfrac{5x}{2} + 1 = 10$

   $\dfrac{5x}{2} = 10 - 1$ ← Subtract 1 from both sides.

   $\dfrac{5x}{2} = 9$

   $5x = 9 \times 2$ ← Multiply both sides by 2.

   $5x = 18$

   $x = \dfrac{18}{5}$ ← Divide both sides by 5.

   $x = 3\frac{3}{5}$ ← Write the answer as a mixed number.

When solving problems, an equation can be written to find an unknown value.

Examples

① The perimeter of the triangle is 32cm.

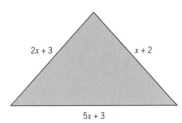

a) Write down an equation for the perimeter.

The equation is...
$2x + 3 + x + 2 + 5x + 3 = 32$

Collecting like terms gives $8x + 8 = 32$

b) Solve the equation.

$$8x + 8 = 32$$
$$8x = 32 - 8$$
$$8x = 24$$
$$x = \frac{24}{8}$$
$$x = 3\text{cm}$$

c) Write down the length of each side of the triangle.

Substitute $x = 3$ into each expression to find the lengths of the triangle:

$$2x + 3 = 2 \times 3 + 3$$
$$= 9\text{cm}$$

$$x + 2 = 3 + 2$$
$$= 5\text{cm}$$

$$5x + 3 = 5 \times 3 + 3$$
$$= 18\text{cm}$$

So the sides are 9cm, 5cm and 18cm.

② The cost of hiring a van is £15 per hour, plus £45. Mr Jones hires a van for x hours and pays a total of £135.

Write an equation and solve it to find out how many hours Mr Jones hired the van for.

$$15x + 45 = 135$$

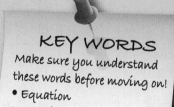

£15 per hour.   Standing charge of £45.

$$15x = 135 - 45$$
$$15x = 90$$
$$x = \frac{90}{15}$$
$$x = 6$$

Mr Jones hired the van for 6 hours.

Quick Test

① Explain how you would solve the equation
$x + 6 = 10$
② Explain how you would solve the equation
$x - 2 = 12$
③ Explain how you would solve the equation
$5x = 20$
④ The solution to the equation $5x + 2 = 17$ is 3.
True or false?
⑤ What is the solution to the equation
$\frac{x}{2} + 1 = 5$?

A 12   **B** 3   **C** 8   **D** 10

> **KEY WORDS**
> Make sure you understand these words before moving on!
> • Equation
> • Solution

Equations

Skills Practice

1 Solve the following:

a) $x + 2 = 6$ f) $x + 6 = 27$ k) $x + 15 = 12$

b) $x + 3 = 9$ g) $x + 10 = 9$ l) $5 + x = 9$

c) $x + 10 = 7$ h) $x + 6 = 4$ m) $7 + x = 2$

d) $x + 12 = 24$ i) $x + 10 = 5$ n) $10 + x = 19$

e) $x + 9 = 12$ j) $x + 9 = 7$

2 Solve the following:

a) $x - 4 = 9$ f) $15 = x - 3$ k) $7 = x - 4$

b) $x - 7 = 2$ g) $x - 6 = 12$ l) $26 = x - 3$

c) $x - 10 = 6$ h) $x - 9 = 7$ m) $38 = x - 1$

d) $x - 9 = 27$ i) $x - 5 = 12.6$ n) $15 = x - 6$

e) $x - 8 = 31$ j) $x - 9 = 15.5$

3 Solve the following:

a) $5x = 10$ f) $7x = 56$ k) $5x = 24$

b) $6x = 18$ g) $2x = 64$ l) $12x = 144$

c) $3x = 6$ h) $8x = 64$ m) $3x = 13$

d) $9x = 27$ i) $5x = 55$ n) $2x = 7$

e) $9x = 81$ j) $7x = 18$

4 Solve the following:

a) $\dfrac{x}{3} = 6$ c) $\dfrac{x}{9} = 10$ e) $\dfrac{x}{7} = 2$

b) $\dfrac{x}{2} = 10$ d) $5 = \dfrac{x}{3}$ f) $9 = \dfrac{x}{4}$

5 Solve the following:

a) $\dfrac{2x}{3} = 6$ c) $\dfrac{4x}{5} = 8$ e) $\dfrac{3x}{5} = 9$

b) $\dfrac{5x}{7} = 5$ d) $\dfrac{6x}{11} = 12$ f) $\dfrac{7x}{9} = 10$

6 Solve the following:

a) $x + 4 = 6$ f) $x + 2 = 11$ k) $5x = 30$

b) $x - 2 = 9$ g) $x - 6 = 10$ l) $6x = 12$

c) $x + 6 = 10$ h) $\dfrac{x}{3} = 2$ m) $7x = 28$

d) $x - 5 = 3$ i) $\dfrac{x}{4} = 8$ n) $10x = 130$

e) $x - 7 = 12$ j) $\dfrac{x}{5} = 6$

Skills Practice (cont.)

7 Solve the following:

a) $2x + 1 = 11$ f) $10x + 5 = 55$ k) $5x - 4 = 36$

b) $3x - 2 = 7$ g) $4x + 6 = 10$ l) $7x + 6 = 20$

c) $5x + 1 = 21$ h) $7x - 2 = 12$ m) $3x - 2 = 6$

d) $4x - 2 = 10$ i) $9x - 1 = 8$ n) $5x - 4 = 20$

e) $7x - 1 = 20$ j) $5x + 3 = 23$ o) $3x + 2 = 36$

8 Solve the following:

a) $\dfrac{5x}{2} + 6 = 9$ b) $\dfrac{3x}{2} + 8 = 12$ c) $\dfrac{5x}{7} + 2 = 10$

9 For each of the following, write an equation to solve the problem.

a) Rachael buys 9 bags of raisins.

   The total cost is £2.88

   How much does each bag of raisins cost?

b) David thinks of a number.

   He multiplies it by 3 and adds 7.

   His answer is 49.

   What number did he think of?

10 Look at the following number pyramid:

The number in each cell is the sum of the
two cells above it.
Copy and complete the number pyramid and
use the information to find the value of n.

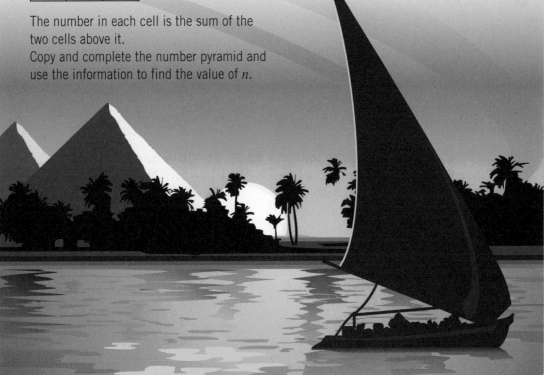

Equations and Inequalities

Equations

It was often claimed that the Babylonians (about 400BC) were the first to solve quadratic equations, that is, equations that have an x^2. They developed a method for working out problems that had only positive answers.

An **equation** has two parts separated by an equals sign. When solving an equation, a **solution** to the equation is found. The balance method (doing the same things to both sides of the equation) is often used to find the solution.

Equations of the Form of $ax + b = c$

When solving equations with an unknown on one side, firstly move anything which is adding or subtracting to the other side of the equals sign. You are then left with $ax = d$ which you can **solve**.

Examples

Solve the following:

① $7x - 2 = 12$

$7x = 12 + 2$ ⟵ Add 2 to both sides

$7x = 14$

$x = \frac{14}{7}$ ⟵ Divide both sides by 7

$x = 2$

② $\frac{x}{3} + 4 = 5$

$\frac{x}{3} = 5 - 4$ ⟵ Subtract 4 from both sides

$\frac{x}{3} = 1$

$x = 1 \times 3$ ⟵ Multiply both sides by 3

$x = 3$

Solving Equations of the Form $ax + b = cx + d$

When solving equations with letters on both sides of the equation (in this case x) get all the letters together on one side of the equals sign and the numbers on the other side.

Examples

① $3x + 2 = x + 6$

$3x + 2 - x = 6$ ⟵ Subtract x from both sides

$2x = 6 - 2$ ⟵ Subtract 2 from both sides

$2x = 4$

$x = \frac{4}{2}$ ⟵ Divide both sides by 2

$x = 2$

② $8x - 10 = 5x + 11$

$8x - 10 - 5x = 11$ ⟵ Subtract $5x$ from both sides

$8x - 5x = 11 + 10$ ⟵ Add 10 to both sides

$3x = 21$

$x = \frac{21}{3}$ ⟵ Divide both sides by 3

$x = 7$

③ $10 - 2x = 5x - 4$

$10 = 5x - 4 + 2x$ ⟵ Add $2x$ to both sides. This will keep the x's positive

$10 = 7x - 4$

$10 + 4 = 7x$ ⟵ Add 4 to both sides

$14 = 7x$

$\frac{14}{7} = x$ ⟵ Divide both sides by 7

$x = 2$

Solving Equations with Brackets

When solving equations with brackets always multiply the brackets out first.

Examples
Solve the following:

1 $3(2x + 1) = 15$ ← Multiply out the brackets
$6x + 3 = 15$
$6x = 15 - 3$ ← Subtract 3 from both sides
$6x = 12$
$x = \frac{12}{6}$ ← Divide both sides by 6
$x = 2$

2 $5(3x - 1) = 25$ ← Multiply out the brackets
$15x - 5 = 25$
$15x = 25 + 5$ ← Add 5 to both sides
$15x = 30$
$x = \frac{30}{15}$ ← Divide both sides by 5
$x = 2$

3 $2(x + 3) + 3(x - 1) = 8$ ← Multiply out each bracket
$2x + 6 + 3x - 3 = 8$ ← Collect like terms
$5x + 3 = 8$
$5x = 8 - 3$ ← Subtract 3 from both sides
$5x = 5$
$x = \frac{5}{5}$ ← Divide both sides by 5
$x = 1$

4 $4(2x + 1) = 2(x - 5)$ ← Multiply both sets of brackets out
$8x + 4 = 2x - 10$
$8x + 4 - 2x = -10$ ← Subtract 2x from both sides
$6x = -10 - 4$ ← Subtract 4 from both sides
$6x = -14$
$x = -\frac{14}{6}$ ← Divide both sides by 6
$x = -2\frac{1}{3}$

Notice that the answers can be positive or negative, whole or fractional.

Constructing and Solving Linear Equations

When solving problems, a linear equation can be written to find an unknown value.

Examples
1 Use the information in the diagram to:
  a) Form an equation.
  b) Solve the equation to find x.

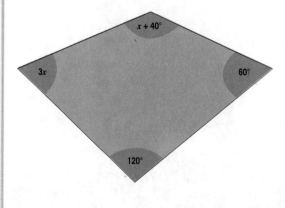

a) $3x + (x + 40°) + 120° + 60° = 360°$
Angles in a quadrilateral add up to 360°

b) $3x + (x + 40°) + 120° + 60° = 360°$
$4x° + 220° = 360°$ ← Collect like terms
$4x = 360° - 220°$
$4x = 140°$
$x = \frac{140°}{4}$
$x = 35°$

2 Joshua thinks of a number. He multiplies it by 4 and adds 3. He gets the same answer as if he multiplied his number by 2 and subtracted 1. What number did Joshua think of?

Let's call the number x.

$4x + 3 = 2x - 1$ ← Form the equation
$4x + 3 - 2x = -1$ ← Subtract 2x from each other
$4x - 2x = -1 - 3$
$2x = -4$
$x = \frac{-4}{2}$
$x = -2$

Equations and Inequalities

Trial and Improvement

In the method of trial and improvement, successive approximations are made to get closer to the correct value.

Example
The equation $x^2 - x = 15$ has a solution between 4 and 5.

You can see from the table that 14.96 is nearer to 15 than 15.75 so to 1 decimal place the solution of the equation $x^2 - x = 15$ between 4 and 5 is $x = 4.4$.

ICT can be used to solve an equation by trial and improvement. Set up a spreadsheet to check the solution of the above equation.

Find the solution to one decimal place. Draw a table to help:

x	$x^2 - x = 15$	Comment
4	$4^2 - 4 = 12$	Too small
5	$5^2 - 5 = 20$	Too big
4.5	$4.5^2 - 4.5 = 15.75$	Too big
4.4	$4.4^2 - 4.4 = 14.96$	Too small

Inequalities

There are four inequality symbols:

> Means 'greater than'

≥ Means 'greater than or equal to'

< Means 'less than'

≤ Means 'less than or equal to'

So, $x > 5$ or $5 < x$ both mean 'x is greater than 5'. $x = 6$ satisfies the inequality $x > 5$.

Example

Put the correct sign between these pairs of numbers:

a) 5 , 9

$5 < 9$

'5 is less than 9'

b) -3 , -5

$-3 > -5$

'-3 is greater than -5'

Inequalities can be represented on a number line:

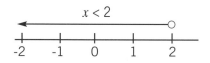

$x < 2$

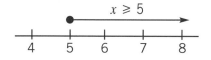

$x \geq 5$

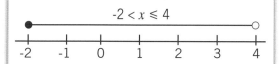

$-2 < x \leq 4$

Use ○ when the end point is not included, $x < 2$.

Use ● when the end point is included, $x \geq 5$.

Equations and Inequalities

Skills Practice

1 Solve the following:

a) $x + 2 = 10$

b) $4x = 16$

c) $x - 3 = 7$

d) $2 + x = 10$

e) $\dfrac{x}{4} = 2$

f) $3x = 12$

g) $\dfrac{x}{6} = 5$

h) $x - 2 = 10$

i) $x + 3 = 4$

j) $x - 6 = -2$

k) $3x = -15$

l) $\dfrac{x}{5} = -3$

2 Solve the following:

a) $5x + 1 = 11$

b) $3x - 2 = 10$

c) $5 + 4x = 21$

d) $3x + 5 = 29$

e) $6x - 1 = 11$

f) $3x - 5 = 10$

g) $2x + 1 = 9$

h) $2x - 6 = 9$

i) $5x - 1 = 9$

j) $3x - 6 = 20$

k) $4x + 3 = 8$

l) $2x - 3 = 19$

3 Solve the following:

a) $\dfrac{3x}{2} + 5 = 7$

b) $\dfrac{2x}{5} + 3 = 4$

c) $\dfrac{5x}{7} + 3 = 10$

4 Solve the following:

a) $5x + 2 = 3x + 6$

b) $3x - 1 = 2x + 8$

c) $7x + 6 = 2x + 11$

d) $3x - 2 = x + 4$

e) $5x - 6 = 3x + 10$

f) $10 - 7x = 3x + 40$

g) $6 - 4x = 2x + 24$

h) $9x - 3 = 4x - 12$

5 Solve the following:

a) $2(x + 1) = 12$

b) $3(x - 2) = 21$

c) $6(x + 1) = 24$

d) $7(2x - 1) = 35$

e) $5(x - 3) = 2(x + 6)$

f) $7(x - 4) = 2(2x + 1)$

g) $5(2x - 3) = 3(2x - 6)$

h) $7(x - 1) = 5(x - 3)$

6 Solve $2x^3 + x = 18$ by trial and improvement. Give your answer of the correct solution to 2 decimal places.

7 Put the correct sign between these pairs of numbers to make a true statement:

a) 5 , 9   b) 7 , 13   c) 15 , 8   d) 9 , 4   e) 7 , 17

8 The perimeter of the rectangle is 40cm.

2x + 5

x + 3

Work out the length and width of the rectangle.

9 Look at the following number pyramid.

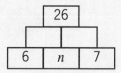

The two numbers in each cell are the sum of the two cells above it. Copy and complete the number pyramid and use the information to find n.

Equations & Inequalities

Equations

An **equation** has two parts separated by an equals sign.

When solving an equation, a **solution** to the equation is found.

Solving Equations of the Form $ax + b = c$

Remember, when solving equations of the form $ax + b = c$, to move anything you're adding or subtracting to the other side of the equals sign.

Examples

Solve the following...

① $7x - 3 = 10$

$7x = 10 + 3$

$7x = 13$

$x = \frac{13}{7}$

$x = 1\frac{6}{7}$ ← Write as a mixed number

② $5 - 2x = 10$

$5 = 10 + 2x$

$5 - 10 = 2x$ ← Subtract $2x$ from both sides to make $2x$ positive

$-5 = 2x$

$-\frac{5}{2} = x$

$x = -2.5$

Solving Equations of the Form $ax + b = cx + d$

Remember, when solving equations of the form $ax + b = cx + d$, to collect all of the letters together on one side of the equals sign and the numbers on the other.

Examples

Solve the following...

①

$5x - 4 = 3x - 12$

$5x - 4 - 3x = -12$

$5x - 3x = -12 + 4$

$2x = -8$

$x = -\frac{8}{2}$

$x = -4$

②

$\frac{x}{4} + 4 = 2x + 6$

$4 = 2x + 6 - \frac{x}{4}$

$4 - 6 = 2x - \frac{x}{4}$

$-2 = \frac{3x}{4}$

$3x = -2 \times 4$

$x = -\frac{8}{3}$

③

$3(x - 6) = 2(x + 4)$ ← Multiply out the brackets

$3x - 18 = 2x + 8$

$3x - 18 - 2x = 8$ ← Collect together the x values

$3x - 2x = 8 + 18$

$x = 26$

④ $5(2x + 1) + 3(x - 2) = 4(2x + 3)$

$10x + 5 + 3x - 6 = 8x + 12$ ← Multiply out the brackets

$13x - 1 = 8x + 12$

$13x - 1 - 8x = 12$

$13x - 8x = 12 + 1$

$5x = 13$

$x = \frac{13}{5}$

$x = 2\frac{3}{5}$

Notice that the answers can be positive, negative, whole or fractional.

Constructing and Solving Linear Equations

Remember to use linear equations to find an unknown value.

Example

A bag contains $b + 3$ green balls, $2b$ blue balls and $3b - 4$ yellow balls. The total number of balls is 35. Form an equation and solve it to find the value of b.

$b + 3 + 2b + 3b - 4 = 35$ ← Form an equation with the information

$$6b - 1 = 35$$
$$6b = 35 + 1$$
$$6b = 36$$
$$b = \frac{36}{6}$$
$$b = 6$$

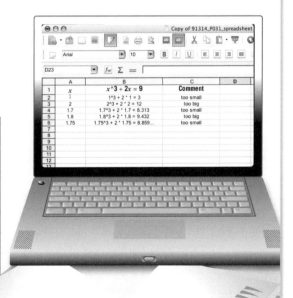

Trial and Improvement

Remember that you can use trial and improvement to get close to a correct value.

Example

The equation $x^3 + 2x = 9$ has a solution between 1 and 2. Use trial and improvement to find the solution. Give your answer correct to one decimal place.

Draw a table to help.

Using spreadsheets is a very useful way of solving equations by trial and improvement, as it's much quicker.

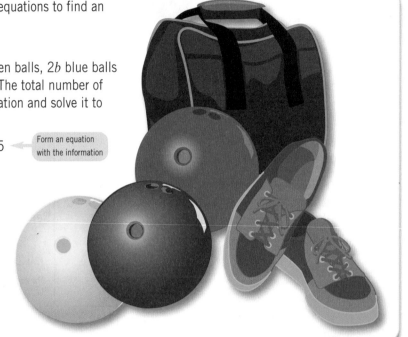

x	$x^3 + 2x = 9$	Comment
1	$1^3 + 2 \times 1 = 3$	too small
2	$2^3 + 2 \times 2 = 12$	too big
1.7	$1.7^3 + 2 \times 1.7 = 8.313$	too small
1.8	$1.8^3 + 2 \times 1.8 = 9.432$	too big
1.75	$1.75^3 + 2 \times 1.75 = 8.859...$	too small

$x = 1.8$ (1 d.p.)

Equations and Inequalities

Simultaneous Equations

You might find that you'll use **simultaneous equations** in your science studies. Simultaneous equations are two equations with two unknown values.

They can be solved in several ways. Solving equations simultaneously involves finding values for the letters which will make both equations work.

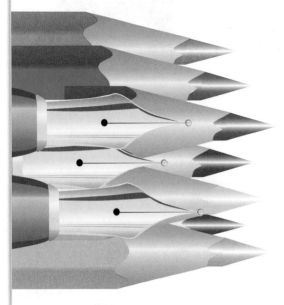

Example

Solve the simultaneous equations using the elimination method.

$2x + 4y = 16$
$3x - y = 3$

Simultaneous equations can be used to solve problems like: 6 pens and 5 pencils cost a total of £4.15, and 3 pens and 7 pencils cost a total of £3.65. Work out the cost of one pen and one pencil.

Try to set up a pair of simultaneous equations and solve them.

Step 1	Label the equations ① and ②.
	$2x + 4y = 16$ ①
	$3x - y = 3$ ②
Step 2	Since the **coefficients** don't match, multiply equation ② by 4. Rename it equation ③.
	$2x + 4y = 16$ ①
	$12x - 4y = 3$ ③
	The coefficient is the number a letter is multiplied by, for example, the coefficient of 4y is 4.
Step 3	The coefficient of y in equations ① and ③ are the same. Add equations ① and ③ together to eliminate y and then solve the remaining equation.
	$14x = 28$
	$x = \frac{28}{14}$
	$x = 2$
Step 4	Substitute $x = 2$ into equation ①. Solve the resulting equation to find y.
	$2x + 4y = 16$
	$(2 \times 2) + 4y = 16$
	$4 + 4y = 16$
	$4y = 16 - 4$
	$4y = 12$
	$y = \frac{12}{4}$
	Therefore, $y = 3$
Step 5	Check in equation ②.
	$3x - y = 3$
	$3 \times 2 - 3 = 3$
	The solution is...
	$x = 2, y = 3$

Inequalities

Inequalities can be used when budgeting. It can help to use a computer program that uses inequalities to set a list of conditions that need to be satisfied.

The four inequality symbols are:

>	means greater than
<	means less than
⩽	means greater than or equal to
⩾	means less than or equal to

So, $x > 3$ and $3 < x$ both mean 'x is greater than 3'.

Inequalities are used in an area of mathematics called linear programming. Linear programming was introduced in the 1940s, but has become much more popular since the revolution in the use of computers.

Linear programming is used for solving allocation problems and is widely used in businesses and organisations.

Solving Inequalities

Inequalities are solved in a similar way to equations.

Examples
Solve the inequalities and show the solution set on a number line.

1 $2x < 10$

$$x < \frac{10}{2}$$ 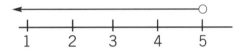 Divide both sides by 2

$$x < 5$$

When the end point is not included, we use an open circle o.

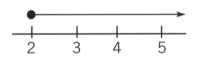

2 $5x - 1 \geqslant 14$
$5x \geqslant 14 + 1$
$5x \geqslant 15$
$x \geqslant \frac{15}{5}$
$x \geqslant 3$

When the end point is included, we use a closed circle ●

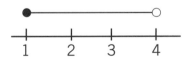

3 $5 \leqslant 6x - 1 < 23$
$6 \leqslant 6x < 24$ 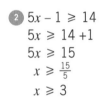 Add 1 to each part
$1 \leqslant x < 4$ Divide each part by 6

The integer values which satisfy this inequality are: 1, 2, 3...

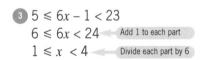

Integers are the set of numbers {...-3, -2, -1, 0, 1, 2, ...}

Equations and Inequalities

Graphical Inequalities

Inequalities can be represented graphically.

The graph of an equation $y = 4$ is a line, whereas the graph of the inequality $y < 4$ is a region that has a line $y = 4$ as its **boundary**.

Example

Leave unshaded the region $x \geq 2$, $y > 1$, $x + y \leq 4$

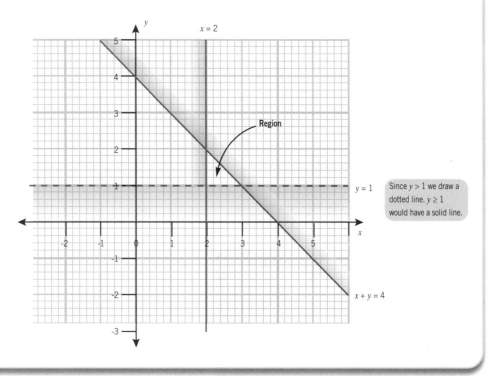

Region

$x = 2$

$y = 1$

Since $y > 1$ we draw a dotted line. $y \geq 1$ would have a solid line.

$x + y = 4$

Quick Test

1. What is the solution to $3x - 1 = 5$?
   a) -2   b) $\frac{4}{3}$ c) 1   d) 2
2. What is the solution to $5(2x - 1) = 30$?
   a) -3   b) 3.5   c) 2.5   d) 3.1
3. The solution to $5x - 1 = 3x + 8$ is $x = 4.5$.
   True or false?
4. What is the solution to $3(2x - 1) = 2(x + 4)$?
   a) 2.75   b) 2.25   c) 2.5   d) -2.75

KEY WORDS

Make sure you understand these words before moving on!
- Equation
- Solution
- Simultaneous equations
- Coefficients
- Inequalities
- Boundary

Skills Practice

1 Solve the following...
a) $3(x - 6) = 9$

b) $5(2x + 1) = 20$

c) $\dfrac{x}{7} = 4$

d) $\dfrac{3x}{2} + 5 = 11$

e) $4x + 2 = 14$

f) $3x - 5 = 22$

2 Solve the following...
a) $7x - 4 = 3x + 12$
b) $5x - 1 = 2x - 6$
c) $10x - 5 = 4x + 19$
d) $3(x - 6) = 2(2x + 1)$
e) $5(2x + 1) = 2(x - 3)$
f) $4(x - 1) = 3(2x + 6)$

3 Solve the following pairs of simultaneous equations.
a) $x + y = 5$
$x - y = 1$

b) $5x + 2y = 3$
$3x - 2y = 5$

c) $5x + 3y = 4$
$x - y = 4$

4 Solve the following inequalities.
Draw a diagram to show the solution set.
a) $x - 2 \leqslant 9$
b) $3x + 1 > 7$
c) $5x - 2 \leqslant 13$
d) $2 < 2x + 4 \leqslant 16$

5 The equation $y^3 + 2y = 7$ has a solution between
1 and 2. Using the trial and improvement method,
find the solution to the equation. Give your answer
correct to one decimal place.

6 A bag contains $2b$ red balls, $3b - 4$ blue balls and
$6b + 1$ black ball. The total number of balls is 52.
Form an equation and solve it to find the value of b.

Coordinates and Graphs

Coordinates

Coordinates are used to locate the position of a point.

When reading coordinates, you read horizontally first (the x-coordinate) and then vertically (the y-coordinate).

The horizontal axis is the x-axis.

The vertical axis is the y-axis.

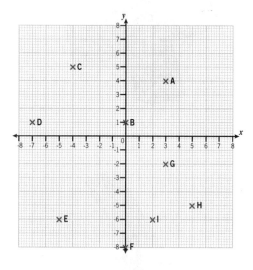

On the above graph, the coordinates of the points, A to I, are...

A (3, 4)	F (0, -8)
B (0, 1)	G (3, -2)
C (-4, 5)	H (5, -5)
D (-7, 1)	I (2, -6)
E (-5, -6)	

Coordinates are always written in brackets with a comma between the two values, for example, (3, 4).

In geography, grid references are similar to coordinates in that they help you to locate the position of a point.

Graphs of the Form $x = a$

A graph of the form $x = a$ is a vertical line with every x-coordinate equal to a.

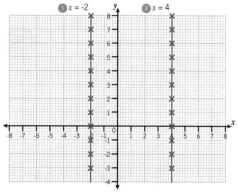

1. The x-coordinate of each point is -2.
   $x = -2$ is the equation of the line.
2. The x-coordinate of each point is 4.
   $x = 4$ is the equation of the line.

Graphs of the Form $y = b$

A graph of the form $y = b$ is a horizontal line with every y-coordinate equal to b.

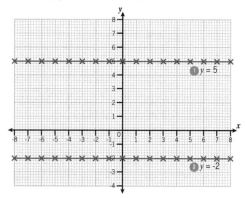

1. The y-coordinate of each point is 5.
   $y = 5$ is the equation of the line.
2. The y-coordinate of each point is -2.
   $y = -2$ is the equation of the line.

Interpreting Graphs

Linear graphs are often used to show relationships.

For example, a hire firm charges £25 per hour to rent a van, plus a standing charge of £50. Using this information, you can work out the first few values and draw up a table:

Number of Hours	1	2	3	4	5
Charge (£)	75	100	125	150	175

You can now plot this information on a graph.

Plotting the points shows a linear relationship between the rental time and the charge.
The graph can be used to find, for example, how long a van is hired for if the charge is £200, in this case 6 hours.

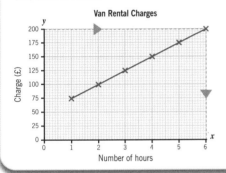

Conversion Graphs

Conversion graphs are used to change one unit of measurement into another unit, for example, kilometres to miles or £ to €.

For example, the graph below shows the conversion rate between GB pounds and US dollars (£1 = $2.10).

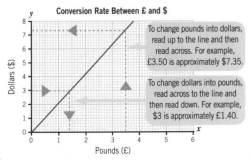

To change pounds into dollars, read up to the line and then read across. For example, £3.50 is approximately $7.35.

To change dollars into pounds, read across to the line and then read down. For example, $3 is approximately £1.40.

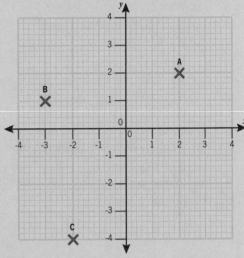

Coordinates and Graphs

Skills Practice

1 Look at this map of a zoo.

   a) What can be found at each of the following coordinates?

     i) (4, 1)

     ii) (7, 5)

     iii) (7, 8)

     iv) (1, 4)

     v) (10, 1)

     vi) (9, 6)

   b) What are the coordinates of...

     i) the gift shop?

     ii) the sea lions?

     iii) the toilets?

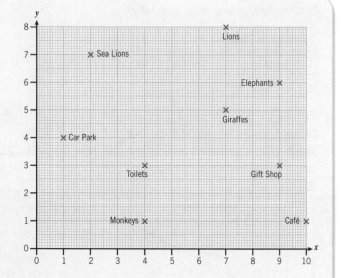

2 The following grid shows the map of an island.

   a) What is at each of the following coordinates?

     i) (3, 4)

     ii) (-4, 2)

     iii) (-4, -6)

     iv) (7, -5)

     v) (4, -2)

   b) From the map, what are the coordinates of the...

     i) lighthouse?

     ii) hostel?

     iii) hospital?

     iv) police station?

     v) farm?

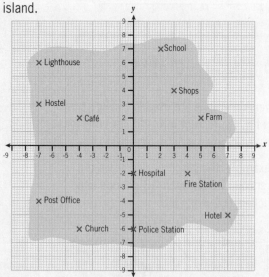

3 From the grid opposite,
write down the equation of...
a) line A
b) line B
c) line C
d) line D

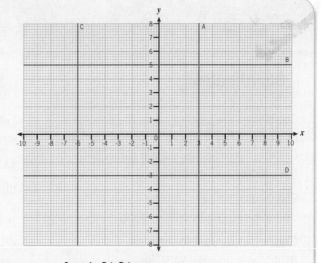

4 The following graph shows the
relationship between inches
and centimetres.

Use the graph to convert...
a) 7 inches into centimetres
b) 15 centimetres into inches
c) 1 inch into centimetres
d) 10 centimetres into inches.

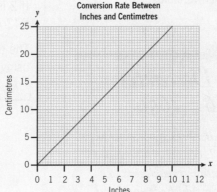

Conversion Rate Between
Inches and Centimetres

5 A cookery book gives these
instructions for roasting a chicken:

Cook for 30 minutes per $\frac{1}{2}$ kilogram (500 grams),
plus 20 minutes.

a) Copy and complete the table.

Mass of Chicken (kg)	0.5	1.0	1.5	2.0
Cooking Time (minutes)		80		

b) Copy the following axes
onto graph paper.
On your axes, plot the values
from the table you completed
in part a).

c) Use your graph to estimate
the cooking time for a chicken
with a mass of 1.25kg.

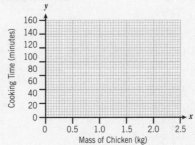

Graphs

Coordinates

Coordinates are used to locate the position of a point. They are more formally known as Cartesian Coordinates and are named after the philosopher Descartes.

Coordinates are used in other subjects, for example, Geography and Science.

Graphs can be used to show the relationship between **variables**.

Rene Descartes
1596 – 1650

Descartes was a French philosopher whose work 'La Geometrie' included his application from algebra to geometry, from which we now have Cartesian Geometry.

Functions and Mapping

Function machines are useful when finding a relationship between two variables.

Example

Input (x) ➤ [× 3] ➤ [-1] ➤ Output (y)

If 1 is fed into the machine, the output is 2 ($1 \times 3 - 1$).

If 2 is fed into the machine the output is 5 ($2 \times 3 - 1$).

The transformation can be illustrated by using a **mapping** diagram like this:

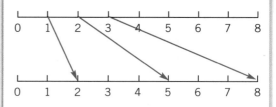

You would describe this mapping by writing,
$x \longrightarrow 3x - 1$.
This is read as 'x becomes $3x - 1$'.

Graphs of the Form $x = a$ and $y = b$

A graph of the form $x = a$ is a vertical line with every x coordinate equal to a.

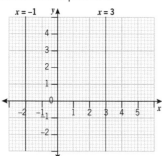

The line $x = -1$ has every x coordinate equal to –1.

A graph of the form $y = b$ is a horizontal line with every y coordinate equal to b.

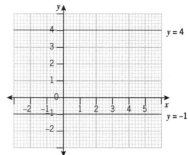

The line $y = 4$ has every y coordinate equal to 4.

Drawing Straight Lined Graphs

To be able to draw any graph, the coordinates that lie on the graph need to be found.

Example

Draw the graphs of $y = x + 1$, $y = x - 3$ and $y = x + 5$ on the same axes.

1 $y = x + 1$

Choose some x coordinates, for example: $x = -2$, $x = 0$ and $x = 2$. You need at least 3 coordinates.

2 Draw up a table:

x	-2	0	2
y	-1	1	3

3 Substitute the values of x into the equation:

when $x = -2$

$y = -2 + 1 = -1$

coordinate is (-2,-1)

when $x = 0$

$y = 0 + 1 = 1$

coordinate is (0, 1)

when $x = 2$

$y = 2 + 1 = 3$

coordinate is (2, 3)

Fill in the table as shown above.

4 Plot the set of three coordinates and join them with a straight line and label (below).

The table of values for the graphs $y = x - 3$ and $y = x + 5$ are:

$y = x - 3$

x	-2	0	2
y	-5	-3	-1

Coordinates (-2, -5) (0, -3) (2, -1)

$y = x + 5$

x	-2	0	2
y	3	5	7

Coordinates (-2, 3) (0, 5) (2, 7)

From these graphs we can see that they all have the same **gradient** (steepness). The point where the graph cuts the y axis (known as the **intercept** on the y axis) changes depending on the equation.

$y = x + 1$ intercepts the y axis at (0, 1)
$y = x - 3$ intercepts the y axis at (0, -3)
$y = x + 5$ intercepts the y axis at (0, 5)

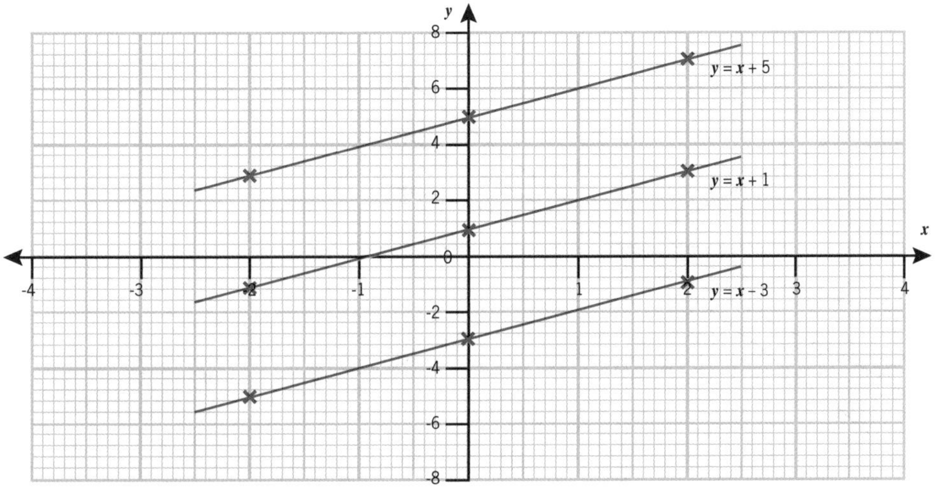

Graphs

Straight Lined Graphs with Different Gradients

The slope of a straight lined graph is known as the gradient of the line.

Example

Draw the graphs of:

a) $y = x$ **c)** $y = 3x$
b) $y = 2x$ **d)** $y = -2x$

1 Copy and complete the tables to work out the coordinates for each graph:

$y = x$

a)

x	-2	0	2
y	-2	0	2

(-2, -2) (0, 0) (2, 2)

$y = 3x$

c)

x	-2	0	2
y	-6	0	6

$y = 2x$

b)

x	-2	0	2
y	-4	0	4

(-2, -4) (0, 0) (2, 4)

$y = -2x$

d)

x	-2	0	2
y	4	0	-4

2 Draw the graphs:

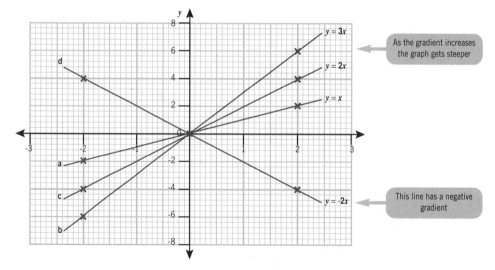

As the gradient increases the graph gets steeper

This line has a negative gradient

Straight Lined Graphs with Different Gradients (cont.)

As the number in front of x increases, the graphs get steeper.

- The number in front of x is called the gradient. The bigger the gradient, the steeper the slope.
- We can also see that the graph of $y = -2x$ (previous page) slopes in the opposite direction.
- A line that slopes up from left to right has a positive gradient.
- A line that slopes down from left to right has a negative gradient.

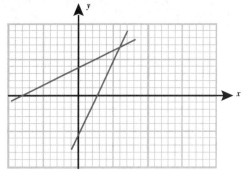

Positive Gradient

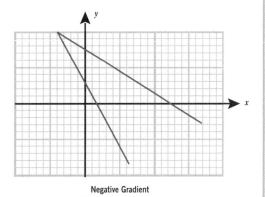

Negative Gradient

Graphs in the Form of $x + y = a$

When asked to draw a graph of the form $x + y = a$, work out the coordinates by choosing some x values.

Example

Draw the graph of $x + y = 6$

when $x = 0$	$y = 6$	$(0 + 6 = 6$ ✓$)$
when $y = 0$	$x = 6$	$(6 + 0 = 6$ ✓$)$
when $x = 2$	$y = 4$	$(2 + 4 = 6$ ✓$)$

So $(0, 6)$ $(6, 0)$ and $(2, 4)$ lie on the graph $x + y = 6$

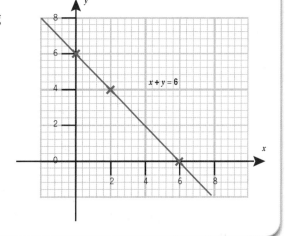

$x + y = 6$

Graphs

Finding the Midpoint of a Line Segment

The diagram shows the straight line joining the points A (1, 1) and B (5, 5). A line joining two points is called a **line segment**.

The midpoint, M, of the line segment AB has coordinates (3, 3). In general, the midpoint of the line joining A (a, b) with B (s, t) is the point $\left(\dfrac{a+s}{2}, \dfrac{b+t}{2}\right)$.

In the example opposite the midpoint is $\left(\left(\dfrac{1+5}{2}\right), \left(\dfrac{1+5}{2}\right)\right)$

$$= \left(\dfrac{6}{2}, \dfrac{6}{2}\right)$$

$$= (3, 3)$$

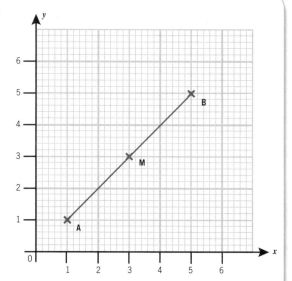

A graph-drawing package can be helpful when investigating gradients of straight lined graphs.

Conversion Graphs

Conversion graphs are used to change one unit of measurement to another unit; for example, litres to pints, km to miles and £ to $.

The exchange rate is very important when buying property off-plan (before it's built) overseas. In November 2007, the exchange rate for United Arab Emirates Dirhams (AED) was £1 = 7.4 AED. In November 2008 it was £1 = 5.7 AED. Buying an apartment for 600 000 AED in November 2007 would cost £81 081, but the same apartment in November 2008 would cost £105 263. A difference of £24 182!

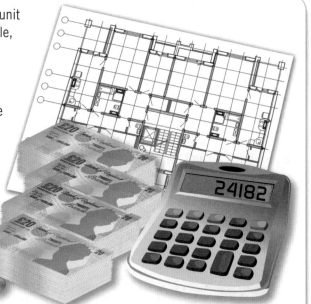

Curved Graphs of the Form $y = ax^2 + b$

You need to be able to draw graphs of more complicated equations.

Example

Draw the graphs of **a)** $y = x^2$ **b)** $y = 2x^2 - 1$ on the same axis.

1 Firstly work out a table of values. Choose some values of x:

$$y = x^2$$

x	-3	-2	-1	0	1	2	3
y	9	4	1	0	1	4	9

Work out the value of y for each value of x. If $x = -3$ then $y = (-3)^2 = 9$

The coordinates of the points of the curve are: (-3, 9) (-2, 4) (-1, 1) (0, 0) (1, 1) (2, 4) (3, 9)

$$y = 2x^2 - 1$$

x	-3	-2	-1	0	1	2	3
y	17	7	1	-1	1	7	17

Work out the value of y for each x coordinate. If $x = -3$ then $y = 2 \times -3^2 - 1$, $y = 17$

The coordinates of the points of the curve are: (-3, 17) (-2, 7) (-1, 1) (0, -1) (1, 1) (2, 7) (3, 17)

2 Plot each of the coordinates and join them with a smooth curve. Don't forget to label the curve.

The curve $y = 2x^2 - 1$ intercepts the y axis at (0, -1). The curve $y = x^2$ goes through the origin (0, 0).

Both graphs are symmetrical about the y axis.

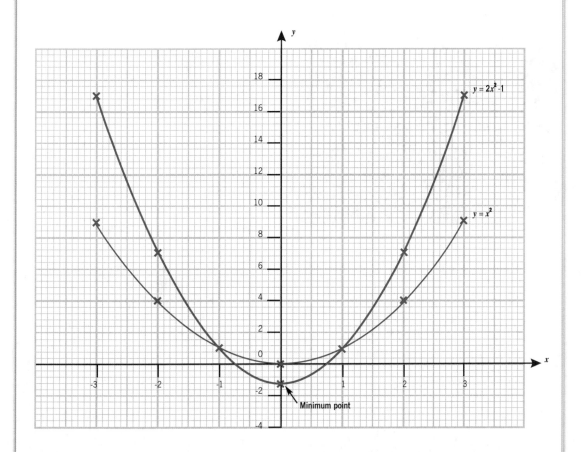

Graphs

Distance–Time Graphs

Distance–time graphs are often called **travel graphs**. Distance is on the **vertical** axis. Time is on the horizontal axis. These graphs can be used to represent journeys.

The gradient of the line is important. The steeper the line, the faster the speed.

A horizontal line indicates a rest or stop, because no distance is being travelled.

The speed can be found by dividing the distance by the time:

$$\text{Speed} = \frac{\text{Distance}}{\text{Time}}$$

Example

Matthew walks to the shops. He stops in the shops to buy some groceries. The graph shows his journey:

- Part A shows that Matthew walked to the shop 1200m away in 15 minutes.
- Part B shows that he stopped for 5 minutes in the shop.
- Part C is his return journey home. Since the slope of the graph is not as steep as part A, he's walking more slowly.
- Part D, Matthew stops for 2 minutes to tie his shoelaces.
- Part E, he continues his journey and arrives home 45 minutes after he set out.

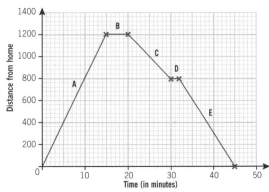

Quick Test

1. Explain how you read coordinates.
2. The vertical axis is called the y axis. True or false?
3. The graphs of $y = x$ and $y = 2x$ will have the same gradient. True or false?
4. The graph of $y = x - 4$ intercepts the y axis at:
   a) (-4, 0) b) (0, -4) c) (4, 0) d) (0, 4)

KEY WORDS

Make sure you understand these words before moving on!

- Coordinates
- Variables
- Function machines
- Mapping
- Gradient
- Intercept
- Line segment
- Conversion
- Distance-time graphs
- Travel graphs
- vertical

Skills Practice

1 **a)** Copy and complete the following tables:

(i) $y = 3x$

x	-3	0	3
y			

(ii) $y = x - 5$

x	-2	0	2
y			

(iii) $y = 2x + 1$

x	-2	0	2
y			

b) Copy the following axes onto graph paper. On your axes, plot the values from the tables you completed in a).

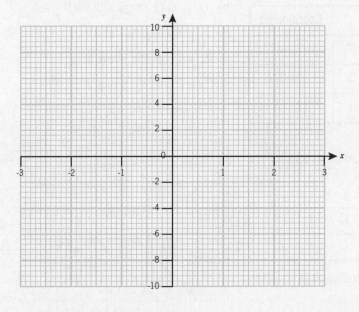

c) From the graphs you have drawn:
   i) Which graph is the steepest?
   ii) Which graph cuts the y axis at (0, -5)?
   iii) What is the intercept of the graph $y = 2x + 1$?

Graphs

Drawing Straight Line Graphs

The following are linear (straight line) graphs. Remember that to draw these graphs you need to work out the coordinates of the points to be plotted.

Example

Draw the graphs of...

a) $y = 2x$
b) $y = 2x - 3$
c) $y = 2x + 2$

Method 1

To use a mapping diagram, choose some x coordinates, e.g. -2, 0, 2 and replace x in the function with the given values.

$$y = 2x$$

x	$2x$	Coordinates
-2	$(2 \times -2) = -4$	(-2, -4)
0	$(2 \times 0) = 0$	(0, 0)
2	$(2 \times 2) = 4$	(2, 4)

Method 2

Another method to use would be a table of values.

$$y = 2x$$

x	-2	0	-2
y	-4	0	4

Each value of x is substituted into the equation $y = 2x$, for example,
$x = -2, y = 2 \times -2, y = -4$.

Plot the set of three coordinates and join them with a straight line and label.

The table of values for the graphs $y = 2x - 3$ and $y = 2x + 2$ are:

$$y = 2x - 3$$

x	-2	0	2
y	-7	-3	1

(-2, -7) (0, -3) (2, 1)

$$y = 2x + 2$$

x	-2	0	2
y	-2	2	6

(-2, -2) (0, 2) (2, 6)

We can see from the graphs below that they all have the same gradient. Depending on the equation, the point where the graph intercepts the y axis will change with each graph.

$y = 2x$ cuts the y axis at (0, 0)

$y = 2x - 3$ cuts the y axis at (0, -3)

$y = 2x + 2$ cuts the y axis at (0, 2)

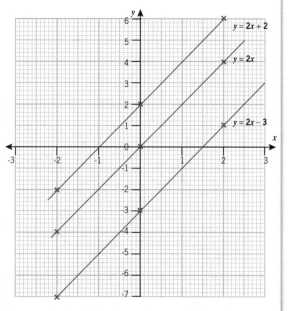

Straight Line Graphs with Different Gradients

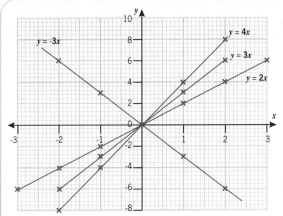

From the graph above we can see that as the number in front of x increases the graph gets steeper.

The number in front of x is called the gradient. The gradient is steeper if the number is bigger.

- A line sloping upwards has a positive gradient.

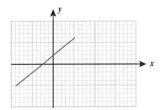

- A line sloping downwards has a negative gradient.

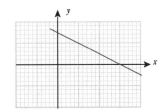

Finding the Gradient of a Straight Line

The general equation of a straight line graph is $y = mx + c$.

m is the gradient and c is the intercept on the y axis.

To find the gradient choose two points that lie on the line.

Gradient	=	$\dfrac{\text{Change in } y}{\text{Change in } x}$

Example

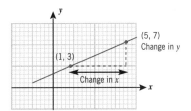

In this example your two points are: (1, 3) and (5, 7).

Use these points to find the change in y (height) and the change in x (base).

Gradient	=	$\dfrac{\text{Change in } y}{\text{Change in } x}$	=	$\dfrac{\text{Height}}{\text{Base}}$

$$= \left(\frac{7 - 3}{5 - 1} \right)$$

$$= \frac{4}{4}$$

$$= 1$$

Decide if the gradient is positive or negative.

Graphs

Simultaneous Equations

The point at which two straight line graphs intersect (meet) represents the simultaneous solution of their equations.

Example
Solve the simultaneous equations:
$y = 3x + 1$
$x + y = 5$

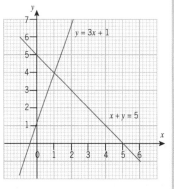

The point of intersection is $x = 1$, $y = 4$. This is the solution of the simultaneous equations.

Highway Code Road Signs

Steep hills are shown using roadsigns.

Steep hill downwards

Steep hill upwards

Gradients may be shown as a ratio, for example, $20\% = 1 : 5$.

Cubic Graphs

When drawing a cubic graph of $y = x^3$, it is important to remember that $x^3 = x \times x \times x$.

Example
Draw the graph of $y = x^3$

x	-3	-2	-1	0	1	2	3
y	-27	-8	-1	0	1	8	27

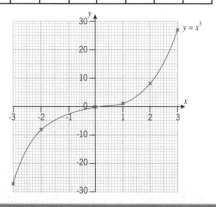

Reciprocal Graphs

The graph of the equation $y = \dfrac{a}{x}$ takes one of two forms, depending on the value of a.

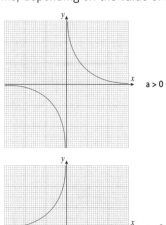

a > 0

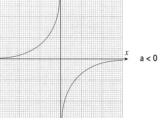

a < 0

Quadratic Graphs

Quadratic graphs are graphs of the form $y = ax^2 + bx + c$, where $a = 0$. These graphs are curved.

If the number in front of x^2 is positive, the curve looks like this:

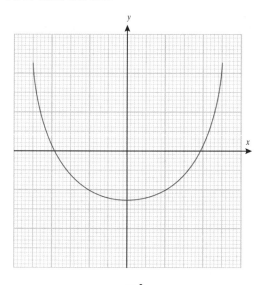

a > 0

If the number in front of x^2 is negative, the curve looks like this:

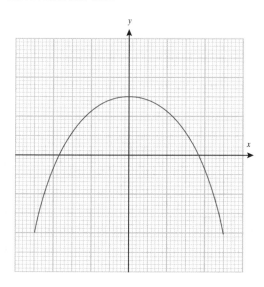

a < 0

Example
Draw the graph of $y = 2x^2 - 5$

Work out a table of values, choosing some values for x.

x	-3	-2	-1	0	1	2	3
y	13	3	-3	-5	-3	3	13

Work out the value of y for each value of x.

When $x = 2$...
$y = 2 \times 2^2 - 5$
$y = 2 \times 4 - 5$
$y = 3$

The coordinates of the points are:
(-3, 13) (-2, 3) (-1, -3) (0, -5) (1, -3) (2, 3) (3, 13)

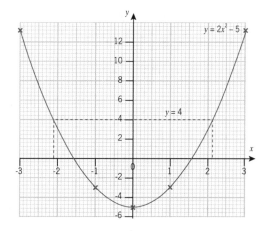

The graph $y = 2x^2 - 5$ has a line of symmetry at $x = 0$. The curve cuts the y axis at (0, -5).

To find the value of x when $y = 4$, read across from $y = 4$ to the graph, then read down to the x axis.

$x = 2.2$ and $x = -2.2$. These are the approximate solutions to $2x^2 - 5 = 4$.

Graphs

Using Graphs

You will find it useful to use graphs in Science and Geography.

Example
These containers are being filled with water at a rate of 100ml per second. The graphs show how the depth of the water changes over time. Match each container with the correct graph.

A

B

C

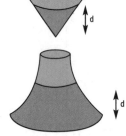

Container A
The depth of the water changes uniformly with time.

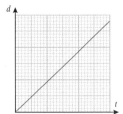

Container B
The depth will rise quickly in the narrow part of the container.

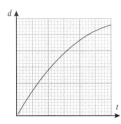

Container C
The depth will increase slowly at the wider part of the container and then increase more quickly at the narrower part.

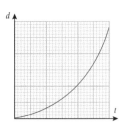

The shape of graphs and their properties can be explored using ICT if you have access to a graphical package.

Quick Test

1. The line $y = 5x - 4$ has a gradient of 4. True or false?
2. The line of $y = 2x + 6$ intercepts the y axis at (0, 6). True or false?
3. $y = x^3$ is a cubic graph. True or false?
4. $y = x^2 - 3$ goes through which coordinate?
   a) (1, 4) b) (2, 0) c) (3, 5) d) (4, 13)

KEY WORDS
Make sure you understand these words before moving on!
- Linear graph
- Coordinates
- Gradient
- Intercept
- Intersect
- Simultaneous equations
- Cubic graph
- Quadratic graph

1
a) Draw the graph of...
  i) $y = 4x - 2$
  ii) $y = 2x + 2$
b) Write down the coordinates of the point of intersection.
c) What is the gradient of $y = 4x - 2$?

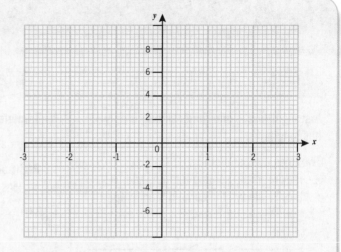

2 From the graph opposite, find the...
a) gradient
b) intercept on the y axis
c) equation of the straight line.

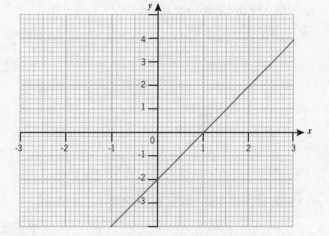

3
a) Draw the graph $y = x^2 - 5$.
b) Write down the equation of the line of symmetry.
c) Using the graph, work out the solution to $x^2 - 5 = 4$.

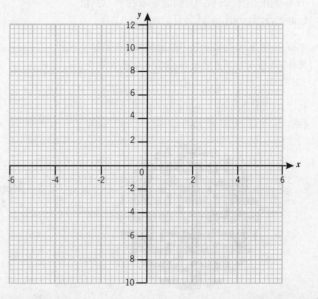

Shapes

Lines

A straight line is one-dimensional; it only has length.

Two lines are parallel if...
- they're in the same direction, and
- they're always the same distance apart.

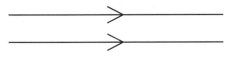

Two lines are perpendicular if they're at right angles to each other.

Vertical

The lines meet at 90° and are therefore perpendicular.

Horizontal

Two-Dimensional Shapes

Two-dimensional shapes have area. They are usually referred to as 2-D shapes.

You need to be able to recognise the 2-D shapes given on these pages, along with some of their important features.

Islamic art is often made up of two-dimensional shapes:

Triangles

Triangles have three sides.

There are several types of triangle:

Right-angled
- Has a 90° angle.

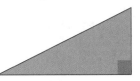

Isosceles
- Two sides are equal.
- Base angles are equal.

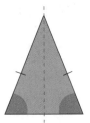

Equilateral
- Three sides are equal.
- Three angles are equal (60°).

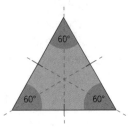

60°

60°   60°

Scalene
- All the sides and angles are different.

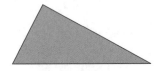

Quadrilaterals

Quadrilaterals have four sides.

There are several types of quadrilateral:

Square
- All angles are 90°.
- All sides are equal.
- Four lines of symmetry.
- Rotational symmetry of order 4.

Rectangle
- All angles are 90°.
- Opposite sides are equal.
- Two lines of symmetry.
- Rotational symmetry of order 2.

Parallelogram
- No lines of symmetry.
- Rotational symmetry of order 2.

Rhombus
- Two lines of symmetry.
- Rotational symmetry of order 2.

Kite
- One line of symmetry.
- No rotational symmetry.

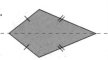

Trapezium
- One pair of parallel sides.
- No lines of symmetry unless it's an isosceles trapezium.
- No rotational symmetry.

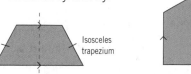

Isosceles trapezium

Three-Dimensional Solids

Three-dimensional (3-D) objects have volume (or 'capacity').

Here are some of the 3-D solids that you should know:

Cube

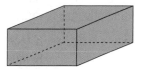

Cuboid

Sphere

Cylinder

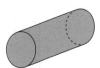

Cone

Triangular prism

Square-based pyramid

Shapes

3-D Solids and Nets

- A **prism** is a solid that can be cut into slices that are all the same shape.
- A **face** is a flat surface of a solid.
- An **edge** is where two faces meet.
- **Vertex** is another word for 'corner'. The plural of vertex is **vertices**.

For example, a cube has: 6 faces
                                 8 vertices
                                 12 edges

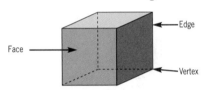

A **net** of a 3-D solid is a 2-D (flat) shape that can be folded to make the 3-D solid.

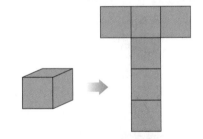

Symmetry

Reflective symmetry – this is when both sides of a shape are the same on each side of a **mirror line**. The mirror line is known as a **line**, or **axis**, **of symmetry**.

2 lines of symmetry

1 line of symmetry

Rotational symmetry – a 2-D shape has rotational symmetry if it can be turned to look exactly the same. The order of rotational symmetry is the number of times the shape can be turned and still look the same.

Order 4

Plane symmetry – a 3-D solid has a plane of symmetry if the plane divides the shape into two halves and one half is the exact mirror image of the other. 3-D solids can have more than one plane of symmetry.

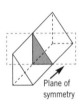

Plane of symmetry

Quick Test

1. Explain what perpendicular lines are.
2. What are the properties of an isosceles triangle?
3. A parallelogram has rotational symmetry of order 2. True or false?
4. How many edges does a cuboid have?
5. How many faces does a triangular prism have?

KEY WORDS
Make sure you understand these words before moving on!
- Parallel
- Perpendicular
- Two-dimensional
- Three-dimensional
- Triangle
- Quadrilateral
- Prism
- Face
- Edge
- Vertex/Vertices
- Net
- Reflective symmetry
- Rotational symmetry
- Plane symmetry
- Mirror line
- Line/Axis of symmetry

Skills Practice

1 a) Sketch a copy of this cuboid:

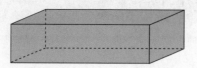

On your sketch, draw in a plane of symmetry.
b) Sketch the net of the cuboid.
c) How many vertices does the cuboid have?

2 A chocolate bar is packaged in a triangular prism.

a) Sketch a copy of the prism and mark in the plane of symmetry.
b) Sketch the net of the chocolate bar's packaging.

3 a) Draw the net of this square-based pyramid.

b) How many faces does the square-based pyramid have?
c) How many edges does the square-based pyramid have?
d) How many vertices does the square-based pyramid have?

4 How many lines of symmetry does each of the following shapes have?

a)   **b)**   **c)**

5 What is the order of rotational symmetry of each of these shapes?

a)   **b)**   **c)**

6 What quadrilaterals are being described?
a) I have no lines of symmetry and rotational symmetry of order two.
My opposite sides are equal in length and parallel.
My opposite angles are equal.
b) I have one line of symmetry, but no rotational symmetry.
My diagonals cross at right angles, but they don't bisect each other.
I have two pairs of adjacent sides that are equal.

Measures and Measurement

Estimating

Estimating is a useful skill in everyday life. Some of the measurements that you might need to estimate are given below:

- Length – for example, an average swimming pool is about 25m long.
- Mass – for example, a bag of sugar has a mass of about 1kg.
- Capacity – for example, a can of soft drink holds about 330ml, or about half a pint.
- Time – for example, it takes approximately $2\frac{1}{2}$ hours to travel from Manchester to London by train.

Metric Units

Metric units include...
- metres (m)
- kilometres (km)
- kilograms (kg)
- litres (l)
- centilitres (cl).

The table below shows the metric equivalents.

Length	Mass	Capacity
10mm = 1cm	1000mg = 1g	1000ml = 1l
100cm = 1m	1000g = 1kg	100cl = 1l
1000m = 1km	1000kg = 1 tonne	1000cm^3 = 1l

When converting units, remember...
- to change from small units to large units, use division
- to change from large units to small units, use multiplication.

Examples
1. 600m = 0.6km (÷ 1000)
2. 3500g = 3.5kg (÷ 1000)
3. 37mm = 3.7cm (÷ 10)
4. 96cm = 960mm (× 10)
5. 5kg = 5000g (× 1000)
6. 7l = 700cl (× 100)
7. 4.2 tonnes = 4200kg (× 1000)

Imperial Units

Imperial units include...
- miles
- yards
- stones
- pounds (lb)
- ounces (oz).

Imperial units are sometimes thought of as old fashioned units of measurement.

The table below shows the imperial equivalents.

Since January 2000, traders have had to weigh and sell loose items, such as fruit and vegetables, in metric units, such as grams and kilograms, rather than imperial measures.

However, there has been opposition from traders and shoppers who still prefer imperial units.

Imperial units can currently be displayed alongside metric units, as long as they are not larger than the metric units.

Length	Mass	Capacity
1 foot = 12 inches	1 stone = 14 pounds	20 fluid oz = 1 pint
1 yard = 3 feet	1 pound = 16 ounces	8 pints = 1 gallon

Converting between Metric and Imperial

This table shows some approximate comparisons between metric and imperial units:

Length	Mass	Capacity
2.5cm ≈ 1 inch	25g ≈ 1 ounce	$1l ≈ 1\frac{3}{4}$ pints
30cm ≈ 1 foot	1kg ≈ 2.2 pounds	4.5l ≈ 1 gallon
1m ≈ 39 inches		
8km ≈ 5 miles		

Examples

1 Change 30km into miles.

8km = 5 miles
So 1km = $\frac{5}{8}$ mile

30km = $30 \times \frac{5}{8}$
= 18.75 miles (to 2 d.p.)

2 Mr Roberts buys 500g of apples.
Approximately how many pounds is this?

500g = $\frac{1}{2}$kg
1kg = 2.2 pounds

So 500g = 1.1 pounds

Measures and Measurement

Choosing the Correct Units of Measurement

The following examples show the units that you should use to measure some everyday quantities.

1 Length
- Thickness of a book (mm).
- Width of a door (cm).
- Height of a house (m).
- Distance from Leeds to Newcastle (km).

2 Mass
- A packet of sweets (g).
- A bag of flour (kg).
- A car (tonnes).

3 Capacity
- A spoonful of gravy powder (ml).
- A bottle of juice (cl).
- The amount of water in a pond (l).

Time

The 12-hour clock uses am and pm:
- Times before midday are am.
- Times after midday are pm.

The 24-hour clock numbers the hours from 0 to 24. Times are written with four figures.

The numbers on the outside show a 12-hour clock and the first 12 hours of a 24-hour clock. The numbers on the inside show the last 12 hours of a 24-hour clock.

From the above clock you can see that...
- 3.47pm is the same as 1547
- 2.30am is the same as 0230.

There are...
- 60 seconds in 1 minute
- 60 minutes in 1 hour
- 24 hours in 1 day
- 7 days in 1 week
- 52 weeks in 1 year.

Example
Josh set off for work at 8.10am and arrived at 9.05am. How long did it take Josh to get to work?

Add 60 minutes

8.10   9.05 9.10

Take away 5 minutes

Total time = 55 minutes.

Reading Scales

It's important that you can read the scales on a range of instruments and objects. Some common examples are shown below.

Weighing scales

The bag of flour on this scale shows 453g.

Measuring cylinder

This cylinder shows 400ml of water.

Jug

This jug contains 75cl of water.

Ruler

This ruler shows 12cm.

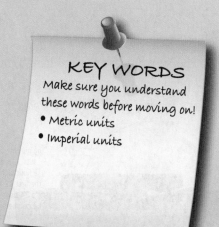

KEY WORDS

Make sure you understand these words before moving on!

- Metric units
- Imperial units

Measures and Measurement

Skills Practice

1 What units would you measure each of these objects in?
  a) Length of a pen.
  b) Length of the M6 motorway.
  c) Thickness of a coin.
  d) Mass of a textbook.
  e) Mass of a bus.
  f) Mass of a fork.

2 Change each of the following quantities into the units given in brackets.
  a) 6200g (kg)
  b) 72cm (mm)
  c) 610m (cm)
  d) 5 tonnes (kg)
  e) 3 litres (cl)
  f) 6.2km (m)
  g) 16.3kg (g)
  h) 725mm (cm)
  i) 96ml (cl)
  j) 52mm (cm)
  k) 86ml (cl)
  l) 3600g (kg)
  m) 525g (kg)
  n) 106cl (l)
  o) 7200m (km)
  p) 6.3kg (g)
  q) 56cm (m)
  r) 7.2 litres (ml)
  s) 2.7kg (g)

3 A glass holds 25cl of liquid when full.
How many times can it be filled from a two-litre bottle?

4 Add together these lengths:

  65cm, 2m, 345cm, 3m 62cm, 5m 35cm

Give the total in...
  a) centimetres
  b) metres.

5 Put these lengths in order of size:

  562cm, 3m 25cm, 1m 62cm, 5700mm, 1m 640mm

6 A lift can carry a maximum mass of 300kg.
The masses of some furniture are as follows:

Sofa 105kg

Chair 16kg

Dresser 93kg

Can all the furniture go into the lift at once, plus Bob, who has a mass of 69kg?

7 Change each of the following to 24-hour clock time.
   a) 7.20am   **c)** 8.36pm
   b) 7.15pm   **d)** 10.25am

8 Change each of the following to 12-hour clock time.
   a) 0916   **c)** 1732
   b) 2218   **d)** 0425

9 Work out how many minutes there are between the following pairs of times:
   a) 0800 and 0847   **e)** 0016 and 0228
   b) 0926 and 1020   **f)** 1407 and 1526
   c) 1251 and 1326   **g)** 1619 and 1623
   d) 1521 and 1727   **h)** 2214 and 2310

10 It takes Katie 25 minutes to walk to school.
   What time must she leave home in order to arrive at school by 8.50am?

11 Reece spends 25 minutes doing maths homework, 38 minutes doing English homework and 42 minutes doing piano practice.
   How long did Reece spend in total doing his homework and piano practice?

12 Change 20km into miles.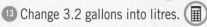

13 Change 3.2 gallons into litres.

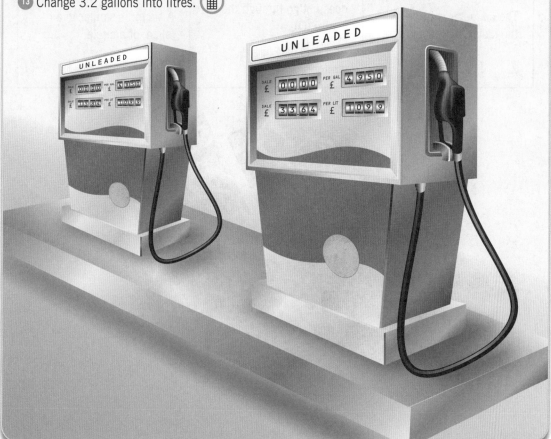

Shapes and Measure

The Circle

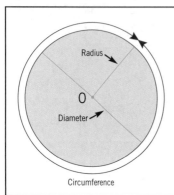	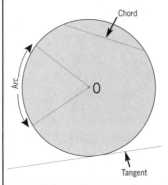	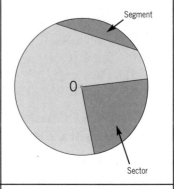
The **circumference** is the distance around the outside edge of a circle. The **diameter** is twice the **radius**.	A **chord** is a line that joins two points on the circumference. A chord does not go through the centre (O). An **arc** is part of the circumference.	A **segment** is part of a circle separated by a chord. A **sector** is similar to a 'slice' of a circle.

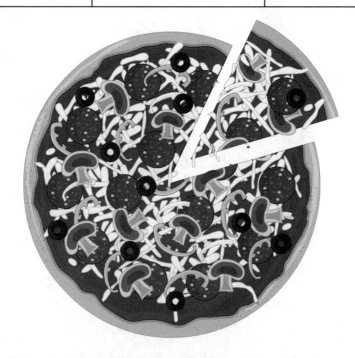

3D Solids and Nets

The net of a 3D solid is a 2D (flat) shape that can be folded to make a 3D solid:

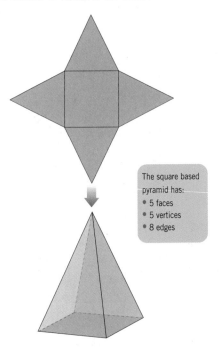

The square based pyramid has:
- 5 faces
- 5 vertices
- 8 edges

Examples

a) You can represent 3D shapes on isometric paper. On this paper you can draw lengths in three perpendicular directions on the same scale. The faces do not appear in their true shape.

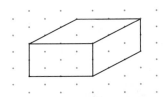

b) The 'T' shaped prism can be shown clearly on isometric paper.

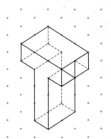

Quadrilaterals

Quadrilaterals have four sides.

There are several types of quadrilateral:

Square
- All angles are 90°.
- All sides are equal.
- Four lines of symmetry.
- Rotational symmetry of order 4.

Rectangle
- All angles are 90°.
- Opposite sides are equal.
- Two lines of symmetry.
- Rotational symmetry of order 2.

Parallelogram
- No lines of symmetry.
- Rotational symmetry of order 2.
- Opposite sides are parallel and equal in length.
- Opposite angles are equal.

Rhombus
- Two lines of symmetry.
- Rotational symmetry of order 2.
- All sides are equal in length.
- Opposite sides are parallel.
- Opposite angles are equal.

Kite
- One line of symmetry.
- No rotational symmetry.
- Has two pairs of adjacent sides equal in length.

Trapezium
- One pair of parallel sides.
- No lines of symmetry unless it's an isosceles trapezium.
- No rotational symmetry.
- Non-parallel sides equal in length.

Isosceles trapezium

Shapes and Measure

Plans and Elevations

A **plan** is what can be seen when a 3D solid is viewed from above.

An **elevation** is seen if the 3D solid is looked at from the side or front view.

Plans are often used in the construction industry.

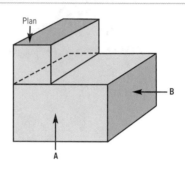

View from A   View from B   Plan

Constructions

When asked to construct shapes and lines, use a compass, ruler and protractor.

Examples

Use a compass to construct these triangles.

1. • Draw the longest side.
   • With the compass point at A, draw an arc of radius 4cm.
   • With the compass point at B, draw an arc of radius 5cm.
   • Join A and B to the point where the two arcs meet at C.

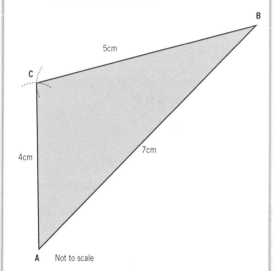

Not to scale

2. • Draw the line AB.
   • Measure the angle B as 52°.
   • Draw the line BC.
   • Join C to A by drawing a line.

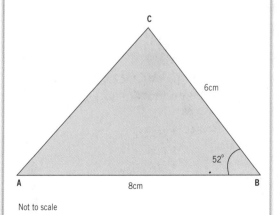

Not to scale

Scale Drawings

A **scale drawing** is very useful for finding lengths that can't be measured directly.

Architects and surveyors use scale drawings to show house and development plans.

Models of buildings are often used when property developments are launched. This gives buyers an idea of what a development might look like.

Example

A house plan has a scale of 1 : 20. If the width of the house on the plan is 72cm, what is the width of the real house?

1cm represents 20cm

72cm represents 72 × 20 = 1440cm

1440 ÷ 100 = 14.4m

The width of the house is 14.4m.

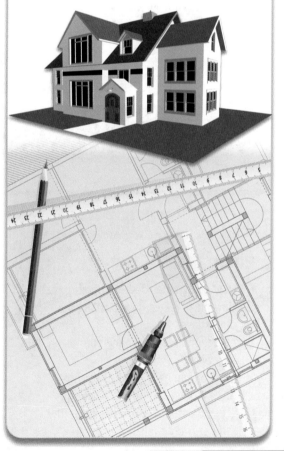

Shapes and Measure

Metric and Imperial Units

The table shows some approximate comparisons between **metric** and **imperial units**.

Length	2.5cm ≈ 1 inch 30cm ≈ 1 foot 1m ≈ 39 inches 8km ≈ 5 miles
Mass	25g ≈ 1 ounce 1 kg ≈ 2.2 pounds
Capacity	$1l ≈ 1\frac{3}{4}$ pints 4.5l ≈ 1 gallon

Examples

1 Change 60km into miles.

$$8km = 5 \text{ miles}$$

$$\text{so } 1km = \frac{5}{8} \text{ mile}$$

$$60km = 60 \times \tfrac{5}{8}$$

$$= 37.5 \text{ miles}$$

2 A patio measures 20 feet. Approximately how many metres is this?

$$30cm = 1 \text{ foot}$$
$$30 \times 20 = 20 \text{ feet}$$
$$600cm = 20 \text{ feet}$$

The patio is approximately 6 metres long.

Quick Test

1 How many faces does a cuboid have?
2 How many edges does a triangular prism have?
3 Approximately how many pounds is in 3.5kg?
   a) 6.5 pounds   c) 5.9 pounds
   b) 8.4 pounds   d) 7.7 pounds
4 The diameter of a circle is twice the radius. True or false?

KEY WORDS

Make sure you understand these words before moving on!

- Circumference
- Diameter
- Radius
- Chord
- Arc
- Tangent
- Segment
- Sector
- Plan
- Elevation
- Scale drawing
- Metric unit
- Imperial unit

Skills Practice

1 Draw lines from the labels to match them with the parts of the circle:

Radius

Arc

Circumference

Tangent

Diameter

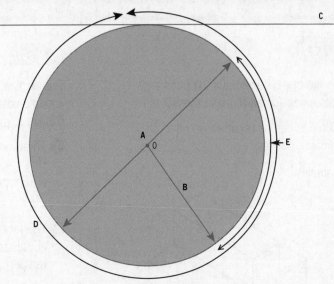

2 Draw the net of this cylinder.

3 Accurately construct this triangle, using a ruler and compass only.

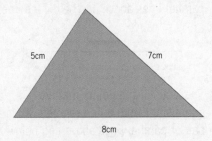

5cm   7cm

8cm

4 A plan of a building has a scale of 1 : 100. If the width of the building on the plan is 5.5cm, how many metres is the actual building?

5 Approximately what is 12 inches in centimetres?

Shapes & Solids

Nets

The **net** of a 3D solid is a 2D flat shape that can be folded to make the 3D solid.

3D solids can be represented on isometric paper.

Examples

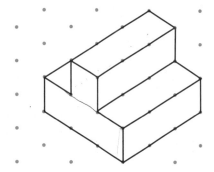

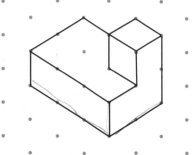

Loci

The **locus** of a point is the set of all the possible positions that point can occupy, subject to some given condition or rule.

① The locus of the points that are equidistant from a fixed point P is a circle.

② The locus of the points that are equidistant from two points X and Y is the perpendicular bisector of XY.

③ The locus of the points that are equidistant from two non-parallel lines is the line that bisects the angle formed by the two lines.

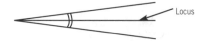

④ The locus of the points that are equidistant from a line is a pair of parallel lines above and below the line.

⑤ The locus of the points that are equidistant from a line segment XY is a pair of parallel lines above and below XY and a semicircle at X and Y.

Loci properties can be applied by town and country planners when proposing new developments.

Constructions

To **construct** a regular hexagon inside a circle:

1 Draw a circle with a radius of 2cm, and mark a point x on its circumference.

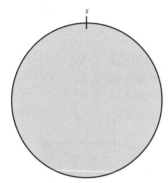

2 Keeping the compass set at 2cm, draw an arc, centre x which cuts the circle at y. y is the centre of the next arc.

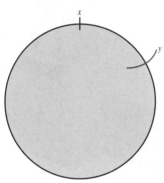

3 Repeat the process until six points are marked on the circumference. Join the points to make a regular hexagon.

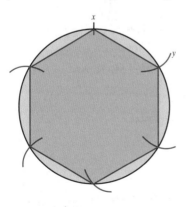

To construct the perpendicular bisector of the line segment XY:

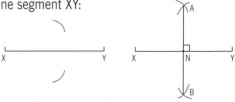

1	Draw two arcs with a compass, using X as the centre.
2	Set the compass at a radius greater than half the length of XY.
3	Draw two more arcs with Y as the centre. (Keep the compasses at the same distance as before.)
4	Join the two points where the arcs cross. AB is the perpendicular bisector of XY. N is the midpoint of XY.

To construct the perpendicular from point P to the line AB:

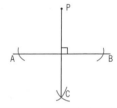

1	From P, draw arcs to cut the line at A and B. From A and B draw arcs with the same radius to intersect at point C below the line.
2	Join P to C; this line is perpendicular to AB.

Using a compass you can construct this triangle.

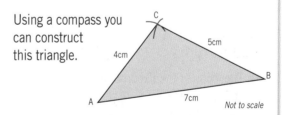

Not to scale

1	Draw the longest side.
2	With the compass point at A, draw an arc of radius 4cm.
3	With the compass point at B, draw an arc of radius 5cm.
4	Join A and B to the point where the two arcs meet at C.

Shapes & Solids

Coordinates in 3D

The normal $x - y$ coordinates describe a plane. Perpendicular to both of them is a third direction, known as z.

All positions in space have three coordinates (x, y, z).

Example

❶ For the cuboid below, the vertices have the following coordinates.

O	(0, 0, 0)	**D**	(3, 0, 4)
A	(0, 2, 0)	**E**	(3, 2, 4)
B	(3, 2, 0)	**F**	(0, 2, 4)
C	(3, 0, 0)	**G**	(0, 0, 4)

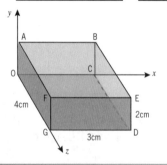

❷ A has coordinate (4, 2, 5)
B has coordinate (0, 0, 5)
C has coordinate (4, 2, 0)

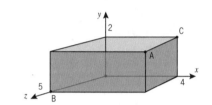

Quick Test

❶ The locus of the fixed point P is a circle. True or false?
Look at the diagram opposite. Use this diagram to answer Q 2-5.

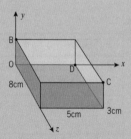

❷ What are the coordinates of point B?
❸ The coordinates of C are (5, 3, 8). True or false?
❹ The coordinates of point D are (5, 0, 0). True or false?

1. Draw a perpendicular bisector on the line RS.

R ——————————————————————————— S

2. Bisect the angle PQR.

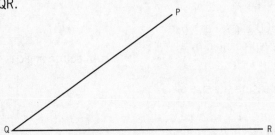

3. On the diagram, draw the locus of the points 4cm from point P.

• P

4. Write down the coordinates of...
   P
   Q
   R
   S
   T

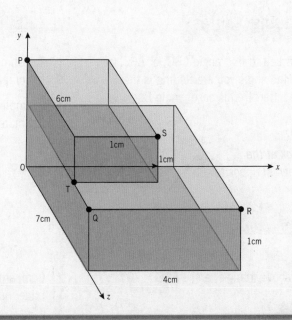

Angles

Angles

An angle is an amount of turning or rotation.

Angles are measured in **degrees**.

A circle is divided into 360 parts. Each part is called a degree and is represented by a small circle °.

A protractor is used to measure the size of an angle.

Always put 0° at the start position and then read from the correct scale.

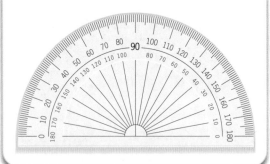

Types of Angle

- An **acute angle** is between 0° and 90°.

- An **obtuse angle** is between 90° and 180°.

- A **reflex angle** is between 180° and 360°.

- A **right angle** is 90°.

Reading Angles

When asked to find angle ABC, or AB̂C, or ∠ABC, the angle you are finding is the middle letter. In this case, angle B.

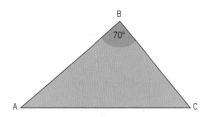

In the above triangle, angle ABC = 70°.

Estimating Angles

To estimate the size of an angle, it's useful to compare it to the size of a right angle.

Example
Estimate the size of this angle.

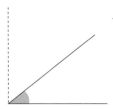

Comparing the angle to a right angle, it's just under half the size, so it's approximately 40°.

Angles not drawn to scale

Angles on a Straight Line

The angles on a straight line add up to 180°.

$a + b + c = 180°$

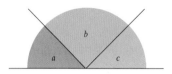

Example

Work out the size of angle x.

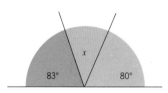

$83° + 80° + x° = 180°$
$163° + x° = 180°$
$x = 180 - 163°$
$x = 17°$

Angles at a Point

The angles at a point add up to 360°.

$a + b + c = 360°$

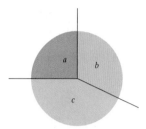

Example

Work out the size of angle y.

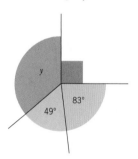

$y + 90° + 83° + 49° = 360°$
$y + 222° = 360°$
$y = 360° - 222°$
$y = 138°$

Vertically Opposite Angles

Vertically opposite angles are formed when two straight lines intersect (cross).

Vertically opposite angles are equal:
* a and c are opposite each other, so $a = c$.
* b and d are opposite each other, so $b = d$.

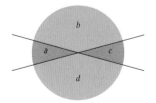

Example

Work out the missing angles.

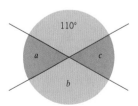

$a = 180° - 110° = 70°$
$b = 110°$
$c = 70°$

Angles

Angles in a Triangle

The angles in a triangle add up to 180°.

$$a + b + c = 180°$$

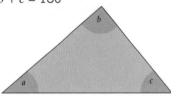

Examples
What angles does the letter a represent?

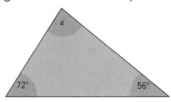

$$a + 72° + 56° = 180°$$
$$a + 128° = 180°$$
$$a = 180° - 128°$$
$$a = 52°$$

Any exterior angle of a triangle is equal to the sum of the two opposite interior angles.

$$a + b = c$$

$$a + 47° = 106°$$
$$a = 106° - 47°$$
$$a = 59°$$

Angles in an Isosceles Triangle

Examples

① Find the missing angles in this isosceles triangle.

$a = 68°$ since the base angles are equal.
$$b + 68° + 68° = 180°$$
$$b = 180° - 136°$$
$$b = 44°$$

② Find the missing angles in this isosceles triangle.

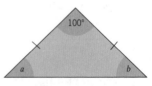

$a = b$ since the base angles are equal.
$$2a = 180° - 100°$$
$$2a = 80°$$
$$a = 40° = b$$

Angles not drawn to scale

Angles in a Quadrilateral

The angles in a quadrilateral add up to 360°.

$a + b + c + d = 360°$

Example

Find the missing angle, a.

$a + 75° + 122° + 107° = 360°$

$$a = 360° - 304°$$
$$a = 56°$$

Constructing Triangles

Triangular shapes are often used in designs for bridges, fun fair rides, etc. because they are strong.

It's important that architects and engineers draw their diagrams accurately. An accurate drawing is called a **construction**.

Example

Construct this triangle:

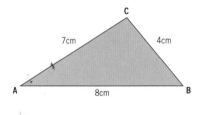

Follow these steps to construct the triangle:

1. Draw the longest side, i.e. AB.
2. With the compass point at A, draw an arc of radius 7cm.
3. With the compass point at B, draw an arc of radius 4cm.
4. Join A and B to the point where the two arcs meet.

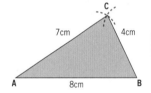

Not to scale. You should construct this triangle accurately.

You can also construct triangles if you're given the angles. You must measure and draw the angles very carefully.

Quick Test

1. Explain what a reflex angle is.
2. An acute angle lies between 0° and 90°. True or false?
3. What do the angles on a straight line add up to?
4. Two angles meet at a point. One of the angles is 217°. What is the size of the other angle?
5. Three angles in a quadrilateral add up to 305°. What is the size of the fourth angle?

KEY WORDS

Make sure you understand these words before moving on!

- Degree
- Acute angle
- Obtuse angle
- Reflex angle
- Right angle
- Construction

Angles

Skills Practice

1 For each of the angles below...
   i) write down the type of angle
   ii) estimate its size.

a)

c)

e)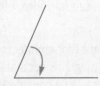

b)

d)

f)

2 Work out the size of the missing angles.

a)

150°

a

b)

75°   *b*   69°

c)

100°   *c*

38°   42°

3 Work out the size of the missing angles.

a)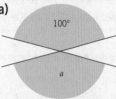

100°

a

c)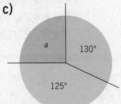

a   130°

125°

e)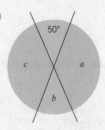

50°

c   *a*

b

b)

a

115°

d)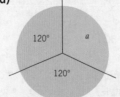

120°   *a*

120°

f)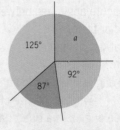

125°   *a*

92°

87°

Angles not drawn to scale

4 Work out the size of the missing angles.

a)

d)

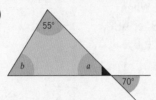

g)

b)

e)

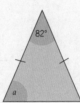

c)

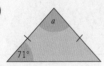

f)

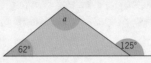

5 Work out the size of the missing angles.

a)

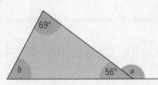

c)

e)

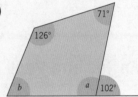

b)

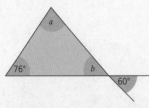

d)

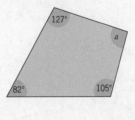

6 The answer to an angle question is 63°.
Write down a question for which the answer is an angle of 63°.

7 Construct these triangles:

a)

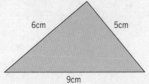

b)

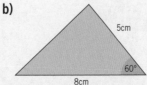

Angles

Angles Revision

An **angle** is an amount of turning or rotation. Angles are measured in **degrees**. When asked to find angle ABC, angle B, or ABĈ, find the middle letter angle, angle B.

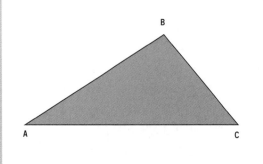

Angles on a Straight Line

The angles on a straight line add up to 180°.

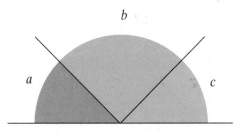

$a + b + c = 180°$.

Angles at a Point

The angles at a point add up to 360°.

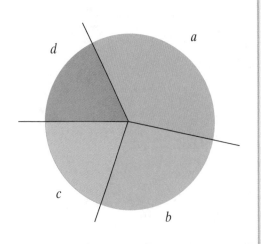

$a + b + c + d = 360°$.

Vertically Opposite Angles

Vertically opposite angles are equal.

$a = b$

$c = d$

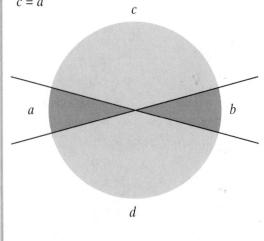

Angles in a Triangle

The angles in a triangle:

$a + b + c = 180°$

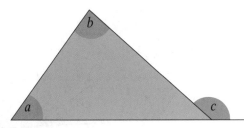

Any exterior angle of a triangle is equal to the sum of the two opposite interior angles.

$a + b = c$

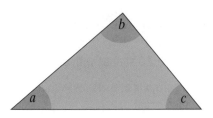

Examples

Work out the size of angle x in each of these triangles:

1

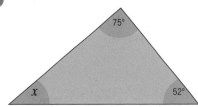

$x + 75° + 52° = 180°$
$x + 127° = 180°$
$x = 53°$

2

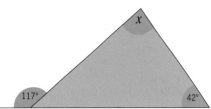

$x + 42° = 117°$
$x = 117° - 42°$
$x = 75°$

3 Since the base angles are equal in an isoceles triangle:

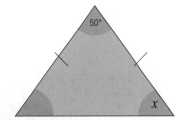

$2x + 50° = 180°$
$2x = 130°$
$x = 65°$

Angles

Angles in a Quadrilateral

The angles in a quadrilateral add up to 360°.

$a + b + c + d = 360°$.

Example
Find the missing angles in this quadrilateral.

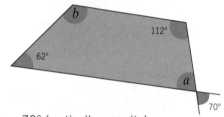

$a = 70°$ (vertically opposite)
$b + 70° + 112° + 62° = 360°$
$b + 244° = 360°$
$b = 116°$

Angles in a Polygon

Polygons are 2D shapes with straight sides.

Regular polygons are shapes with all sides and angles equal.

There are two types of angles in any polygon: **interior** (inside) and **exterior** (outside).

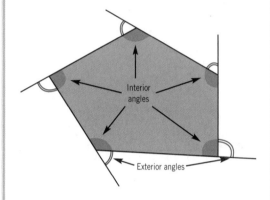

For a regular polygon:
- The sum of the exterior angles adds up to 360°.
- For 'n' exterior angles, size of an exterior angle $= \frac{360°}{n}$
- Interior angle + exterior angle = 180°
- Sum of the interior angles
  $= (n - 2) \times 180°$ or $(2n - 4) \times 90°$.

Examples
1 A regular polygon has 8 sides. What is the size of the interior angle?

$n = 8$, so exterior angle $= \frac{360°}{8} = 45°$

Since the exterior angle + interior angle = 180°

Interior angle $= 180° - 45°$

$= 135°$.

Angles in a Polygon (cont.)

2 Work out the size of angle x in this pentagon.

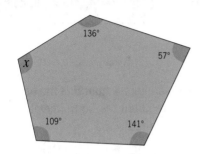

Sum of the interior angles $= (n - 2) \times 180°$
$= (5 - 2) \times 180°$
$= 540°$
$x + 136° + 57° + 109° + 141° = 540°$
$x + 443° = 540°$
$x = 540° - 443°$
$x = 97°$

Angles in Parallel Lines

a) **Alternate angles** are equal

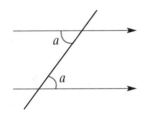

b) **Corresponding angles** are equal

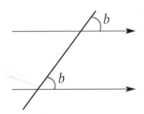

c) **Supplementary angles** add up to 180°
$c + d = 180°$

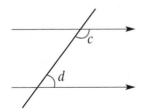

Examples
Find the angles labelled by letters in the diagrams below:

1

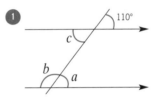

$a = 110°$ (corresponding)
$b = 70°$ (angles on a straight line)
$c = 110°$ (vertically opposite)

2

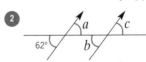

$a = 62°$ (vertically opposite)
$b = 62°$ (alternate)
$c = 62°$ (vertically opposite)

3

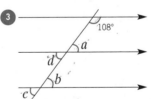

$a = 180° - 108°$
$\quad = 72°$ (supplementary)
$b = 72°$ (corresponding)
$c = 72°$ (vertically opposite)
$d = 72°$ (alternate)

Angles not drawn to scale

Angles

Bearings

A **bearing** is the direction travelled between two points, given as an angle in degrees.

Aeroplanes and ships use bearings when travelling on a journey. This helps to avoid collisions as each plane flies on a particular bearing at a particular speed and altitude (height).

All bearings are measured from the North line in a clockwise direction. They are always written as three figures.

Examples

1. Use a protractor to measure the bearing of:
   a) A from B
   b) B from A

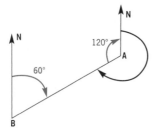

a) The bearing of **A from B** is the angle measured from the North line at B (shown in red) = 60°.

   Bearing = 060°

b) The bearing of **B from A** is the angle measured from the North line at A (shown in black) = 240°.

   This could be calculated since both North lines are parallel lines.

   $180° - 60° = 120°$

   The bearing of B from A is $360° - 120°$
   $= 240°$.

2. The bearing of P from Q is 130°
   The bearing of Q from P is
   $360° - 50°$
   $= 310°$

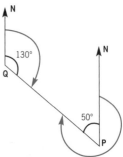

Quick Test

1. What do the angles in a triangle add up to?
2. Bearings are measured in an anticlockwise direction. True or false?
3. Supplementary angles add up to 180°. True or false?
4. Three angles in a quadrilateral add up to 310°. What is the size of the fourth angle?
5. A five-sided polygon is called a...
   a) hexagon   c) pentagon
   b) nonagon   d) octagon

KEY WORDS

Make sure you understand these words before moving on!

- Angle
- Degree
- Isosceles triangle
- Polygon
- Regular polygon
- Interior angle
- Exterior angle
- Alternate angles
- Corresponding angles
- Supplementary angles
- Bearings

Skills Practice

1 Work out the size of the missing angles:

a)

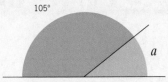

105°

a

b)

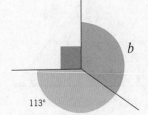

b

113°

c)

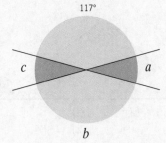

117°

c   *a*

b

d)

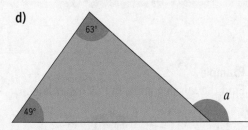

63°

49°   *a*

e)

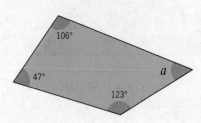

76°

a

f)

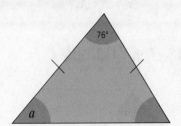

106°

47°   *a*

123°

g)

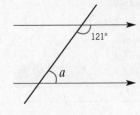

121°

a

h)

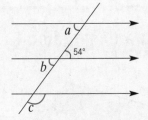

a

54°

b

c

2 Work out the size of **i)** interior and **ii)** exterior angles of a regular octogon.

3 Work out the following:
   a) The bearing of C from D.
   b) The bearing of D from C.

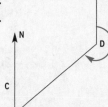

N

N

D

C

Angles & Compound Measures

Angles in a Triangle

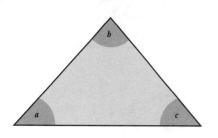

$$a + b + c = 180°$$

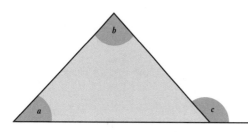

$$a + b = c$$

Examples
Work out the size of **angle** x in each of these triangles.

1

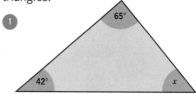

$$x + 63° + 42° = 180°$$
$$x + 105° = 180°$$
$$x = 180° - 105°$$
$$x = 75°$$

2

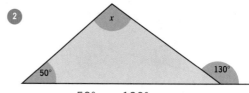

$$x + 50° = 130°$$
$$x = 130° - 50°$$
$$x = 80°$$

Angles in a Quadrilateral

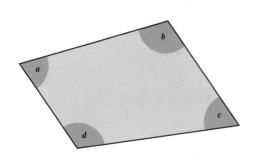

$$a + b + c + d = 360°$$

Example
Find the missing angle in this **quadrilateral**.

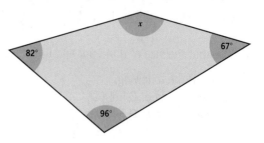

$$x + 82° + 96° + 67° = 360°$$
$$x + 240° = 360°$$
$$x = 360° - 245°$$
$$x = 115°$$

Angles in a Polygon

For a regular **polygon** the sum of the **exterior angles** adds up to 360°.

> For 'n' exterior angels, size of an exterior angle $= \dfrac{360°}{n}$

> Interior angle $+$ exterior angle $= 180°$

> Sum of the interior angles $= (n-2) \times 180°$ or $(2n-4) \times 90°$

Example

A regular polygon has 12 sides. What is the size of the **interior angles**?

$n = 12$ so the exterior angles $= \dfrac{360°}{12}$

Since exterior angle + interior angle = 180°

Interior angle = 180° – 30°

= 150°

Angles in Parallel Lines

Alternate angles: $a = b$

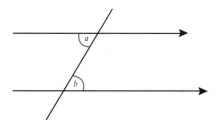

Corresponding angles: $c = d$

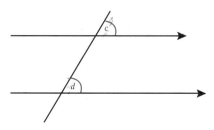

Supplementary angles: $e + f = 180°$

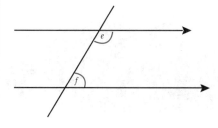

Examples
Find the angles labelled with letters in the diagrams below.

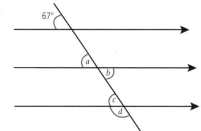

$a = 67°$ (corresponding angles)
$b = 67°$ (opposite to a)
$c = 67°$ (corresponding to 67°)
$d = 113°$ (angles on a straight line)

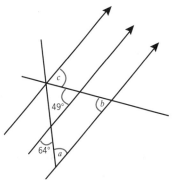

$a = 64°$ (alternate)
$b = 49°$ (corresponding)
$c = 49°$ (corresponding)

Angles & Compound Measures

Bearings

Bearings are always written in three figures and measured from the North line in a clockwise direction.

Example

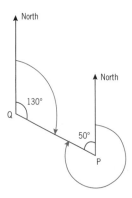

The bearing of P from Q is 130°.
The bearing of Q from P is
360° − 50° = 310°

2 A ship sails 20km due North and then 25km on a bearing of 075°. Using a scale of 1cm = 5cm, draw an accurate scale drawing of the ship's journey.

N.B. Diagram not drawn to scale

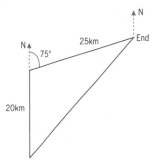

How far and on what bearing is the ship from its starting point?

Distance: 7.3cm = 7.3 × 5
= 36.5km
Bearing = 041°

Compound Measures

Speed can be measured in kilometres per hour (km/h), miles per hour (mph), and metres per second (m/s). These are all compound measures because they involve a combination of basic measures.

To calculate speed...

$$\text{average speed}(s) = \frac{\text{total distance travelled}(d)}{\text{total time taken }(t)}$$

$s = \dfrac{d}{t}$, $t = \dfrac{d}{s}$ and $d = s \times t$

$$\frac{D}{S \times T}$$

Examples

1 A car travels at 60 km/h for three and a half hours. Find the distance travelled in km.

$s = \dfrac{d}{t}$, so $d = s \times t$

$d = 60 \times 3.5$

$= 210$km.

2 A car travels 50km in 40 minutes. Work out the average speed in km/h.

$s = \dfrac{d}{t}$ ← 40 minutes needs to be written as a fraction of one hour

$\dfrac{40}{60} = \dfrac{2}{3}$ hour

$s = \dfrac{50}{\frac{2}{3}}$

$= 75$km/h

Concorde

Concordes were the fastest commercial aeroplanes built. A Concorde took off at a speed of 250mph and cruised at a speed of 1350mph, which is more than twice the speed of sound.

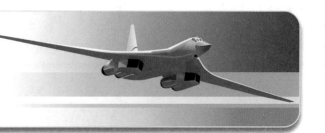

Density

$$\text{Density} = \frac{\text{Mass}}{\text{Volume}}$$

$$D = \frac{M}{V}$$

so $M = D \times V$ or $V = \frac{M}{D}$

Example

Find the density of an object of mass 600g and volume 50cm³.

$$D = \frac{M}{V} = \frac{M}{V} = \frac{600}{50} = 12\text{g/cm}^3$$

Quick Test

1. Two angles in a triangle are 102° and 31°. What is the size of the third angle?
2. Bearings are measured from the north in an anticlockwise direction. True or false?
3. A car travels at 70 mph for two and a half hours. How far has the car travelled?
4. A car travels 120 miles in 1 hour and 40 minutes. What is the speed of the car in mph?

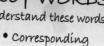

KEY WORDS

Make sure you understand these words before moving on!

- Angle
- Quadrilateral
- Polygon
- Exterior angle
- Interior angle
- Alternate angle
- Corresponding angle
- Supplementary angle
- Bearing
- Speed
- Density
- Mass
- Volume

Angles & Compound Measures

Skills Practice

1 Work out the size of the missing angles:

a)

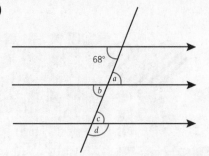

d)

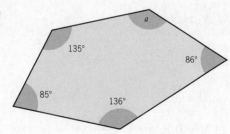

b)

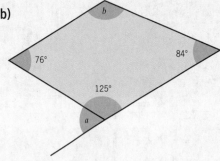

e)

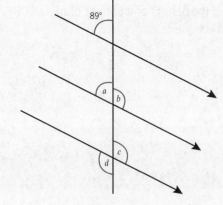

c)

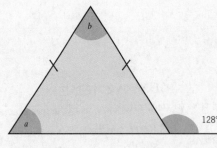

f)

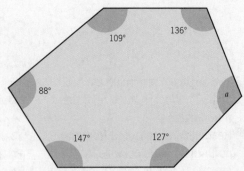

2 Work out the size of the interior and exterior angles of a regular octagon.

3 Work out the size of an exterior angle of a regular shape with 12 sides.

4 For the following, work out...
  i) the bearing of A from B
  ii) the bearing of B from A.

a)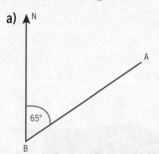

b)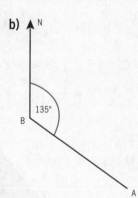

c)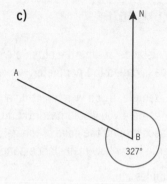

5 For the following, work out...
  i) the bearing of P from Q
  ii) the bearing of Q from P

a)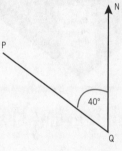

b)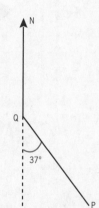

c)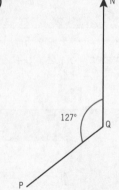

6 A car travels at 85km/h for 2 hours. Find the distance travelled in kilometres.

7 Find the density of an object of mass 7kg and volume 75m³. 🖩

8 A car travels 75km in 40 minutes. What is the speed of the car? 🖩

9 The density of an object is 0.65 kg/cm³. The volume of the object is 12g. 🖩 What is the mass of the object?

Perimeter, Area and Volume

Perimeter

The distance around the outside edge of a shape is called the **perimeter**.

For example, if you were erecting a fence in your garden, you would need to find the distance around the edge of the garden in order to know how many fence panels to buy.

Examples
The following shapes are drawn on cm^2 paper. Find the perimeter of each shape.

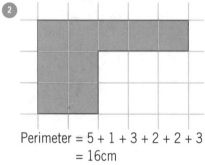

Perimeter = 5 + 2 + 5 + 2
= 14cm

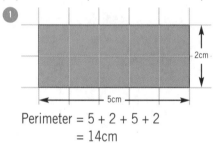

Perimeter = 5 + 1 + 3 + 2 + 2 + 3
= 16cm

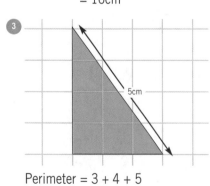

Perimeter = 3 + 4 + 5
= 12cm

Area

The **area** of a 2-D shape is the amount of space it covers.

Units of area include mm^2, cm^2 and m^2.

Rug (3m²)

Carpet off-cut (6m²)

Area of an Irregular Shape

The area of an irregular shape drawn on squared paper can be found by counting the number of squares the shape covers.

Example
This shape is drawn on cm^2 paper. What is its area?

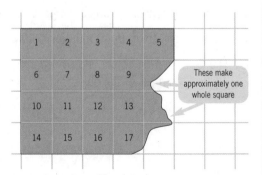

These make approximately one whole square

The area of the shape is approximately $18cm^2$.

Area of a Rectangle

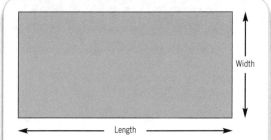

Width

Length

For any rectangle:

Area	=	Length	×	Width

This can be written as:

A	=	l	×	w

Examples
Find the area of the following:

1

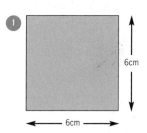

6cm

6cm

Area = $l \times w$
= 6×6 ← A square has all lengths equal.
= 36cm^2

2

7cm

10.5cm

Area = $l \times w$
= 10.5×7
= 73.5cm^2 ← Remember the units are squared.

Area of a Triangle

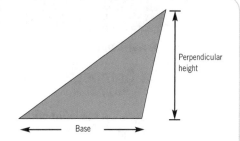

Perpendicular height

Base

The area of a triangle is:

Area	=	$\frac{1}{2}$	×	Base	×	Perpendicular height

This can be written as:

A	=	$\frac{1}{2}$	×	b	×	h

Examples
Find the area of each of these triangles:

1

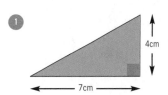

4cm

7cm

Area = $\frac{1}{2} \times b \times h$
= $\frac{1}{2} \times 7 \times 4$
= 14cm^2

2

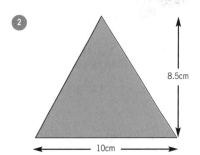

8.5cm

10cm

Area = $\frac{1}{2} \times b \times h$
= $\frac{1}{2} \times 10 \times 8.5$
= 42.5cm^2

Perimeter, Area and Volume

Area of a Compound Shape

Quite often, shapes are made up of different-sized rectangles and triangles. These are called compound shapes.

The area of a compound shape can be worked out in parts.

Example
Jonathan wants to tile his bathroom floor. Work out the area of the floor.

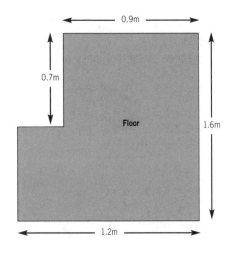

The floor can be split up into two rectangles and the area of each rectangle can be worked out.

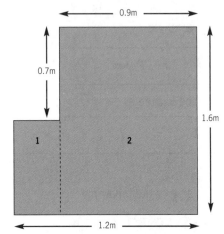

For rectangle 1, new lengths have to be calculated.

Area of rectangle 1: $A = l \times w$
$$= 0.3 \times 0.9 = 0.27\text{m}^2$$

$1.2 - 0.9 = 0.3\text{m}$ $1.6 - 0.7 = 0.9\text{m}$

Area of rectangle 2: $A = l \times w$
$$= 0.9 \times 1.6 = 1.44\text{m}^2$$

$$\text{Total area} = 1.44 + 0.27$$
$$= 1.71\text{m}^2$$

Volume of 3-D Solids

The **volume** of an object is the amount of space it occupies.

Units of volume include mm^3, cm^3 and m^3.

The volume of a 3-D solid can be found by counting the number of 1cm^3 cubes it can hold.

For example, the solid opposite is made up of 9 cubes, so its volume is 9cm^3.

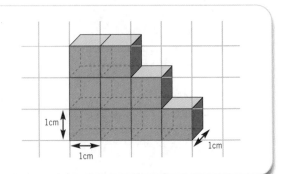

Volume of a Cuboid

A **cuboid** is a solid with rectangular faces.

Example

Work out the volume of this cuboid.

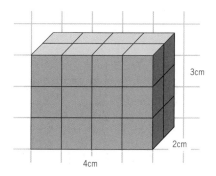

By counting cubes: Volume = 24cm^3

Alternatively:

Volume of a cuboid	=	Length	×	Width	×	Height

This can be written as:

$$V = l \times w \times h$$

Example

Work out the volume of this empty box.

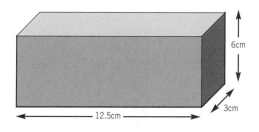

Volume = $l \times w \times h$
     = $12.5 \times 3 \times 6$
     = 225cm^3

Quick Test

1. Explain what is meant by the perimeter of a shape.
2. A rectangle has an area of 20cm^2. If the width is 2cm what is the length?
   A 10cm
   B 20cm
   C 18cm
   D 5cm
3. What is the area of this triangle?

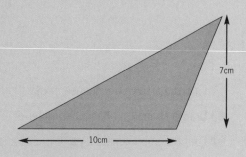

   A 70cm^2
   B 140cm^2
   C 35cm^2
   D 35cm
4. cm^2 is a unit of volume. True or false?
5. The length of a cuboid is 6cm, its height is 2cm and its width is 3cm. What is the volume of the cuboid?
   A 11cm^3
   B 15cm^3
   C 30cm^3
   D 36cm^3

KEY WORDS

Make sure you understand these words before moving on!
• Perimeter
• Area
• Volume
• Cuboid

Perimeter, Area and Volume

Skills Practice

1 Find the perimeter of each of the following shapes drawn on cm squared paper:

a)

b)
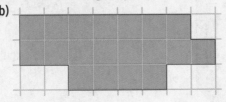

c)
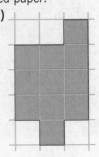

2 Find the area of the shapes in question 1 by counting squares.

3 Draw a shape that has a perimeter of 20cm.

4 Find the approximate area of this shape drawn on cm squared paper:

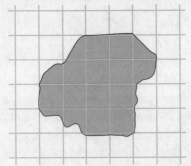

5 Find the area of each of these rectangles: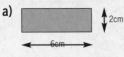

a)
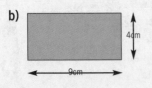
6cm, 2cm

c)
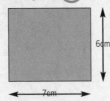
7cm, 6cm

e)
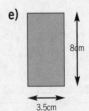
8cm, 3.5cm

b)
9cm, 4cm

d)
12.5cm, 8cm

f)
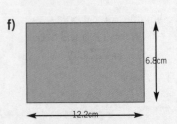
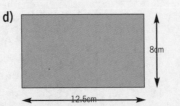
12.2cm, 6.8cm

6 A rectangular picture frame measures 36cm by 42cm.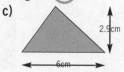
Work out...
a) the perimeter of the picture frame
b) the area of the picture frame.

7 Find the area of each of these triangles: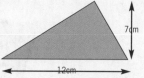

a)
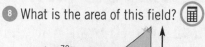
5cm
8cm

c)
2.9cm
6cm

e)
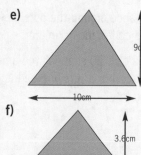
9cm
10cm

b)
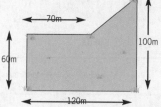
6cm
9cm

d)
7cm
12cm

f)
3.6cm
6.8cm

8 What is the area of this field?

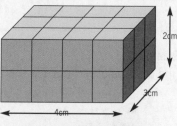
70m
100m
60m
120m

9 Find the volume of each of the following boxes:

a)
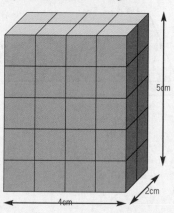
2cm
3cm
4cm

c)
2cm
5cm
4cm

b)
5cm
4cm
2cm

d)
5cm
10cm
7cm

e)
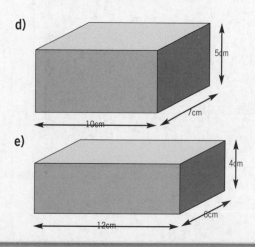
4cm
12cm
6cm

Perimeter, Area and Volume

Perimeter and Area

The distance around the outside edge of a shape is called the **perimeter**.

The **area** of a 2D shape is the amount of space it covers. Units of area include mm^2, cm^2 and m^2.

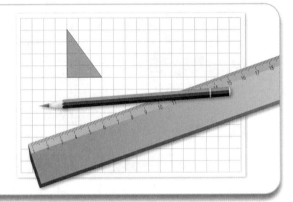

Area of a Rectangle

For any rectangle:

Area	=	Length	×	Width

This can be written as:

$$A = l \times w$$

Example
Find the area of this rectangle.

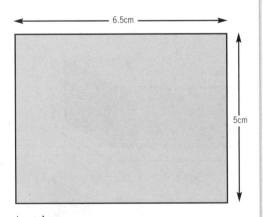

$A = l \times w$
$ = 6.5 \times 5$
$ = 32.5 \text{cm}^2$

Area of a Triangle

The area of a triangle is:

Area	=	$\frac{1}{2}$	×	Base	×	Perpendicular height

This can be written as:

$$A = \tfrac{1}{2} \times b \times h$$

Example
Find the area of this triangle.

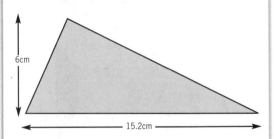

$A = \frac{1}{2} \times b \times h$
$ = \frac{1}{2} \times 15.2 \times 6$
$ = 45.6 \text{ cm}^2$

Area of a Parallelogram

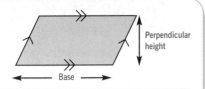

Perpendicular height

Base

| Area | = | Base | × | Perpendicular height |

This can be written as: ,

$$A = b \times h$$

Example
Find the area of this parallelogram.

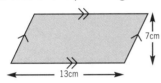

7cm

13cm

$A = b \times h$
$ = 13 \times 7$
$ = 91\text{cm}^2$

Area of a Trapezium

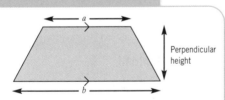

a

Perpendicular height

b

The area of a trapezium is:

| Area | = | $\frac{1}{2}$ | × | $\begin{pmatrix} \text{sum of} \\ \text{parallel sides} \end{pmatrix}$ | × | $\begin{array}{c} \text{perpendicular height} \\ \text{between them} \end{array}$ |

Example
Find the area of the trapezium.

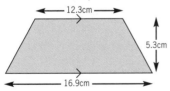

12.3cm

5.3cm

16.9cm

$$A = \frac{1}{2} \times (a + b) \times h$$

$A = \frac{1}{2} \times (12.3 + 16.9) \times 5.3$
$ = 77.38\text{cm}^2$

Area of Compound Shapes

Compound shapes are made up of different sized shapes. The area can be worked out in parts.

Example
A sewing pattern is this shape.

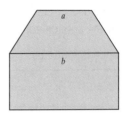

a

b

The sewing pattern can be split up into a rectangle (2) and a trapezium (1). The area of each one can then be worked out.

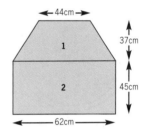

44cm

37cm

1

2

45cm

62cm

Area of 1 $= \frac{1}{2} \times (a + b) \times h$
$\phantom{\text{Area of 1}} = \frac{1}{2} \times (44 + 62) \times 37$
$\phantom{\text{Area of 1}} = 1961\text{cm}^2$

Area of 2 $= l \times w$
$\phantom{\text{Area of 2}} = 62 \times 45$
$\phantom{\text{Area of 2}} = 2790\text{cm}^2$

Total Area $= 2790 + 1961$
$\phantom{\text{Total Area}} = 4751\text{cm}^2$

Perimeter, Area and Volume

Circumference of a Circle

The **circumference** of a circle is the distance around the outside edge.

The circumference is found by:

$$C = \pi \times \text{diameter}$$

or

$$C = \pi \times 2 \times \text{radius}$$

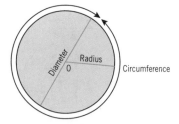

Remember: The **radius** is half the **diameter**.

This can be written as:

$$C = \pi d \quad \text{or} \quad C = 2\pi r$$

π is one of the most important numbers in mathematics and is widely used in Geometry. In Greek the name of this letter is pronounced 'pi'. The value of π has been calculated to more than a trillion (10^{12}) digits. We usually use π to 2 or 3 decimal places. $\pi = 3.142$ (3dp)

Examples

Find the circumference of these circles. Use $\pi = 3.14$

a)

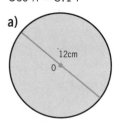

b)

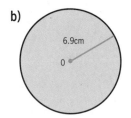

$C = \pi d$
$\quad = \pi \times 12$
$\quad = 37.68\text{cm}$

$C = 2\pi r$
$\quad = 2 \times \pi \times 6.9$
$\quad = 43.332\text{cm}$

Area of a Circle

The area of a circle is found by:

$$\text{Area} = \pi \times \text{radius}^2$$

Which is written as:

$$A = \pi r^2$$

Examples

Find the area of these circles. Use $\pi = 3.14$

a)

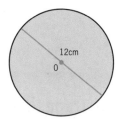

$A = \pi r^2$
$\quad = \pi \times 6^2$ ← Remember $6^2 = 6 \times 6$
$\quad = 113.04\text{cm}^2$

b)

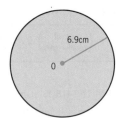

$A = \pi r^2$
$\quad = \pi \times 6.9^2$
$\quad = 149.50\text{cm}^2$

Volume and Surface Area of a Cuboid

The **volume** of an object is the amount of space it occupies. Units of volume include mm^3, cm^3 and m^3. A cuboid is a solid with rectangular faces.

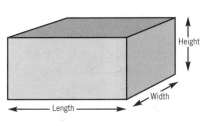

Volume of a cuboid	=	Length	×	Width	×	Height

This can be written as:

$$V = l \times w \times h$$

To find the **surface area** of a cuboid it is best to consider the net of the cuboid.

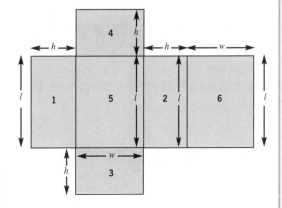

Faces 1 and 2: $A = (l \times h) \times 2$
$A = 2(h \times l)$

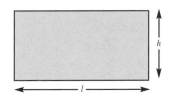

Faces 5 and 6: $A = (l \times w) \times 2$
$A = 2(l \times w)$

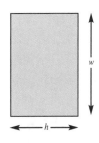

Faces 3 and 4: $A = (h \times w) \times 2$
$A = 2(h \times w)$

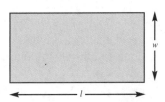

Total surface area	=	**2hl**	×	**2hw**	×	**2lw**

Volume and Surface Area of a Cuboid (cont.)

Examples

1 Work out the volume and surface area of this cuboid.

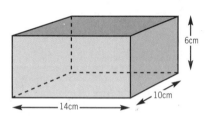

Volume $= l \times w \times h$
$= 14 \times 10 \times 6$
$= 840\text{cm}^3$

Surface area $= 2hl + 2hw + 2lw$
$= (2 \times 6 \times 14) + (2 \times 6 \times 10)$
$\quad + (2 \times 14 \times 10)$
$= 168 + 120 + 280$
$= 568\text{cm}^2$

2 Work out the volume of this solid.

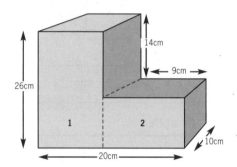

Draw a dashed line to split the solid in two:

Volume of 1: $V = l \times w \times h$
$= 11 \times 10 \times 26$
$= 2860\text{cm}^3$

Volume of 2: $V = l \times w \times h$
$= 9 \times 10 \times 12$
$= 1080\text{cm}^3$

Total volume $= 2860 + 1080$
$= 3940\text{cm}^3$

Quick Test

1 cm^3 is a unit of volume. True or false?

2 A rectangle has an area of 40cm^2. If the height is 8cm, what is the width?

3 The volume of a cuboid is 64cm^3. If the height is 8cm and the width 4cm, what is the length?

4 The volume of a cube is 27cm^3. What is the length of each side?

5 To find the area of a trapezium you use this formula: $A = \frac{1}{2}(a \times b) + h$.
True or false?

KEY WORDS

Make sure you understand these words before moving on!

- Perimeter
- Area
- Perpendicular height
- Circumference
- Radius
- Volume
- Diameter
- Surface area

Skills Practice

1 Find the area of each of these shapes:

a)
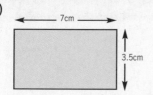
7cm
3.5cm

c)
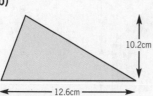
8.3cm
19.5cm

e)
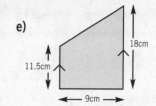
18cm
11.5cm
9cm

b)
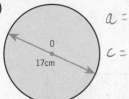
10.2cm
12.6cm

d)
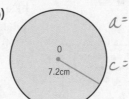
14cm
10cm
27cm

f)
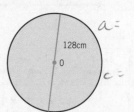
5.6cm
21.2cm
26.3cm

2 For these circles, work out using π = 3.14 to 2dp the:
i) Circumference
ii) Area

a)
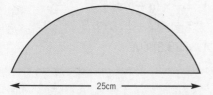
0
17cm
a =
c =

b)
0
7.2cm
a =
c =

c)
128cm
0
a =
c =

3 Work out the area of this semicircle. Use π = 3.14. Give your answer to 2dp.

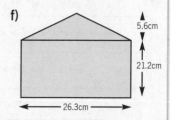
25cm

4 Find the volume and surface area of this cuboid.

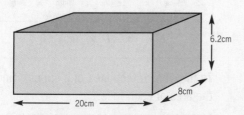
6.2cm
8cm
20cm

Area and Volume

Area Formulae

There are formulae for calculating the **area** of 2D shapes.

Area of Parallelogram	**=**	base	**✕**	perpendicular height

$$A = b \times h$$

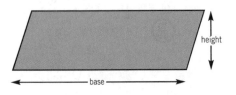

Area of Trapezium	**=**	$\frac{1}{2}$	**✕**	[sum of parallel sides]	**✕**	[perpendicular distance between them]

$$A = \tfrac{1}{2} \times (a + b) \times h$$

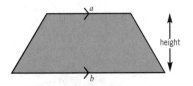

Examples
Find the area of the following shapes.

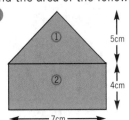

Split into two shapes, ① and ②.
a) $A = \frac{1}{2} \times b \times h$
$\qquad = \frac{1}{2} \times 7 \times 5 = 17.5\text{cm}^2$
b) $A = b \times h = 7 \times 4 = 28\text{cm}^2$
Total $= 28 + 17.5$
$\qquad A = 45.5\text{cm}^2$

2

7cm
6.3cm
11cm

$A = \frac{1}{2} \times (a + b) \times h$
$\quad = \frac{1}{2} \times (7 + 11) \times 6.3$
$A = 28.35\text{cm}^2$

Volume of a Solid

The **volume** of an object is the amount of space it occupies. Units of volume include mm^3, cm^3, m^3, etc.

A **prism** is a 3D solid. No matter where you cut, it has a constant cross sectional area.

cross sectional area

Volume of a Cuboid

Volume	**=**	Length	**✕**	Width	**✕**	Height

$$V = l \times w \times h$$

To find the **surface area** of a cuboid, find the area of each face.

$$SA = 2hl + 2hw + 2lw$$

Volume of a Prism

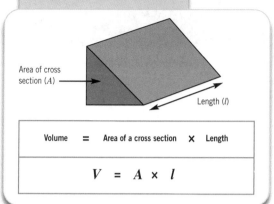

Area of cross section (A)

Length (l)

Volume	=	Area of a cross section	×	Length

$$V = A \times l$$

Circles

Circumference

The equation for circumference uses the diameter or radius:

$$C = \pi \times \text{diameter} \quad \text{or} \quad C = \pi \times 2 \times \text{radius}$$

This can be written as:

$$C = \pi d \quad \text{or} \quad C = 2\pi r$$

π is usually used to two or three decimal places, $\pi = 3.241$ (3 d.p.) or the π button on the calculator can be used.

Area

The equation for area is:

$$\text{Area} = \pi \times \text{Radius}^2$$

This is written as:

$$A = \pi r^2$$

Example

Find the circumference and area of this circle.

$C = \pi d$
$C = \pi \times 12$
$C = 37.7\text{cm}$

$A = \pi r^2$
$A = \pi \times 6^2$
$A = 113.04\text{cm}^2$

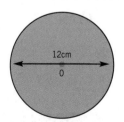

12cm

0

Cylinders

A cylinder is a prism.

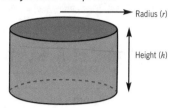

Radius (r)

Height (h)

To work out the volume...

$$V = \pi r^2 \times h$$

area of cross section   height

To work out the surface area...

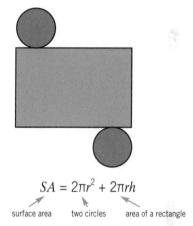

$$SA = 2\pi r^2 + 2\pi r h$$

surface area   two circles   area of a rectangle

When finding the surface area, draw the net of the solid and work out the area of each face.

Example

Work out the volume and surface area of this cylinder.

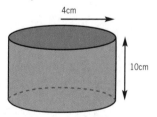

4cm

10cm

Volume $= \pi r^2 h$
$\quad\quad = \pi \times 4^2 \times 10$
$\quad\quad = 502.65\text{cm}^3$ (2d.p.)

Surface $= 2\pi r^2 + 2\pi r h$
Area $\quad = (2 \times \pi \times 4^2) + (2 \times \pi \times 4 \times 10)$
$\quad\quad = 351.86\text{cm}^2$

Area and Volume

Converting Units of Area and Volume

$1cm^2$	$= 10 \times 10 = 100mm^2$
$1m^2$	$= 100 \times 100 = 10\,000cm^2$
$1cm^3$	$= 10 \times 10 \times 10 = 1000mm^3$
$1m^3$	$= 100 \times 100 \times 100 = 1000\,000cm^3$

Examples

1 $6m^2 = 6 \times 10\,000$
$\quad\quad = 60\,000cm^2$

2 $5cm^3 = 5 \times 1000$
$\quad\quad = 5000mm^3$

Quick Test

1 mm^2 is a unit of area. True or false?

2 Work out the circumference of a circle 🖩 of diameter 22cm, to 2 d.p.

3 The volume of the cylinder below 🖩 is $763m^3$ (nearest whole number). True or false?

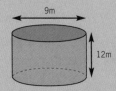

9m

12m

KEY WORDS

Make sure you understand these words before moving on!

- Area
- Perpendicular height
- Volume
- Prism
- Surface area
- Circumference
- Diameter
- Radius

1 Work out the area of the shape below.

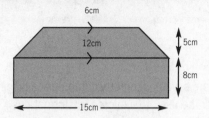

2 A circle has a circumference of 50m. Work out its radius to 2 d.p.

3 Work out the **volume** of these solids.

a)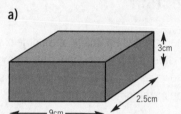

b)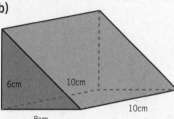

c)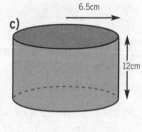

4 Work out the **surface area** of these solids.

a)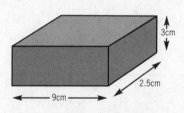

b)

c)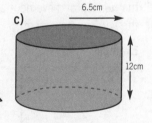

5 Work out the volume and surface area of the solid below.

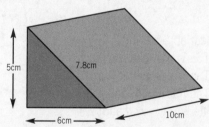

6 Change the following measurements to the units given.

a) $6cm^2$ = _____ m^2

b) $5m^3$ = _____ cm^3

c) $16m^2$ = _____ cm^2

d) $4cm^3$ = _____ m^3

Transformations

Transformation

A **transformation** changes the position or size of a shape. There are four types of transformations: **translation**, **reflection**, **rotation** and **enlargement**.

There are several geometry computer packages that can be used to explore transformations.

Translation

A translation moves an object from one place to another. The size and shape of the object are not changed.

Vectors can be used to describe the distance and direction of a transformation.

The vector is written as $\binom{a}{b}$. 'a' represents the **horizontal** movement and 'b' represents the **vertical** movement.

Example

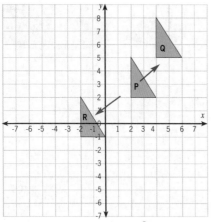

1. Translate P by the vector $\binom{2}{3}$ (this means 2 to the right and 3 up). Call it Q.

2. Translate P by the vector $\binom{-4}{-3}$ (this means 4 to the left and 3 down). Call it R.

Triangles P, Q and R are **congruent** – two or more shapes are congruent if they have exactly the same size and shape.

Reflection

A reflection creates an image of an object on the other side of the **mirror line**. The mirror line is known as an **axis of reflection**. The size and shape of the **object** are not changed.

Example

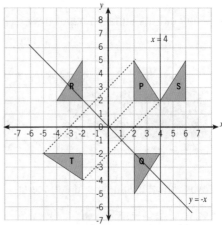

Reflect object P in:
a) The x axis, call it Q.
b) The y axis, call it R.
c) The line $x = 4$, call it S.
d) The line $y = -x$, call it T.

All the triangles are congruent.

Transformations in Art

Transformations have been used by artists and designers for thousands of years. Many patterns go around in a circle. Rose windows are particularly characteristic of Gothic architecture and may be seen in all the major Gothic cathedrals of Northern France. Their origins are much earlier and rose windows can be seen in the medieval period.

Rotations

A rotation turns a object through an angle about a fixed point. This fixed point is called the **centre of rotation**. The size and shape of the object are not changed.

Example

Rotate P:
a) 90° clockwise about (0,0), call it Q.
b) 180° clockwise about (0,0), call it S.
c) 90° anticlockwise about (0,1), call it T.

When describing a rotation give:
i) The angle of the turn.
ii) The direction of the turn.
iii) The centre of rotation.

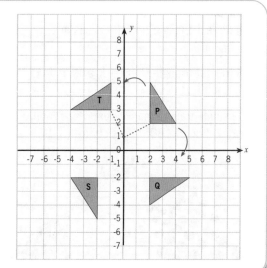

Enlargements

An enlargement changes the size but not the shape of an object.

The **centre of enlargement** is the point from which the enlargement takes place.

The **scale factor** indicates how many times the lengths of the original figure have increased in size. If the scale factor is greater than 1 the shape becomes bigger. If the scale factor is less than 1 the shape becomes smaller.

Example

❶ Enlarge triangle A by a scale factor of 3 to give triangle B, centre (0,0).

❷ Enlarge triangle A by a scale factor of $\frac{1}{2}$ to give triangle C, centre (0,0).

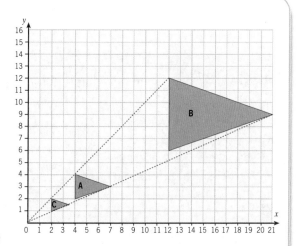

Triangle B is three times the size of triangle A. Triangle C is half the size of triangle A.

Transformations

Combining Transformations

Transformations can be combined in a series of two or more transformations.

Example

1 Reflect triangle A in the x axis and call it B.

2 Reflect triangle B in the y axis and call it C.

The single transformation that maps A onto C is a rotation of 180° about centre (0,0).

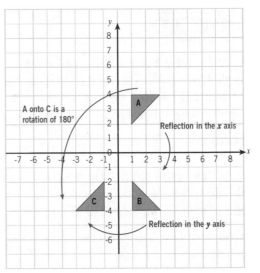

A onto C is a rotation of 180°

Reflection in the x axis

Reflection in the y axis

Quick Test

1 What are the four transformations called?

2 If a shape is enlarged by a scale factor 2, each length is twice the size of the original. True or false?

3 A translation by a vector $\begin{pmatrix} -3 \\ -6 \end{pmatrix}$ means 3 to the left and 6 up. True or false?

4 A translation by a vector $\begin{pmatrix} 3 \\ -2 \end{pmatrix}$ means 3 to the right and 2 down. True or false?

KEY WORDS

Make sure you understand these words before moving on!

- Transformation
- Translation
- Reflection
- Rotation
- Enlargement
- Vector
- Horizontal
- Vertical
- Congruent
- Mirror line
- Axis of reflection
- Object
- Centre of rotation
- Centre of enlargement
- Scale factor

Skills Practice

1 Copy the coordinate axes opposite.

   a) Translate triangle A by the vector
$\begin{pmatrix} -4 \\ 2 \end{pmatrix}$. Call it B.

   b) Translate triangle A by the vector
$\begin{pmatrix} 1 \\ -8 \end{pmatrix}$. Call it C.

   c) Reflect triangle A in the line $x = 5$.
Call it D.

   d) Reflect triangle C in the y axis. Call it E.

   e) Reflect triangle A in the line $y = -x$.
Call it F.

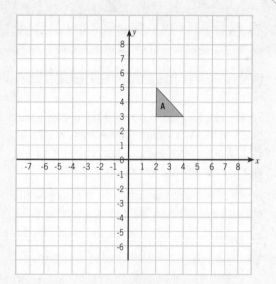

2 Copy the coordinate axes opposite.

   a) Rotate triangle A by 90° clockwise
about (0,0). Call it B.

   b) Rotate triangle A by 90° anticlockwise
about (0,0). Call it C.

   c) Rotate triangle A 180° about (0,0).
Call it D.

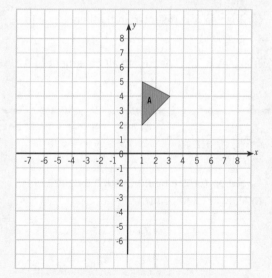

3 On a separate piece of paper enlarge shape
A with a scale factor of 3 about point P.

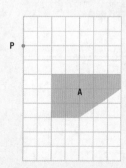

Transformations

Translations and Reflections

Vectors can be used to describe the distance and direction of a translation. The vector is written as $\binom{a}{b}$, where a represents the horizontal movement and b represents the vertical movement.

A reflection creates an image of an object on the other side of a mirror line (the axis of reflection).

Examples
1. Triangle A is translated by the vector $\binom{-3}{-4}$ to give B.
2. Triangle A is translated by $\binom{4}{-6}$ to give C.
3. Triangle A is reflected in the line $x = 3$ to give D.
4. Triangle A is reflected in the line $y = -x$ to give E.

Triangles B, C, D and E are all congruent to A.

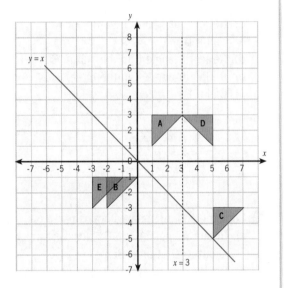

Rotations

A rotation turns a figure through a centre of rotation (a fixed point).

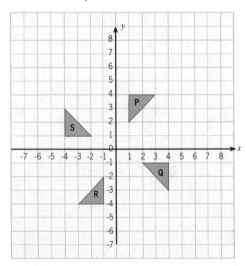

1. P is rotated 90° clockwise about (0, 0) to give Q.
2. P is rotated 90° anticlockwise about (0, 0) to give S.
3. P is rotated 180° about (0, 0) to give R.

Enlargements

The point from which an enlargement takes place is the **centre of enlargement.**

The increase in length is indicated by the **scale factor:**
- Greater than 1 and the shape becomes larger.
- Less than 1 and the shape becomes smaller.

A negative scale factor puts the image on the opposite side of the centre of enlargement to the object.

Examples

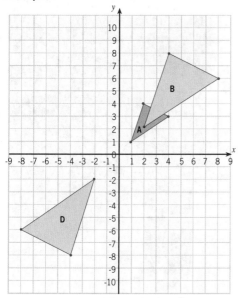

1. B is an enlargement of A, scale factor 2, centre (0, 0).
2. D is an enlargement of A, scale factor -2, centre (0, 0).

Congruent Triangles

Two triangles are congruent if one of the following sets of conditions is true.

S = side, A = angle, R = right angle, H = hypotenuse

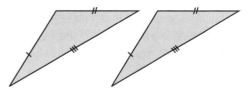

SSS The three sides of one triangle are the same lengths as three sides of another.

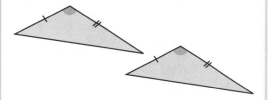

SAS Two sides and the angle between them in one triangle are equal to two sides and the included angle in the other.

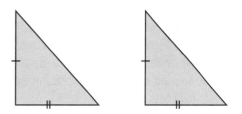

RHS Each triangle contains a right angle. The hypotenuse and the other pair of sides are equal.

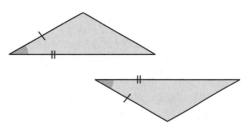

AAS Two angles and a side in one triangle are equal to the two corresponding angles and the corresponding side in the other.

Transformations

Tessellations

Transformation of objects can make tessellations. A tessellation is a pattern of 2D shapes that fit together without leaving any gaps.

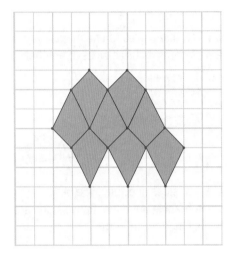

Tessellations frequently appeared in the art of M.C. Escher. Tessellations are seen throughout art history from ancient to modern art. Tessellations can also be used in computer graphics in order to manage data sets of polygons.

Quick Test

1. If a shape is enlarged by a scale factor 3, each length is three times the size of the original. True or false?
2. Two triangles are congruent if all three sides are the same length. True or false?
3. A translation by a vector $\begin{pmatrix} -6 \\ 9 \end{pmatrix}$ means 6 to the right and 9 up. True or false?
4. Rectangles can tessellate. Draw a sketch of tessellated rectangles.

KEY WORDS

Make sure you understand these words before moving on!

- Vector
- Translation
- Reflection
- Congruent
- Rotation
- Centre of enlargement
- Scale factor
- Transformation
- Tessellation

1 For triangle A, carry out the following transformations.

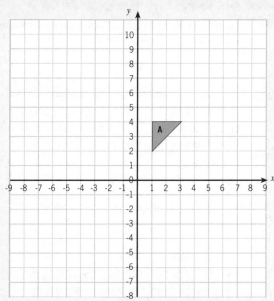

a) Rotate A about (0, 0) by a 90° clockwise rotation. Call the shape B.

b) Translate A by the vector $\binom{-5}{6}$. Call the shape C.

c) Reflect A in the line $y = -2$. Call the shape D.

d) Rotate A by 90° anticlockwise about the point (0, 1). Call the shape E.

2 Continue the tessellation below. Draw at least six more shapes.

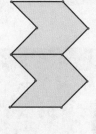

3 Decide whether these pairs of triangles are congruent, giving a reason for your answer.

a)

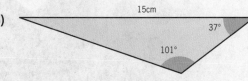

4cm   9.5cm   12cm

9.3cm   4cm   12cm

b)

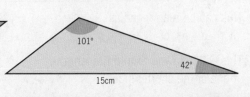

15cm   37°   101°

101°   42°   15cm

Pythagoras' Theorem

Pythagoras

Pythagoras, a Greek philosopher and mathematician, was born about 570 BC in Samos, Ionia, and died about 490 BC. Much of his work was said to have been influenced by the philosopher and mathematician Plato.

Pythagoras founded the Pythagorean school of mathematics in Crotone, a Greek seaport in Southern Italy. The Pythagorean Theorem is Pythagoras' most famous contribution to mathematics.

Pythagoras' Theorem

Pythagoras' Theorem states: 'In any right angled triangle, the square of the hypotenuse is equal to the sum of the squares on the other two sides.'

The hypotenuse is the longest side of a right angled triangle; it is always opposite the right angle.

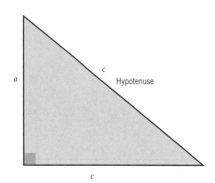

The distance between two towns is found by using pythagoras' theorem on a satellite navigation system.

Using the letters in the diagram, the theorem is written as:

$$c^2 = a^2 + b^2$$

This can be rearranged as:
$a^2 = c^2 - b^2$ or $b^2 = c^2 - a^2$

This will help you to find the length of one of the shorter sides.

Finding the Length of the Hypotenuse

You need to follow the steps below to find the hypotenuse of a right angled triangle.

Examples

1 Find the length AB in the triangle below. Give your answer to one decimal place.

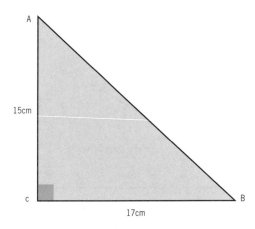

- Square the two lengths of the shorter sides that you are given.

$(AB)^2 = (AC)^2 + (BC)^2$
$= 15^2 + 17^2$

- To find the hypotenuse, add the two squared numbers.

$(AB)^2 = (AC)^2 + (BC)^2$
$= 15^2 + 17^2$
$= 225 + 289$
$= 514$

- Take the **square root** of the sum.

$AB = \sqrt{514}$
$AB = 22.7m \ (1 \ d.p.)$

2 Town A is 15km due north of town C. Town B is 12km due east of town A. Work out the direct distance between town B and town C.

$(CB)^2 = 15^2 + 12^2$
$(CB)^2 = 225 + 144$
$(CB)^2 = 369$
$CB = \sqrt{369}$
$CB = 19.2km \ (3 \ s.f.)$

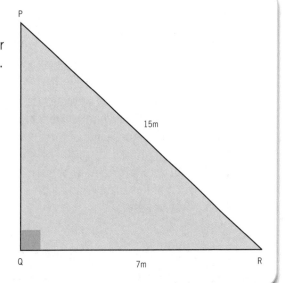

Finding the Length of a Shorter Side

The method for finding the length of the shorter side is the same as finding the hypotenuse. Remember, instead of adding the two sides together you subtract the smaller value from the larger value.

Example

Find the length of PQ in the triangle alongside. Give your answer to one decimal place.

- $(PR)^2 = (PQ)^2 + (QR)^2$
  $15^2 = (PQ)^2 + 7^2$
- $15^2 - 7^2 = (PQ)^2$
  $225 - 49 = (PQ)^2$
  $176 = (PQ)^2$
- $PQ = \sqrt{176}$
  $PQ = 13.3m \ (1 \ d.p.)$

Pythagoras' Theorem

Applications of Pythagoras' Theorem

Pythagoras' Theorem can be used to solve problems.

Examples

1. A ladder of 12m in length rests against a wall. The foot of the ladder is 6.8m away from the wall. How high up the wall does the ladder reach? Give your answer to 3 s.f.

Call the height of the wall h.

$$12^2 = h^2 + 6.8^2$$
$$12^2 - 6.8^2 = h^2$$
$$144 - 46.24 = h^2$$
$$h^2 = 97.76$$
$$h = \sqrt{97.76}$$
$$h = 9.89m$$

The height that the ladder reaches up the wall is 9.89m.

2. Calculate the length of a line XY, which connects X (2, 5) and Y (5, 12). Give your answer to 3 s.f.

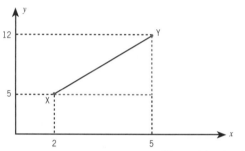

Diagram not drawn to scale

Horizontal distance = 3
Vertical distance = 7

$$\text{Length of } (XY)^2 = 3^2 + 7^2$$
$$= 9 + 49$$
$$= 58$$
$$XY = \sqrt{58}$$
$$XY = 7.62 \text{ (3 s.f.)}$$

Quick Test

1. The hypotenuse is the longest side of a right angled triangle. True or false?
2. Explain what other property a hypotenuse has.
3. Two sides of a right angled triangle are 3cm and 4cm. What is the length of the hypotenuse?
   a) 12cm b) 7cm c) 25cm d) 5cm
4. The length x of this triangle to 1 d.p. is 7.1cm. True or false?

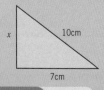

Skills Practice

1 Work out the missing length, x, in each of the triangles below.

a)
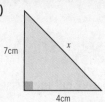
7cm
4cm
x

c)
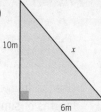
10m
6m
x

e)

62.3m
45m
x

g)

x
6.2m
7.3m

b)
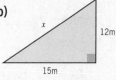
x
12m
15m

d)
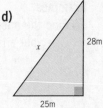
x
28m
25m

f)
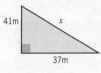
41m
x
37m

h)

x
19.3m
24.6m

2 Work out the missing length, y, in each of the triangles below.

a)

19m
12m
y

c)

y
36m
10.5m

e)

26m
y
10m

g)

15m
y
13.5m

b)

y
21m
14m

d)
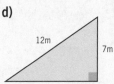
12m
7m
y

f)
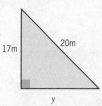
17m
20m
y

h)
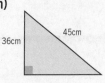
36cm
45cm
y

3 The diagram shows a rectangle of length 12cm and width 9cm.
Work out the length of the diagonal of the rectangle.

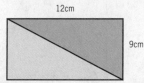
12cm
9cm

4 Work out the perimeter of the triangle below. Give your answer to one decimal place.

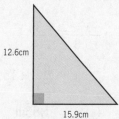
12.6cm
15.9cm

Similarity

Similar figures

Similar figures are those that are the same shape but different sizes. For example, models are similar to real-life objects.

For similar shapes, corresponding angles are equal and corresponding lengths are in the same ratio.

Corresponding sides are in the same ratio. The length of the bigger triangle is twice the size of the small triangle.

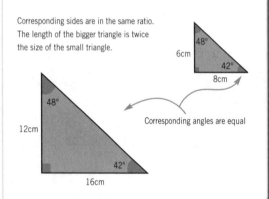

Corresponding angles are equal

Finding Missing Lengths

Use the following to work out the missing lengths of similar figures.

Examples

① Find the missing length x.
Give your answer to 3 s.f.

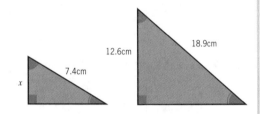

Since the corresponding sides are in the same ratio

$$\frac{x}{7.4} = \frac{12.6}{18.9}$$

Multiply both sides by 7.4

$$x = \frac{12.6}{18.9} \times 7.4$$

$$x = 4.9\dot{3}$$

② Find the missing length x.

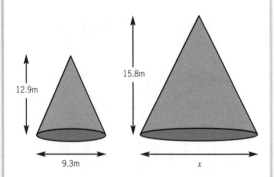

Since the corresponding sides are in the same ratio

$$\frac{x}{15.8} = \frac{9.3}{12.4}$$

Multiply both sides by 15.8

$$x = \frac{9.3}{12.4} \times 15.8$$

$$x = 11.85\text{m}$$

KEY WORDS
Make sure you understand these words before moving on!
- Similar
- Corresponding
- Ratio

1 Work out the missing length x in each pair of similar shapes below. 🖩
Give your answer to one decimal place.

a)

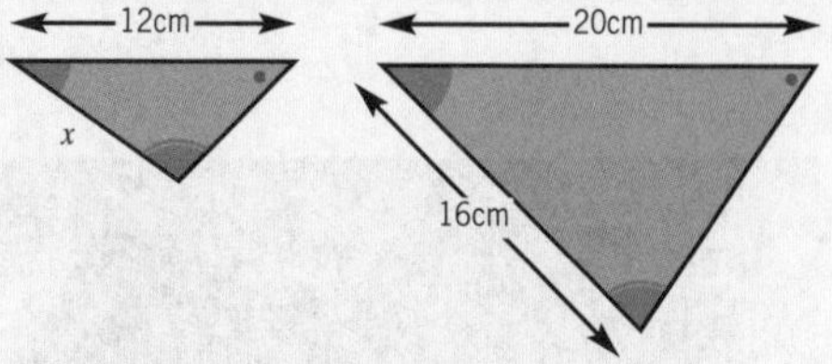

←12cm→
x

←20cm→
16cm

b)

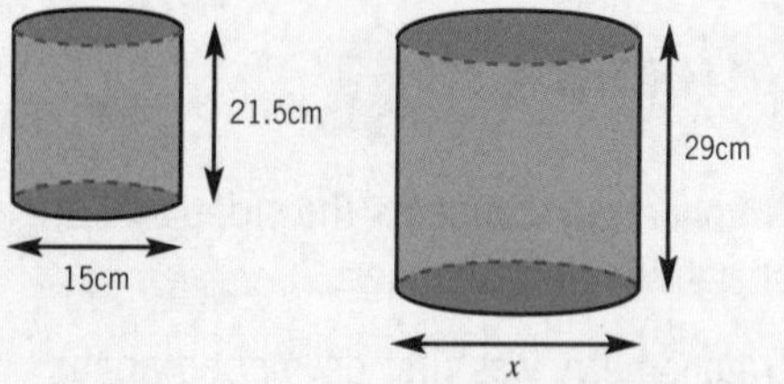

21.5cm
15cm

29cm
x

c)

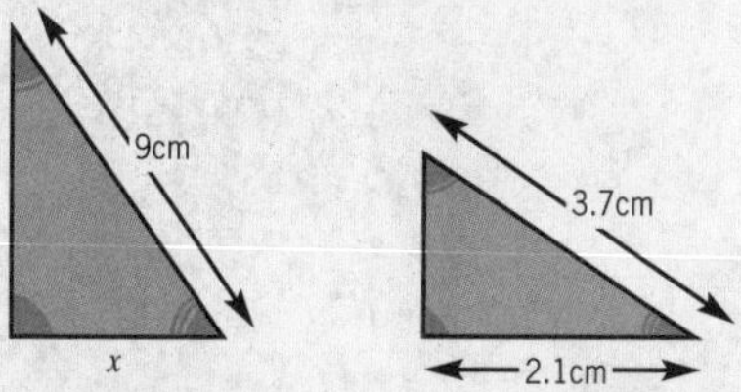

9cm
x

3.7cm
←2.1cm→

d)

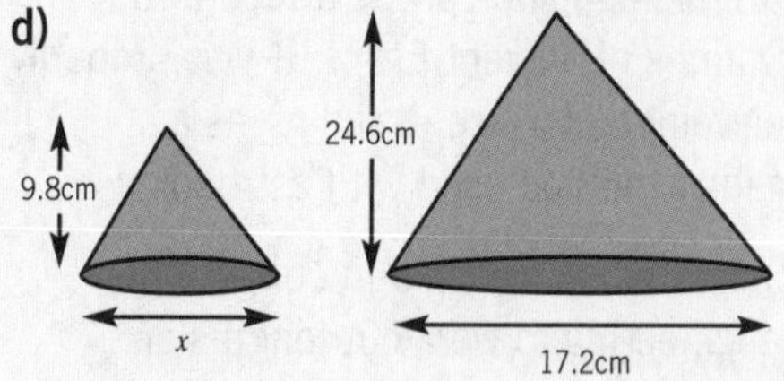

9.8cm
x

24.6cm
17.2cm

e)

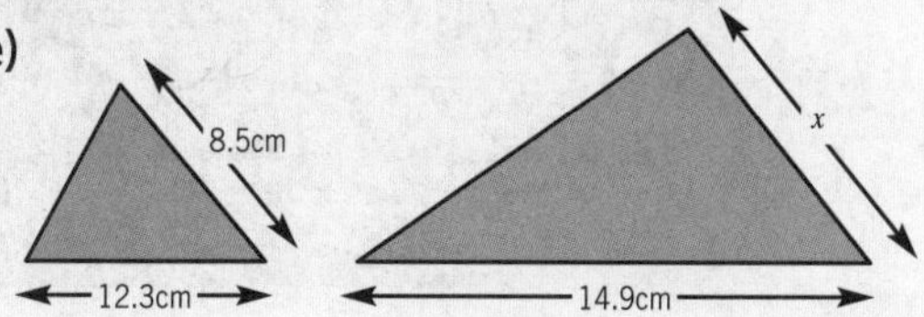

8.5cm
←12.3cm→

x
←14.9cm→

2 Decide whether each pair of shapes is similar or not similar. 🖩

a)

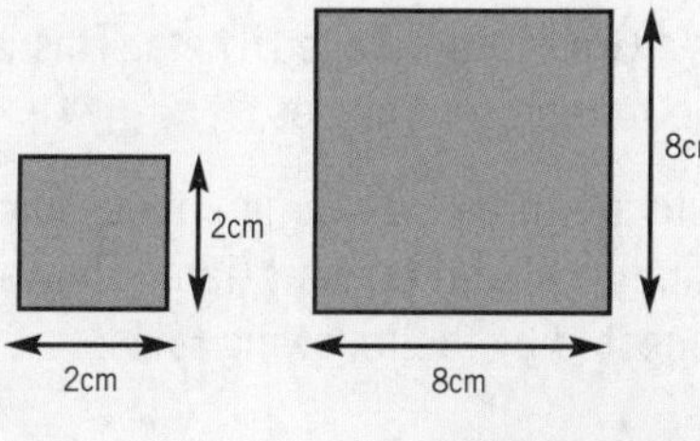

2cm
2cm

8cm
8cm

b)

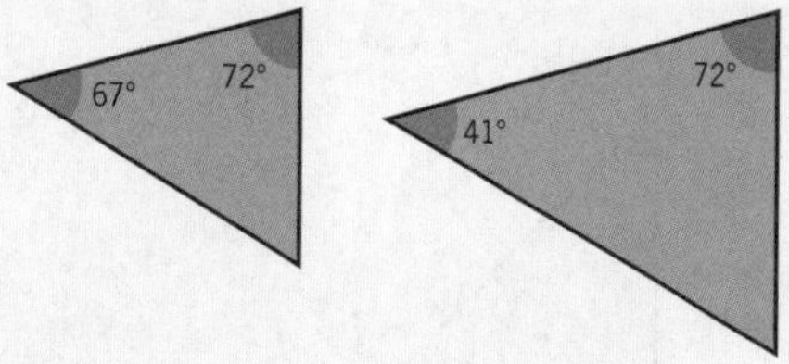

67° 72°

41° 72°

c)

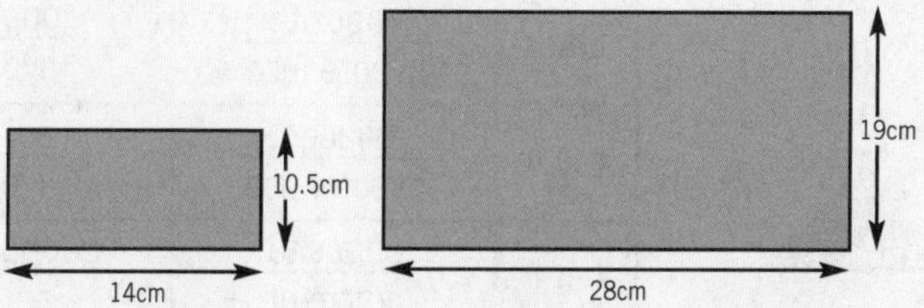

10.5cm
14cm

19cm
28cm

d)

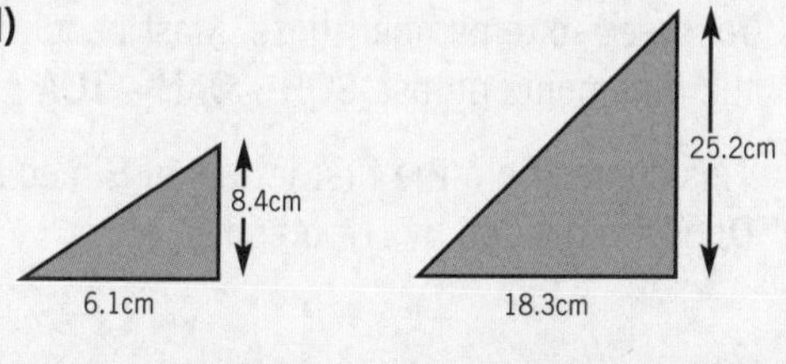

8.4cm
6.1cm

25.2cm
18.3cm

e)

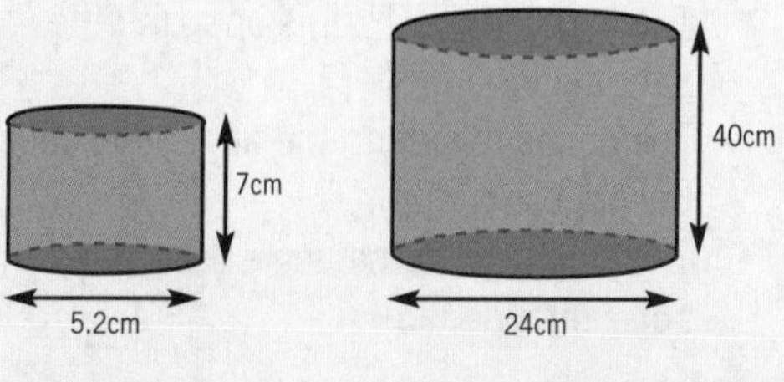

7cm
5.2cm

40cm
24cm

Trigonometry

Trigonometry

Trigonometry connects the sides and angles of right angled triangles.

Trigonometry was first developed about 4000 years ago and can be traced to the civilizations of ancient Egypt. It was probably first developed for use in sailing as a navigation method used with astronomy.

Trigonometry is now used in construction and engineering to work out lengths and angles on plans.

Labelling the Sides of the Triangle

In this triangle:

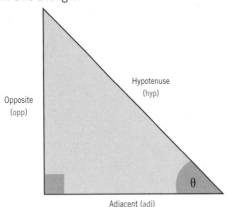

θ is a Greek letter called Theta. This is often used to represent angles.

There are three trigonomic ratios, **sine** (sin), **cosine** (cos) and **tangent** (tan). They are connected by the following rules:

sin θ	$\dfrac{\text{opposite}}{\text{hypotenuse}}$	$\dfrac{\text{opp}}{\text{hyp}}$
cos θ	$\dfrac{\text{adjacent}}{\text{hypotenuse}}$	$\dfrac{\text{adj}}{\text{hyp}}$
tan θ	$\dfrac{\text{opposite}}{\text{adjacent}}$	$\dfrac{\text{opp}}{\text{adj}}$

- The **hypotenuse** (hyp) is opposite the right angle.
- The opposite side to the angle θ is called the **opposite** (opp).
- The side next to the angle θ is called the **adjacent** side (adj).

You need to remember these. Most people use the mnemonic phrase **SOH – CAH – TOA**

This comes from the first letters of **S**in equals **O**pposite divided by **H**ypotenuse, etc.

Finding the Length of a Side

To solve a trigonometric problem there are several steps.

Example

Calculate the length of x in this triangle.

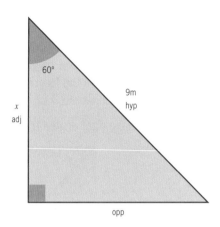

1️⃣ Label the sides of the triangle relative to the angle given.

2️⃣ Decide on the ratio. In this case use cosine ratio.

$$\cos 60° = \frac{\text{adj}}{\text{hyp}}$$

3️⃣ Substitute the values into the ratio.

$$\cos 60° = \frac{x}{9}$$

$$9 \times \cos 60° = x \quad \blacktriangleleft\!\!-\!\!\boxed{\text{Rearrange the formula to find } x}$$

$$x = 4.5\text{m}$$

Make sure that you know how to key this into your calculator.

Calculating the Size of an Angle

The method of calculating an angle is similar to finding the length of a side.

Example

Calculate the angle PQR.

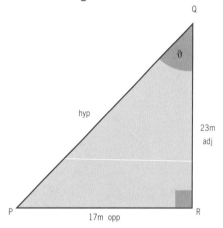

1️⃣ Label the sides of the triangle relative to the angle you're finding.

2️⃣ Decide on the ratio. In this case use the tangent ratio.

$$\tan \theta = \frac{\text{opp}}{\text{adj}}$$

$$\tan \theta = \frac{17}{23}$$

$\tan \theta = 0.739...$(keep all the digits on your calculator display)

$$\theta = \tan^{-1} 0.739... \quad \blacktriangleleft\!\!-\!\!\boxed{\begin{array}{l}\theta = \tan^{-1} 0.739... \text{ means the} \\ \text{inverse tan of } 0.739..., \\ \text{which is the angle that has} \\ \text{a tan of } 0.739.\end{array}}$$

$$\theta = 36.5° \text{ to 1 d.p.}$$

Make sure you know how your calculator works in order to calculate these equations.

Trigonometry

Angles of Elevation and Depression

- The **angle of elevation** is measured from the horizontal upwards.

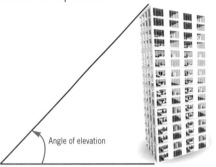

Angle of elevation

- The **angle of depression** is measured from the horizontal downwards.

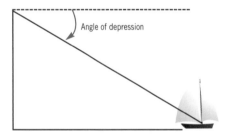

Angle of depression

Example

John looks down from a cliff to a boat below. The angle of depression is 52°. The height of the cliff is 100m. How far from the foot of the cliff is the boat? Give your answer to 3 s.f.

Put this information into a right angled triangle.

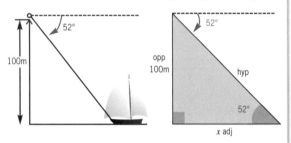

$$\tan 52° = \frac{\text{opp}}{\text{adj}}$$

$$\tan 52° = \frac{100}{x}$$

$$x \times \tan 52° = 100 \quad \longleftarrow \boxed{\text{Rearrange to make } x \text{ the subject}}$$

$$x = \frac{100}{\tan 52°}$$

$$x = 78.1\text{m (3 s.f.)}$$

Quick Test

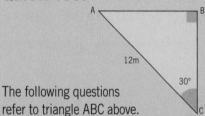

The following questions refer to triangle ABC above.

1. What is the length of AB in relation to BCA?
   a) Hypotenuse b) Opposite c) Adjacent
2. The length AC is the hypotenuse. True or false?
3. If the length AB is being calculated, which ratio would you use?
4. Work out the length of AB.

1 For each of the triangles below, work out the value of x.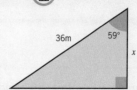

a)
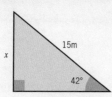
15m
x
42°

b)
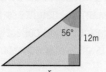
56° 12m
x

c)

31° 25m
x

d)
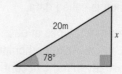
36m 59°
x

e)
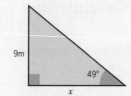
20m
x
78°

f)

9m
49°
x

2 For each of the triangles below, work out the size of angle x.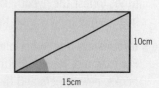

a)

x
15m
9m

b)
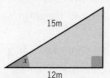
15m
x
12m

c)
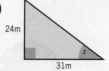
24m
x
31m

d)
104m
x
72m

e)
x
9cm
6cm

f)
12cm
x
20cm

3 Mehnaz stands 25m from the base of a 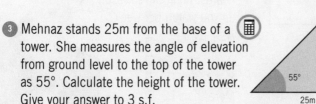 tower. She measures the angle of elevation from ground level to the top of the tower as 55°. Calculate the height of the tower. Give your answer to 3 s.f.
55°
25m

4 For the rectangle opposite work out the angle between the diagonal and the base. Give your answer to 3 s.f.
10cm
15cm

Handling Data

Data

People are bombarded with information every day. This information is called data.

There are several different types of data:
- Discrete data can only take particular values and is usually found by counting. Examples include the number of people with brown hair.

- Continuous data can take any value in a range. This data is often found by measuring, for example, heights of people.
- Primary data is data that you collect yourself.
- Secondary data is data that somebody else has collected.

Collecting Data

Data can be collected in several ways:

1 By observation
An observation sheet (sometimes known as a data collection sheet) can be used.

For example, an observation sheet to test the hypothesis, 'Most students have brown hair' might look like this:

Hair Colour		
Colour	Tally	Frequency
Brown		
Black		
Blonde		
Ginger		

2 By experiment
An experiment can be carried out to collect data. For example, throwing a coin 100 times to test the hypothesis, 'Throwing a head is more likely than throwing a tail'.

3 Information from other places
For example, taking information from books, newspapers and the internet.

4 By questionnaire
Questionnaires are often used by market research companies. When designing or using questionnaires, the following points must be considered:
- Keep the questions simple and make sure that they cover the purpose of the survey.
- Make sure that your personal opinion doesn't show, for example, 'Do you agree that netball is better than football?'.
- Allow for all possible outcomes.

This is an example of a well-written question: How many hours, to the nearest hour, of television do you watch per week?

Under 3 ☐
3–7 ☐
8–12 ☐
More than 12 ☐

Organising Data

Data that's been collected can be sorted by putting it into a table called a **tally chart** or a **frequency table**. For example...

Colour of Car	Tally	Frequency
Silver	JHT JHT III	13
Red	JHT II	7
Black	II	2
Other	JHT JHT	10

A tally is a mark: **I**.

Marks are grouped into fives to make them easy to count. The fifth mark forms a gate: **JHT**.

When data cover a large range of results, it's usual to group them into **class intervals**. Usually, the class intervals are the same width.

For example, in a test out of 30, the scores might be grouped as:

1–5, 6–10, 11–15, 16–20, 21–25, 26–30

A frequency table for this test might look like this:

Score	Frequency
1–5	0
6–10	6
11–15	4
16–20	10
21–25	7
26–30	3

Once the data has been sorted, it can be shown in several different types of diagram.

Pictograms

Pictograms use identical symbols, where each symbol represents a certain number of items.

Example

Number of Pizzas Sold

Ham	
Cheese	
Vegetarian	

Key:

 = 4 pizzas

5 vegetarian pizzas were sold.

Bar Charts

Bar charts have bars of equal width to represent the frequency of discrete data.

Example

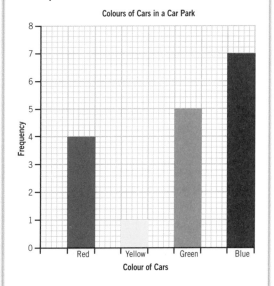

7 cars in the car park are blue.

Handling Data

Bar Charts for Grouped Data

Bar charts (sometimes called frequency diagrams) can also be drawn for grouped data.

Example

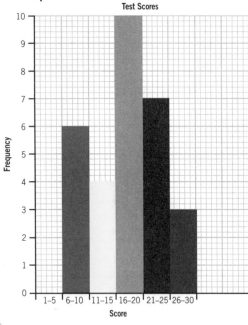

Bar Line Graphs

Bar line graphs are similar to bar charts, except they use lines instead of bars to represent data.

Example

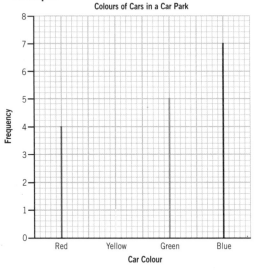

7 cars in the car park are blue.

Pie Charts

In a **pie chart**, the data is shown in a circle, which is split up into sections. Each section represents a certain number of items.
You need to be able to interpret pie charts.

Example
William drew a pie chart to show how he spent his monthly pocket money of £48.
How much did William spend on CDs and DVDs?
(360° represents £48)

Amount spent on CDs and DVDs is represented by 150° (360° − 120° − 90° = 150°).
$$\frac{150}{360} \times £48 = £20$$

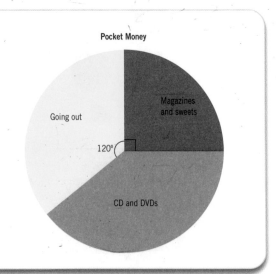

Line Graphs

A **line graph** is a set of points joined by lines.

Line graphs can be used to show…
- continuous data
- how a quantity changes over time.

Example

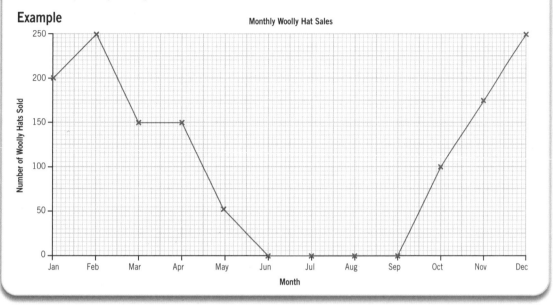

Monthly Woolly Hat Sales

Quick Test

1. Vinay wants to find out how many pets each of his classmates has.
   a) What would be an appropriate way to collect this data?
   b) Will his data be primary or secondary?
   c) Will his data be discrete or continuous?
   d) What would be the best way of organising his data? Explain your answer.
   e) Name one method he could use to display the data.

2. What is the difference between a tally chart and a frequency table?

3. The line graph opposite shows the number of greeting cards sold by a newsagent over a year.
   a) Explain what happens to the sale of cards during the year.
   b) Why do you think sales rose in specific months?

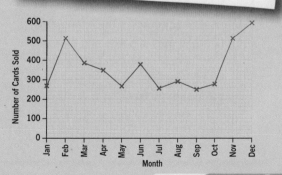

Skills Practice

Skills Practice

1. Hattie is doing a survey on the types of books people like to read.
   Design a data collection sheet that Hattie could use.

2. Ahmed included this question on his questionnaire:

> **How much pocket money do you receive per week?**
>
> £1 or less ☐
>
> £1–£3 ☐
>
> Over £3 ☐

Explain what is wrong with Ahmed's question.

3. A leisure centre asked 20 people what sport
   they had come to do. The answers were as follows:

Swimming	Yoga	Badminton	Squash	Yoga
Squash	Swimming	Swimming	Squash	Squash
Badminton	Yoga	Badminton	Swimming	Swimming
Yoga	Yoga	Yoga	Swimming	Squash

a) Copy and complete the tally chart below:

Sport	Tally	Frequency
Swimming		6
Squash		5
Badminton		3
Yoga		6

20

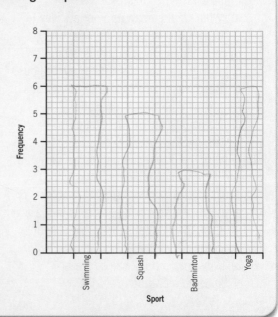

b) Draw a pictogram of the information.
c) Copy the axes opposite and draw a
   bar chart of the leisure centre data.
d) Which sports are the most popular at
   the leisure centre?

4 The bar line graph opposite shows the sales of hot drinks in a café in one day.
  a) Which drink sold the most?
  b) How many hot drinks were sold in total?
  c) Explain why the sales of soup might have been so low.

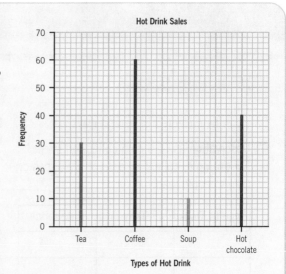

5 Using a survey, Erin decided to find out what method of transport the students in her class had used to get to school that morning. Her findings are shown in the pie chart. There are 24 students in Erin's Class.
  a) How many students walked to school?
  b) How many students came to school by car?
  c) Give a possible reason why so few students came to school by car.

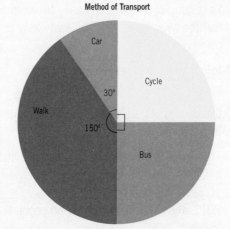

6 The line graph shows the number of cups of tea sold in a café during a week.
  a) Give possible reasons why only five cups of tea were sold on Wednesday.
  b) Give possible reasons why 40 cups of tea were sold on Saturday.

Handling Data

Collecting Data

Data can be collected in several ways.

1 **Observation** using a **data collection sheet**. For example, collecting data on the types of books people read.

Type of Book	Tally	Frequency

2 **Experiments** can be used to collect data. For example, throwing a die 60 times to test the hypothesis 'A six is least likely to come up'.

3 **Information from resources** e.g. books, newspapers and Internet.

4 **Questionnaires** are often used to find out information.

The **census** is a survey of the whole population in England and Wales. It takes place every 10 years. The next one will take place in 2011. The census collects data on population, transport, health, housing and employment.

The information is used to help the government plan the future running of the country.

When writing questionnaires:
* Keep the questions simple.
* Make sure your personal opinion doesn't show.
* Allow for all possible outcomes.

Example
How many hours of sport to the nearest hour do you do per week?

Under 2 ☐

2 – 4 ☐

5 – 7 ☐

More than 7 ☐

Discrete data is usually found by counting. **Continuous data** is usually found by measuring.

Data that has been collected can be put into a table called a tally chart or frequency table.

Representing Data

Data can be represented using pictograms, bar charts and bar line graphs for discrete data.

When there is a large amount of data, the data is often grouped, e.g., 1 – 5, 6 – 10, 11 – 15, etc for discrete data. Continuous data is put into **class intervals**, usually of equal width.

Example
The table below shows information about the height of 40 people.

$155 \leq h < 160$ means a height of 155cm or more, but less than 160cm.

The class intervals here are 5cm.

This data can be put into a **frequency diagram**. This is similar to a bar chart but since it represents continuous data there are no gaps between the bars. This is sometimes known as a **histogram**.

Height (hcm)	Frequency
$155 \leq h < 160$	4
$160 \leq h < 165$	6
$165 \leq h < 170$	15
$170 \leq h < 175$	7
$175 \leq h < 180$	8

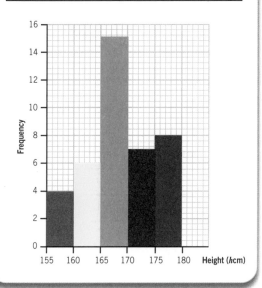

Interpreting Pie Charts

In a **pie chart**, the data is shown in a circle that is split up into sections. Each section represents a certain number of items.

Example
90 students were asked where they went on holiday in the summer. The pie chart shows the result of this survey.

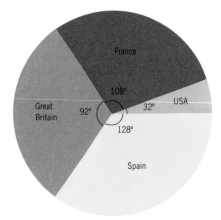

We can see that Spain is the most popular holiday destination.

$\dfrac{108°}{360°} \times 90 = 27$ — 27 students went on holiday to France

$\dfrac{32°}{360°} \times 90 = 8$ — 8 students went on holiday to the USA

Handling Data

Drawing Pie Charts

To draw a pie chart:
- Draw a circle and mark the centre.
- Work out the angles.

Example
Toby asked 30 friends to name their favourite flavour of crisps. The table shows his results:

Flavour	Bacon	Beef	Cheese	Plain	Salt n' Vinegar
Frequency	5	5	7	3	10

Draw a pie chart.

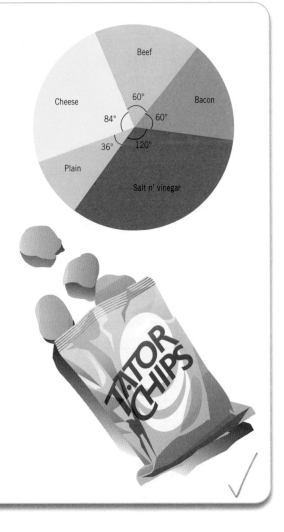

Method 1

$\frac{5}{30} \times 360° = 60°$ (5 out of 30 students chose Bacon and 5 chose Beef).

$\frac{7}{30} \times 360° = 84°$ (Cheese)

$\frac{10}{30} \times 360° = 120°$ (Salt n' Vinegar)

$\frac{3}{30} \times 360° = 36°$ (Plain)

Method 2

$360° \div 30 = 12°$ (12° represents 1 student. Multiply each frequency by 12).

Bacon = 12° × 5 = 60° = Beef and 60° = Bacon

Plain = 12° × 3 = 36°

Cheese = 12° × 7 = 84°

Salt n' Vinegar = 12° × 10 = 120°

Two-Way Tables

A two-way table contains information that is totalled in both directions.

Example
Here is a two-way table showing the number of adults in a numeracy and literacy class.

There are 12 men in the numeracy class.
There are 25 women in total.

	Numeracy	Literacy	Total
Male	12	7	19
Female	15	10	25
Total	27	17	44

Scatterdiagrams and Correlation

A **scatterdiagram** (scattergraph) is used to show two sets of data at the same time.

A scatterdiagram is also used to show the **correlation** (connection) between two sets of data.

Types of correlation:

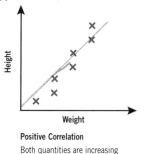

Positive Correlation
Both quantities are increasing

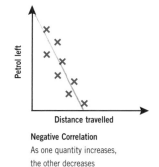

Negative Correlation
As one quantity increases, the other decreases

Zero / No Correlation
There is little or no linear relationship between the variables

Drawing a Scatterdiagram

Work out the scales first and plot the points carefully. Each time a point is plotted, tick it off.

Example

The table shows the height in cm and weight in kg of 10 women.

Line of best fit is a line that best fits the data. There is roughly the same number of points above and below the line.

A line of best fit is used to make predictions.

Height (cm)	155	158	154	164	165	161	157	159	161
Weight (kg)	57	57	54	62	67	65	60	62	64

The scatterdiagram is used to show this information:

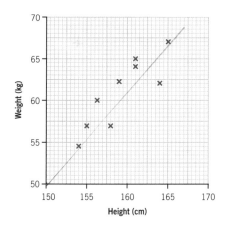

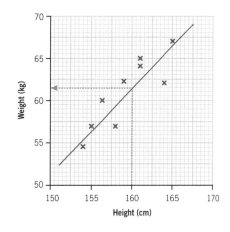

Using a line of best fit, a woman of 160cm in height is approximately 61.5kg.

There is a positive correlation. The taller the women are the more they weigh.

Scatterdiagrams can be drawn using a spreadsheet package on the computer.

Handling Data

Stem and Leaf Diagrams

A **stem and leaf diagram** is used for recording and displaying information.

The stem often represents tens and the leaves represent the units.

Stem and leaf diagrams should be ordered and have a key.

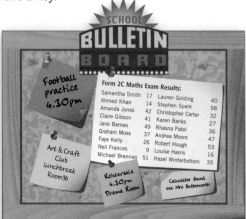

Example

These are some marks gained by students in a Maths exam:

17 14 42 41 49 37 26 9 51
40 58 32 27 36 47 53 16 35
Key 2|6 = 26

When the information is put into a stem and leaf diagram it looks like this:

Unordered

Stem	Leaf
0	9
1	7 4 6
2	6 7
3	6 7 2 5
4	2 7 1 0 9
5	1 3 8

Ordered

Stem	Leaf
0	9
1	4 6 7
2	6 7
3	2 5 6 7
4	0 1 2 7 9
5	1 3 8

Quick Test

1. A stem and leaf diagram is a type of plant. True or false?
2. In a questionnaire a question reads: 'For how many hours do you watch TV?'. Write down a better way of asking this question.
3. For $160 \leq h < 170$ the class interval is 10. True or false?
4. What are the three types of correlation?
5. Decide what type of correlation, if any, there is between these variables:
   a) Height and IQ.
   b) Height and shoe size.
   c) Height and Age.
   d) Age of car and price.
   e) Cost of petrol and price of food.

KEY WORDS

Make sure you understand these words before moving on!
- Data collection sheet
- Questionnaire
- Census
- Discrete data
- Line of best fit
- Continuous data
- Class intervals
- Frequency diagram
- Histogram
- Pie chart
- Stem and Leaf
- Scatterdiagram
- Correlation

Skills Practice

1 Charlotte included this question in her questionnaire:

'What type of books do you read?'

Rewrite Charlotte's question so that it is improved.

2 Draw a pie chart of this data:

Favourite ice cream flavour	Vanilla	Strawberry	Chocolate	Mint
Frequency	3	8	6	7

3 Complete the two-way table which shows how some students travel to school:

	Walk	Car	Coach	Total
Boys	5	11	26	42
Girls	12	12	19	43
Total	17	23	45	85

4 These results show the number of seconds it takes for some adults to complete a puzzle. Draw a stem and leaf diagram of this data.

26, 39, 32, 38, 41, 62, 41, 25, 58, 25, 37, 65, 46, 58, 59, 27

Handling Data

Collecting Data

Remember that there are several ways to collect data:
- Information from resources: books, the Internet and newspapers.
- Data collection sheets.
- Experiments.
- Questionnaires.

Keep the questions simple when writing questionnaires. Ensure that your personal opinion doesn't show and allow for all possible outcomes.

Make sure when carrying out a questionnaire that you don't introduce bias. For example, if you're conducting a questionnaire on coffee consumption you wouldn't stand outside a cafe and ask people which coffee they prefer.

Continuous data is found by measuring whilst discrete data is found by counting. Data that has been collected can be put into a frequency table.

Representing Data

One way to represent continuous data is to put it into class intervals; the class intervals are usually equal in width.

Example
The table below gives information about the weights, in grams, of 25 apples.

The class intervals are 5 grams.

Weight (w g)	Frequency
$90 \leqslant w < 95$	5
$95 \leqslant w < 100$	7
$100 \leqslant w < 105$	9
$105 \leqslant w < 110$	3
$110 \leqslant w < 115$	1

A frequency polygon can be used instead of a frequency diagram to show data. To draw a frequency polygon of the data above, plot the midpoint of the class interval against the frequency.

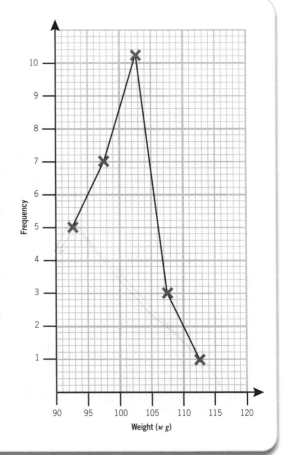

Pie Charts

Remember each section in a **pie chart** represents a certain number of items.

Example

Will counted 24 cars in a car park and noted their colour. The table shows his results.

Car colour	Blue	Red	Silver	Black
Frequency	4	5	9	6

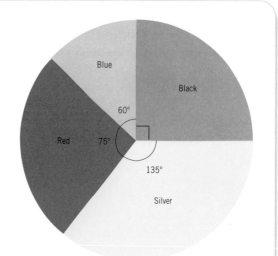

Draw a pie chart.
- Draw a circle and mark the centre.
- Work out the angles.

$$\frac{360}{24} = 15°$$

1 car represents 15°.

Multiply each colour by 15.

Blue: $4 \times 15 = 60°$
Red: $5 \times 15 = 75°$
Silver: $9 \times 15 = 135°$
Black: $6 \times 15 = 90°$

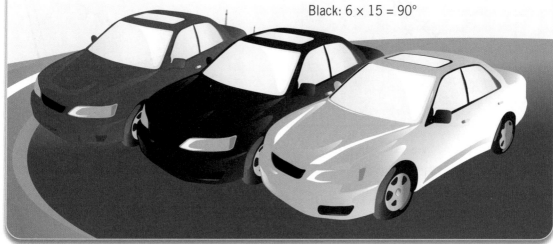

Scatterdiagrams and Correlation

As a quick reminder there are three types of **correlation**:

1 **Positive correlation** – both values increase.
2 **Negative correlation** – one value increases and the other decreases.
3 **Zero correlation** – no linear correlation between variables.

Handling Data

Lines of Best Fit

The scatterdiagram below shows the Maths and Science test results of some students.

A line of best fit has been added, which has roughly the same number of points above the line as below it.

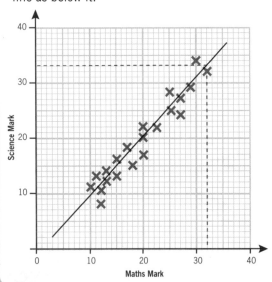

There is a positive correlation. The higher the student's Maths score the higher their Science score.

For example, a score of 32 on the Maths test is approximately a score of 33 on the Science test.

Scatterdiagrams can easily be drawn using a spreadsheet package on a computer.

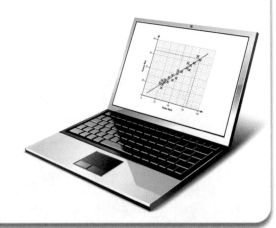

Quick Test

1. For $20 \leqslant h < 30$, the class interval is 10. True or false?
2. For this scatter diagram, what type of correlation is shown?

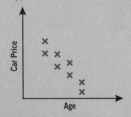

3. A frequency polygon joins the midpoints of the class intervals. True or false?

KEY WORDS

Make sure you understand these words before moving on!

- Data collection sheet
- Questionnaire
- Continuous data
- Discrete data
- Frequency table
- Class intervals
- Frequency polygon
- Frequency diagram
- Pie chart
- Correlation
- Positive correlation
- Negative correlation
- Zero correlation
- Scatter diagram
- Line of best fit

1 Erin carried out a survey on how often people use a leisure centre. She did her survey by standing outside the leisure centre on a Tuesday morning. Explain why her results may be biased.

2 Draw a frequency polygon of this data on the graph paper below.

Height (*h* cm)	Frequency
$0 \leqslant h < 20$	3
$20 \leqslant h < 40$	5
$40 \leqslant h < 60$	6
$60 \leqslant h < 80$	10
$80 \leqslant h < 100$	9
$100 \leqslant h < 120$	4
$120 \leqslant h < 140$	1

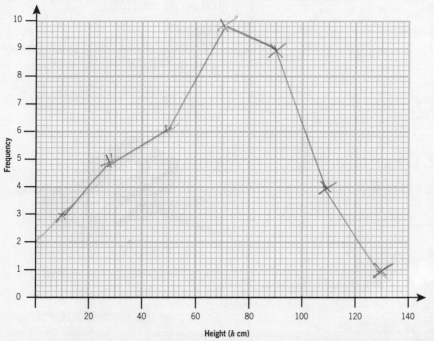

3 Draw a pie chart of this data:

Travel to school	Walk	Car	Bus	Bike
Frequency	16	4	20	5

Averages

Averages

The word 'average' is very common.
Some examples of its use are...
- 'the average weight of a ten-year-old boy is 47kg'
- 'the average height of a ten-year-old girl is 120cm'
- 'the average rainfall in August is 22mm'.

The average is the best representation of a set of data.

There are three different types of average that you can find for a set of data:
- the mean
- the mode
- the median.

Mean

The mean is one of the most commonly used averages.

$$\text{Mean} = \frac{\text{Sum of a set of values}}{\text{Number of values used}}$$

Examples

1 Lottie got the following marks in ten mental arithmetic tests:

12, 15, 6, 9, 12, 11, 10, 9, 9, 5

What is Lottie's mean mark?

$$\text{Mean} = \frac{12 + 15 + 6 + 9 + 12 + 11 + 10 + 9 + 9 + 5}{10}$$

$$= \frac{98}{10} = 9.8$$

2 The number of cups of tea sold daily in a café during a week are:

36, 42, 31, 49, 28, 48, 54

What is the mean number of cups of tea sold that week?

$$\text{Mean} = \frac{36 + 42 + 31 + 49 + 28 + 48 + 54}{7}$$

$$= \frac{288}{7} = 41.1 \text{ (to 1 d.p.)}$$

Mode

In any set of data, the mode is the value that occurs most often.

Example
The number of matches in ten matchboxes is counted. The results are as follows:

37, 41, 37, 36, 38, 38, 39, 40, 40, 40

What is the mode of this data?

Since three boxes contain 40 matches, the mode is 40.

You can say that the 'modal number' of matches is 40.

Example
What is the mode of this data?

6, 9, 4, 3, 6, 6, 5, 3, 7, 3, 6, 3

There are two modes: 3 and 6. This is known as bimodal.

Median

The median of a set of data is the middle value when the data is put in order of size.

Examples

1 The number of goals scored by a football team in their first nine matches of the season is:

3, 2, 1, 3, 4, 2, 1, 2, 3

What is the median number of goals scored?

First, arrange the data in order of size:

1, 1, 2, 2, 2, 3, 3, 3, 4

Cross off numbers from both ends to locate the middle value:

1̸ ,1̸ ,2̸ ,2̸ ,②,3̸ ,3̸ ,3̸ ,4̸

So, the median is 2 goals.

2 Molly wants to find the median weight, to the nearest kg, of the girls in her dance group. Their weights, in kg, are:

48, 52, 47, 46, 52, 55, 53, 49, 50, 47

Find the median weight.

First, arrange the data in order of size:

46, 47, 47, 48, 49, 50, 52, 52, 53, 55

Next, locate the middle value(s):

4̸6̸,4̸7̸,4̸7̸,4̸8̸, (49, 50), 5̸2̸,5̸2̸,5̸3̸,5̸5̸

Since there are two values in the middle, you need to find the midpoint of these:

$$\frac{49 + 50}{2} = 49.5$$

Median weight = 49.5kg

Range

The range of a set of data tells you how 'spread out' the data is.

It's the difference between the highest and lowest values.

Range	=	Highest value	−	Lowest value

Example

The data shows the rainfall, in mm, of the twelve months in one year.

161, 172, 165, 152, 112, 110, 92, 27, 31, 87, 136, 141

What is the range of this data?

Range = 172 − 27 = 145mm

Making Comparisons

The average and range can be used to compare two or more sets of data.

Example

Two brands of batteries are compared. The results are shown in the table.

Brand	Mean (hours)	Range (hours)
Best Buy	16.3	5.8
Durable	16.2	1.2

Which brand represents the best value?

From the information in the table, you can see that 'Durable' is the better-value brand.

Although the average number of hours that 'Durable' batteries last for is slightly less than 'Best Buy' batteries, their range is much smaller (the spread is lower), which means that 'Durable' batteries are more reliable.

Averages

Averages from a Frequency Table

Data is often shown in frequency tables.

Frequency tables can be used to find the mean, mode and range of data.

Example
The frequency table shows the number of televisions the students of Class 7K have at home.

Number of Televisions	Frequency
0	1
1	5
2	7
3	8
4	4

Find the mean, mode and range of this set of data.

The table shows...
- 1 student has 0 televisions
- 5 students have 1 television
- 7 students have 2 televisions, and so on.

$$\text{Mean} = \frac{\text{Total (Frequency} \times \text{Number of televisions)}}{\text{Total of the frequency}}$$

$$\text{Mean} = \frac{(1 \times 0) + (5 \times 1) + (7 \times 2) + (8 \times 3) + (4 \times 4)}{1 + 5 + 7 + 8 + 4}$$

$$= \frac{59}{25} = 2.36 \text{ televisions}$$

Mode – this is the number of televisions with the highest frequency. The modal number of televisions is 3.

Range = Highest number of televisions – Lowest number of televisions
= 4 – 0 = 4 televisions

Quick Test

1. Explain how you would find the mode of a set of data.
2. The mode of 8, 9, 4, 8, 7, 3, 8, 7 is 7. True or false?
3. What is the range of these numbers?
   7, 9, 15, 2, 6, 3, 13
   A 9 **B** 13 **C** 2 – 15 **D** 17
4. What is the median of these numbers?
   7, 2, 9, 3, 4, 4, 6
   A 9 **B** 3 **C** 4 **D** 6
5. Explain how you would find the mean of a set of data.
6. 4.7 is the mean of these numbers:
   2, 9, 3, 7, 4, 6, 5, 1, 9, 1
   True or false?

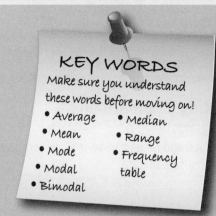

KEY WORDS
Make sure you understand these words before moving on!
- Average
- Mean
- Mode
- Modal
- Bimodal
- Median
- Range
- Frequency table

Skills Practice

1 For this set of data:

3, 7, 9, 6, 7, 7, 4, 8, 5

find the...

a) mean   **b)** median   **c)** mode   **d)** range.

2 For this set of data:

7, 4, 9, 11, 3, 3, 8, 3

find the...

a) mean   **b)** median   **c)** mode   **d)** range.

3 For this set of data:

2.6, 4.8, 4.7, 5.2, 9.3, 4.7, 4.8, 4.7, 5.1, 4.7

find the...

a) mean   **b)** median   **c)** mode   **d)** range.

4 Class 7M got a mean score of 63% in a maths test.
The top mark was 100% and the lowest mark was 14%.

Class 7K got a mean score of 82% in the same maths test.
The top mark was 92% and the lowest mark was 71%.

Which class performed the best? Explain your answer.

5 The table shows the number of experiments carried out by some students.

Number of Experiments	0	1	2	3	4
Frequency	2	7	12	20	4

Find the mean number of experiments carried out.
Give your answer correct to one decimal place.

6 The number of goals scored by teams in a local football league one week is shown in the table.

Number of Goals	0	1	2	3
Frequency	5	7	6	2

a) Work out the mean number of goals scored.
b) Work out the modal number of goals scored.
c) Find the range of this data.

Averages

Averages

There are three types of **averages** that you can find for a set of data:

- The **mean**.
- The **median**.
- The **mode**.

Example

During August an ice cream van sold the following number of ice creams each day over a one-week period.

28, 32, 31, 28, 24, 17, 28

Work out the mean, median, mode.

The **mean** is the (sum of a set of values) ÷ (number of values used).

$$\text{Mean} = \frac{(28 + 32 + 31 + 28 + 24 + 17 + 28)}{7}$$

$$= \frac{188}{7}$$

Mean = 26.86 (2dp)

The **mode** in any set of data is the value that occurs the most often. If there are two modes, this is known as bimodal.

Mode = 28 ice creams.

The **median** of a set of data is the middle value when the data is put in to order.

28, 32, 31, 28, 24, 17, 28

reordered goes:

17, 24, 28, (28), 28, 31, 32

Median = 28 ice creams sold.

Range

Use the following formula to find the **range**.

Range	=	Highest Value	—	Lowest Value

Example

The range in the number of ice creams sold is:

Range = 32 – 17

= 15 ice creams.

Making Comparisons

Remember that the average and range are used to compare two or more sets of data.

Example

During the Olympics, two archery competitors had the following results:

Competitor	Mean score	Range
Australia	9.3	3
France	9.2	1

Each shot carries a maximum of 10 points.

From the results we can see that the Australian competitor had a higher mean score. But, since their range is higher than the French competitor their accuracy is not as consistent.

Averages from a Frequency Table

You will remember that a **frequency table** can be used to find the mean, median, mode and range.

Example

The frequency table show the marks for 20 students in a times tables test.

The table shows that...
* 1 student gained 4 marks
* 2 students gained 5 marks, and so on.

$$\text{Mean} = \frac{\text{Total (of frequency} \times \text{number of marks)}}{\text{Total of the frequency}}$$

Mark (x)	Frequency (f)	$x \times f$
4	1	4
5	2	10
6	0	0
7	1	7
8	8	64
9	5	45
10	3	30

$$\frac{(1 \times 4) + (2 \times 5) + (0 \times 6) + (1 \times 7) + (8 \times 8) + (5 \times 9) + (3 \times 10)}{1 + 2 + 0 + 1 + 8 + 5 + 3}$$

$$= \frac{160}{20}$$

$$= 8$$

Median: Since there are 20 students the median must lie between the 10th and 11th mark.

Counting up the frequency table gives the value as 8 marks.

Mode: This is the mark that occurs the most or has the highest frequency.

$= 8$ marks.

Range = highest mark – lowest mark

$= 10 - 4$

$= 6$ marks.

Mark (x)	Frequency (f)
4	1
5	2
6	0
7	1
8	8	← 10th, 11th value in here
9	5
10	3

Averages

Using Stem and Leaf Diagrams to Find Averages

Stem and leaf diagrams can be used to find averages.

Example
John records the number of text messages he receives each day. Here are the results for the last 15 days.

Stem	Leaf
0	2 2 6
1	3 3 7 7 ⑦ 8 9
2	2 4 5 8
3	1

Key
2|5 = 25 texts

Range = 31 – 2

     = 29 texts

Median = this is the 8th day. John got 17 texts

Mode   = 17 texts, since 17 texts were received on 3 of the days.

Quick Test

1. The mode of these numbers is 1. True or false?
   7, 2, 1, 1, 2, 1, 4, 6, 1
2. Explain how you would find the range of a set of data?
3. What is the range of this data?
   7, 9, 11, 4, 1, 7, 2
   a) 12   **b)** 10   **c)** 9   **d)** 8

KEY WORDS
Make sure you understand these words before moving on!
- Average
- Mean
- Median
- Mode
- Range
- Frequency table
- Stem and leaf

Skills Practice

1 For this set of data:
7, 9, 4, 1, 5, 5, 5, 6

Find the:
a) Mean **b)** Median **c)** Mode **d)** Range

2 Nigel needs to pick a forward for the football team. He looks at the scoring record for Paulo and Cesc.

In Paulo's last seven matches he has scored 2, 2, 1, 0, 0, 3 and 2 goals.

In Cesc's last seven matches he has scored 3, 2, 2, 1, 1, 1 and 1 goals.

Work out the mean, medium, mode and range for Paulo and Cesc. Who should Nigel choose and why?

3 The number of merits awarded to each student in a class last week is shown in the table below:

Mark (x)	0	1	2	3	4	5
Frequency (f)	2	1	1	12	8	7

Work out:
a) The modal number of merits awarded.
b) The range of the number of merits awarded.
c) The mean number of merits awarded.
d) The median number of merits awarded to students.

4 Eleven swimmers had their times recorded (to the nearest 10th of a second) for the 50m freestyle. Their times are shown in the stem and leaf diagram below:

Use the diagram to find:
a) The range of the times. **b)** The median time. **c)** The modal time.

```
Stem | Leaf
  28 | 6  7
  29 | 5
  30 | 8  9  9
  31 | 4  4  4  7
  32 | 1
```

Key
29|5 = 29.5 seconds

Averages

Averages from a Frequency Table

The average you calculate from a frequency table will not always be a whole number.

Example
The **frequency** table shows the number of sisters 12 students had:

Number of Sisters (x)	Frequency
0	5
1	3
2	2
3	2

The table shows that 5 students had no sisters.

$$\text{Mean} = \frac{\text{Total of frequency} \times \text{Number of sisters}}{\text{Total of frequency}}$$

$$\text{Mean} = \frac{(0 \times 5) + (1 \times 3) + (2 \times 2) + (3 \times 2)}{5 + 3 + 2 + 2}$$

$$\text{Mean} = \frac{0 + 3 + 4 + 6}{12}$$

$$= \frac{13}{12}$$

$$= 1.08\dot{3} \text{ sisters.}$$

Median
Since there are 12 students the **median** must lie between the 6th and 7th students.

Counting up the frequency column gives the 6th and 7th students having three sisters.

Mode
The number of sisters that occurs the most is none. So the **mode** of the data is none.

Range
The **range** of sisters is...

$$\text{Range} = \text{Highest number} - \text{Lowest number}$$
of sisters   of sisters

$$3 - 0$$

$$= 3 \text{ sisters}$$

Averages of Grouped Data

Continuous data is grouped into class intervals since the exact data set is not known.

The mean can be estimated by using the midpoint of the class interval. The midpoint is the halfway value.

Weight (w kg)	Frequency (f)	Midpoint (x)	fx
40 ≤ w < 45	6	42.5	255
45 ≤ w < 50	5	47.5	237.5
50 ≤ w < 55	3	52.5	157.5
55 ≤ w < 60	2	57.5	115
60 ≤ w < 65	1	62.5	62.5
Total	17		827.5

Adding these extra columns helps to show working out

Example

The table opposite shows the weight (w kg) of some year 10 students.

Σf means 'the sum of f'.

$$\text{mean} = \frac{\Sigma fx}{\Sigma f}$$

$$= \frac{827.5}{17}$$

mean $= 48.7$kg (1 d.p.)

Modal class is $40 \leqslant w < 45$

The class interval containing the median is:
$45 \leqslant w < 50$
Since there are 17 students, the median must be in the class interval in which the 9th student lies.

Quick Test

1 Find the mean of the data below.

a)

Number of Brothers (x)	Frequency
0	4
1	5
2	3
3	2

b) The mode of the data is 5.
   True or false?
c) The median of the data is 1.
   True or false?
d) The range of the data is 0 – 3.
   True or false?

Averages

Skills Practice

1 Molly made this table to show how many minutes (t) late students were for registration.

Number of Minutes Late (t)	0	1	2	3	4	5	6
Frequency (f)	14	2	2	1	3	1	1

Calculate...

a) the mean   **b)** the median   **c)** the mode   **d)** the range

2 The table shows the height (h cm) of some year 7 students.

Height (h cm)	Frequency (f)
$130 \leqslant h < 135$	5
$135 \leqslant h < 140$	7
$140 \leqslant h < 145$	4
$145 \leqslant h < 150$	3
$150 \leqslant h < 155$	2

a) Calculate an estimate for the mean height of this data.
b) Write down the modal class.
c) Which class interval has the median height?

3 The table shows the weight (w kg) of some year 7 students.

Weight (w kg)	Frequency (f)
$30 \leqslant w < 40$	4
$40 \leqslant w < 50$	8
$50 \leqslant w < 60$	12
$60 \leqslant w < 70$	3
$70 \leqslant w < 80$	3

a) Calculate an estimate for the mean weight of this data.

b) Write down the modal class.

c) Which class interval has the median weight?

4 The table shows information about the number of minutes some students spent doing homework on one evening.

Number of Minutes (t)	Frequency (f)
$0 < t \leqslant 20$	10
$20 < t \leqslant 40$	15
$40 < t \leqslant 60$	25
$60 < t \leqslant 80$	8
$80 < t \leqslant 100$	2

a) Find the class interval that contains the median.

b) Work out an estimate for the mean number of minutes that the students spent doing homework.

Cumulative Frequency Graphs

Cumulative Frequency Graphs

Cumulative frequency graphs are very useful for finding the median and spread of grouped data.

Example
The table shows information about the amount of time 50 students spent doing homework one evening.

A cumulative frequency table can be drawn for this data.

When a cumulative frequency graph is drawn, plot the upper class boundaries, so plot (10, 5) (20, 17) (30, 34) (40, 44) (50, 48) (60, 50). Join the points with a smooth curve.

Time (x minutes)	Frequency
$0 < x \leqslant 10$	5
$10 < x \leqslant 20$	12
$20 < x \leqslant 30$	17
$30 < x \leqslant 40$	10
$40 < x \leqslant 50$	4
$50 < x \leqslant 60$	2

Time (x minutes)	Cumulative Frequency
$0 < x \leqslant 10$	5
$0 < x \leqslant 20$	(5 + 12 =) 17
$0 < x \leqslant 30$	(17 + 17 =) 34
$0 < x \leqslant 40$	(34 + 10 =) 44
$0 < x \leqslant 50$	(44 + 4 =) 48
$0 < x \leqslant 60$	(48 + 2 =) 50

To complete the cumulative frequency column add the frequencies.

Cumulative frequency graphs are S-shaped.

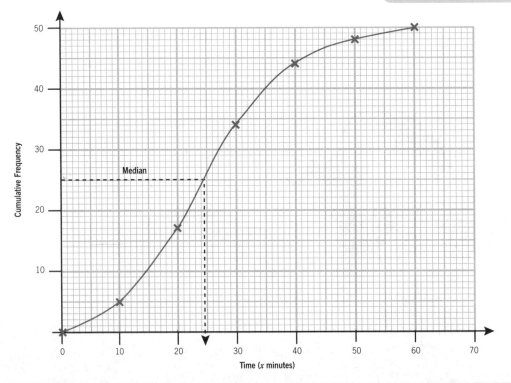

Cumulative Frequency Graphs (cont.)

The median is the middle value of the distribution.

Median = $\frac{1}{2}$ × total of cumulative frequency

$= \frac{1}{2}$ × 50 = 25

Reading across on the previous page from 25 to the y axis and then down gives a median time of approximately 24.5 minutes.

Finding the Interquartile Range

The **upper quartile** is the value three quarters of the way into the distribution.

$\frac{3}{4}$ × 50 = 37.5

Using the graph below gives an approximate time of 32.5 minutes.

The **lower quartile** is the value one quarter of the way into the distribution.

$\frac{1}{4}$ × 50 = 12.5

Using the graph gives an approximate time of 16.5 minutes.

The **interquartile range** is found by subtracting the lower quartile from the upper quartile.

Interquartile range	=	upper quartile	−	lower quartile

The interquartile range would be:

Interquartile range = upper quartile – lower quartile

$= 32.5 - 16.5$

$= 16$ minutes.

A large interquartile range indicates that the middle half of the data is widely spread about the median.

A small interquartile range indicates that the middle half of the data is concentrated about the median.

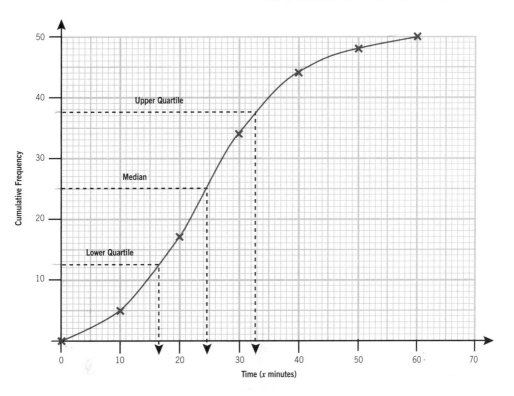

Cumulative Frequency Graphs

Box Plots

A box plot shows the interquartile range as a box, which makes it useful when comparing distributions.

The box plot for the homework data on p.78 would look like this:

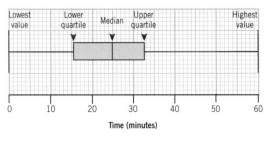

Example

The times in seconds taken by 11 students to solve a puzzle is listed in order:

3, 3, 5, 6, 7, 7, 8, 9, 11, 13, 14

Draw a plot of this data.

3, 3, ⑤, 6, 7, ⑦, 8, 9, ⑪, 13, 14

Lower quartile   Median   Upper quartile

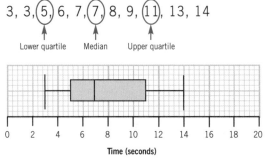

Quick Test

1. These two box plots show the results of two classes, R and T, who took the same maths test.

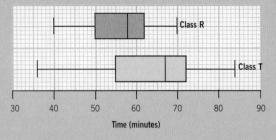

   a) Which class has the student who scored the lowest mark?
   b) What was the median mark of class T?
   c) The students in class R generally did better in the test than those students in class T. True or false?
   d) The interquartile range of marks was larger in class R than class T. True or false?

> **KEY WORDS**
> Make sure you understand these words before moving on!
> • Cumulative frequency graphs
> • Median
> • Upper quartile
> • Lower quartile
> • Interquartile range

1. The following data shows the distance (d km) from a shopping centre.

Distance (d km)	Frequency	Cumulative Frequency
$0 \leqslant d < 5$	8	
$5 \leqslant d < 10$	22	
$10 \leqslant d < 15$	25	
$15 \leqslant d < 20$	18	
$20 \leqslant d < 25$	14	
$25 \leqslant d < 30$	3	

a) Complete the cumulative frequency column in the table above.

b) On the graph paper below, complete the cumulative frequency graph.

c) Use your graph to find the median distance.

d) Use your graph to find the interquartile range.

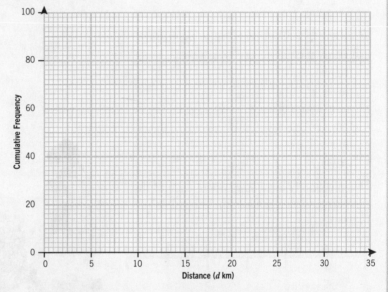

e) On the graph paper opposite, draw a box plot of the data.

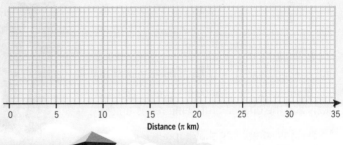

Probability

Probability

Probability is the chance that something will happen.

The idea of chance comes up every day. For example...

- the chance of winning the lottery
- the likelihood that it'll snow on Christmas Day.

When you talk about probability, you might use words such as...

- likely
- unlikely
- evens / even chance
- fair
- impossible
- certain.

This probability line shows where each of the words comes on a scale from 'impossible' to 'certain'.

Impossible | Very unlikely | Unlikely | Even chance | Likely | Very likely | Certain

For example, a bag contains three green beads and one red bead. If a bead is taken out of the bag at random, the chance of it being green is likely and the chance of it being red is unlikely.

An event is something that happens. Every event has a set of possible outcomes. In probability, events are considered that have one or more possible outcomes.

For example, the possible outcomes when a fair die is thrown are 1, 2, 3, 4, 5, 6.

Expressing Probabilities

The probability that an event can happen lies between 0 and 1.

The probability scale...
- starts at 0 for something that's impossible
- finishes at 1 for something that's certain.

| A person has six legs | Getting a tail when a coin is thrown | The Sun will set tomorrow |

0   0.5   1

Probabilities can be written as...
- fractions
- decimals
- percentages

Never write probabilities using the words 'out of'.

Example
A bag contains five red counters, one blue counter and four yellow counters.
A counter is chosen at random.
On a probability scale...
a) mark with an R the probability of choosing a red counter
b) mark with a B the probability of choosing a blue counter
c) mark with a G the probability of choosing a green counter.

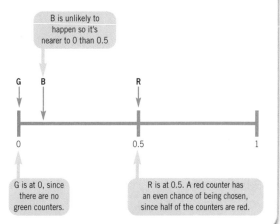

B is unlikely to happen so it's nearer to 0 than 0.5

G is at 0, since there are no green counters.

R is at 0.5. A red counter has an even chance of being chosen, since half of the counters are red.

Calculating Probabilities

Probabilities can be calculated by...
- doing experiments
- using theory
- collecting data.

If you know what all the possible outcomes of an event are, you can calculate the probability of something happening:

| Probability of an outcome | = | Number of ways an outcome can happen / Total number of outcomes |

P(outcome) is the shortened way of writing the probability of an outcome.

The total of the probabilities for all possible outcomes of an event is 1.

Example
The letters that spell out the word 'trigonometry' are placed in a container.
A letter is taken out at random.
What is the probability of taking out...
a) a letter T?
   $P(T) = \frac{2}{12} = \frac{1}{6}$

b) a vowel?
   $P(vowel) = \frac{4}{12} = \frac{1}{3}$

c) a letter A?
   $P(A) = 0$ Since there's no letter A, the probability is zero.

Probability

Experimental Probability

Sometimes an experiment is carried out to show all the possible outcomes of an event, before estimating probabilities of particular outcomes.

For example, Samuel threw a fair die 60 times to estimate the probability of getting a six. Here are his results:

Six	Not six
13	47

There are 60 possible outcomes of which 13 are favourable so...
P(landing on a six) = $\frac{13}{60}$

Theoretically, you would expect...
P(landing on a six) = $\frac{10}{60}$

It's unlikely if Samuel was to repeat the experiment that he would get exactly the same result, but he will get a score similar to $\frac{10}{60}$.

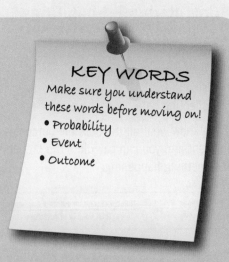

Quick Test

1. Explain what probability is.
2. A bag contains three red beads and two green beads.
   A bead is taken out of the bag at random.
   What is the probability that it's...
   a) red?
      A $\frac{2}{5}$ B 1 C $\frac{3}{5}$ D 0
   b) green?
      A $\frac{2}{5}$ B 1 C $\frac{3}{5}$ D 0
   c) red or green?
      A $\frac{2}{5}$ B 1 C $\frac{3}{5}$ D 0
3. The number of outcomes when a fair die is thrown is 6. True or false?
4. The probability of getting a head on a fair coin is $\frac{1}{2}$. True or false?

① Write down whether each of the following outcomes is 'certain', 'impossible' or 'possible':
a) You'll throw a 9 with a regular die.
b) You'll have a birthday on the same date each year.
c) Your friend will go to Mars next summer.
d) You'll receive an email from a friend tonight.

② Copy the likelihood scale below.

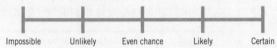

Impossible   Unlikely   Even chance   Likely   Certain

Mark each of these outcomes on the scale.
a) It'll rain in Manchester next year.
b) The next baby born will be female.
c) You'll live until you're 300 years old.
d) The next person you'll see is famous.

③ A, B, C and D are four outcomes that have been marked on this probability scale:

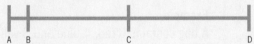

A   B   C   D

Write down possible outcomes that A, B, C and D could be.

④ List all possible outcomes for each of the following events:
a) Spinning this spinner.
b) Picking a counter from this box without looking.

⑤ A bag contains three red, four blue and two green counters.
A counter is taken from the bag at random.
What is the probability that the chosen counter is...
a) red?   b) yellow?   c) blue?

⑥ A multipack of crisps contains two cheese and onion, four ready salted, four salt and vinegar and one smoky bacon.
Thomas takes a bag of crisps without looking at the flavours.
What is the probability that Thomas picks...
a) cheese and onion?   c) smoky bacon?
b) ready salted?   d) prawn cocktail?

Activity

Throw a coin 200 times. Record your results in a tally chart.

$$\text{Experimental probability of landing on tails} = \frac{\text{Number of times your coin landed on tails}}{\text{Total number of times you threw the coin}}$$

Work out the experimental probability of the coin landing on tails.

Compare the theoretical probability with the experimental probability.

Probability

Probability

Probability is the chance or **likelihood** that something will happen.

An **event** is something that happens. Every event has a set of possible outcomes. In probability, events are considered that have one or more possible **outcomes**. For example, when a coin is thrown the possible outcomes are a head or a tail.

The probability that an event can happen lies between 0 and 1.

The probability scale:
- starts at 0 for something that's impossible.
- finishes at 1 for something that's certain.

```
├─────────────┼─────────────┤
0              Evens          1
Impossible     chance       Certain
```

Probabilities can be written as:
- Fractions.
- Decimals.
- Percentages.

Theoretical Probability

The theoretical probability (or probability of an outcome) is calculated in the following way:

| Probability of an outcome | $=$ | Number of ways an outcome can happen / Total number of outcomes |

P (outcome) is the shortened way of writing the probability of an outcome.

Example
A bag contains 6 red, 4 blue and 3 yellow counters. A counter is taken from the bag at random. What is the probability of choosing a...

a) red counter? $\frac{6}{13}$

b) blue counter? $\frac{4}{13}$

c) yellow counter? $\frac{3}{13}$

d) green counter? 0

Experimental Probability

The experimental probability of an outcome can be calculated after an experiment has been completed.

| Experimental probability | $=$ | Number of times the outcome happened / Total number of times experiment carried out |

The experimental probability is the **relative frequency** of the event happening.

Example
Molly threw a coin 100 times to estimate the probability of getting a tail.

Head	Tail
59	41

There are 100 outcomes of which 41 are favourable (i.e. tails).

Experimental Probability: P (tail) $= \frac{41}{100} = 0.41$

The Theoretical Probability of a tail: P (tail) $= \frac{50}{100} = 0.5$

Probability of an Event Not Happening

If two outcomes of an event can't occur at the same time then:

P (Outcome will happen)
= 1 – P (Outcome will not happen), or

P (Outcome will not happen)
= 1 – P (Outcome will happen)

Examples

① The probability that a train arrives late is $\frac{2}{11}$. What is the probability that a train does not arrive late?

P (train late) = 1 – P (train on time)
$$1 - \frac{2}{11}$$
$$= \frac{9}{11}$$

② The probability that Pradnya gets a grade C in GCSE Maths is 0.81. What is the probability that Pradnya will not get a grade C?

P (not get a C) = 1 – P (will get a C)
= 1 – 0.81
= 0.19

Possible Outcomes for Two or More Events

Tests, diagrams and tables can be used when considering outcomes of two or more events.

Examples

① **Sample Space Diagrams**

Two spinners are spun at the same time, and their scores added. Represent the outcomes on a sample space diagram.

		Spinner 2		
+		1	1	3
Spinner 1	1	2	2	4
	2	3	3	5
	3	4	4	6
	3	4	4	6

There are 12 outcomes.

What is:

a) P (score of 4) = $\frac{5}{12}$

b) P (odd score) = $\frac{3}{12} = \frac{1}{4}$

c) P (score of 9) = 0

Probability

Possible Outcomes for Two or More Events (cont.)

2 The diagrams show two spinners. One is coloured and the other is numbered: 4, 5 and 6. Write a list of all possible outcomes:

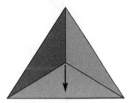 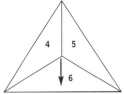

Red 4	Green 4	Blue 4
Red 5	Green 5	Blue 5
Red 6	Green 6	Blue 6

3 The diagram shows a two-way table for pupils in a class who are studying either French or German.

Language	Male	Female	Total
French	6	2	**8**
German	4	5	**9**
Total	**10**	**7**	**17**

If a pupil is chosen at random, what is the probability that they are studying German?

P (German) = $\frac{9}{17}$

If a boy is chosen at random, what is the probability he is studying French?

P (French) = $\frac{6}{10}$ 6 boys study French
10 boys in total

Quick Test

1 What is probability?

2 In a bag there are 6 red and 3 green beads. The probability of choosing a green bead at random is $\frac{6}{9}$. True or false?

3 The probability of being late is $\frac{7}{9}$. What is the probability of not being late?

4 The probability of getting 4 on a fair die is $\frac{1}{6}$. True or false?

KEY WORDS

Make sure you understand these words before moving on!

- Probability
- Likelihood
- Event
- Outcome
- Relative frequency
- Sample space diagrams

Skills Practice

1 A drawer has 3 red, 4 black and 2 grey socks. A sock is taken out of the drawer at random.

What is the probability of choosing:
a) A red sock?
b) A black sock?
c) A grey sock?
d) A blue sock?

2 The probability that it will snow on any day in December is 23%. Work out the probability that it will not snow on any day in December.

3 The probability of winning the premium bonds is 0.1. What is the probability of not winning the premium bonds?

4 The probability that a traffic light is red is $\frac{2}{5}$. What is the probability that it isn't red?

5 During the options process you can choose one subject from each option block.

Option 1	Option 2
Geography	History
French	German
Technology	ICT

Write down all the possible outcomes.

6 Two dice are thrown and their scores are added. Copy and complete the sample space diagram.

What is the probability of a score of:
a) 3
b) 7
c) 12
d) 15

Dice 2

	1	2	3	4	5	6
1	2	3	4	5	6	7
2	3	4	5	6	7	8
3	4	5	6	7	8	9
4	5	6				
5	6	7				
6	7	8				12

Dice 1

Probability

Theoretical Probability

The theoretical **probability** can be calculated in the following way:

$$\text{Probability of an outcome or P (outcome)} = \frac{\text{Number of ways an outcome can happen}}{\text{Total number of outcomes}}$$

Examples

1 A drawer has 3 keys, 4 coins and 2 paperclips inside it. An item is picked out of the drawer at random. What is the probability of choosing the following?

a) A key
$\frac{3}{9} = \frac{1}{3}$

b) A coin
$\frac{4}{9}$

c) A rubber band
0

2 A bag has 6 pink and 4 blue beads. A bead is taken out of the bag at random. What is the probability of choosing the following?

a) Pink bead
$\frac{6}{10} = \frac{3}{5}$

b) Blue bead
$\frac{4}{10} = \frac{2}{5}$

c) Green bead
0

3 The letters T R I G O N O M E T R Y are put on pieces of card and placed in a bag. A piece of card is chosen at random. What is the probability of choosing the following?

a) The letter M $= \frac{1}{12}$

b) The letter T $= \frac{2}{12} = \frac{1}{6}$

c) A vowel $= \frac{4}{12} = \frac{1}{3}$

d) The letter K $= 0$

Experimental Probability

The experimental probability (**relative frequency**) can be calculated in the following way:

$$\text{Experimental probability} = \frac{\text{Number of times the outcome happened}}{\text{Total number of times experiment carried out}}$$

Examples

1 When a fair dice was thrown 120 times during an experiment, a five came up 16 times. What is the relative frequency of getting a five?

Relative frequency $= \frac{16}{120}$

$= \frac{2}{15}$

The theoretical probability of a five $= \frac{1}{6}$

As the number of times a dice is thrown increases, the nearer the experimental probability approaches the theoretical probability.

2 When a fair coin was thrown 250 times during an experiment, a tail came up 138 times. What is the relative frequency and theoretical probability of getting a tail?

Relative frequency $= \frac{138}{250}$

Theoretical probability of a tail $= \frac{1}{2}$

As the number of times the coin is thrown increases, the experimental probability approaches the theoretical probability.

The Language of Probability

The language of probability is often seen in newspapers.

Olympic Bid

It seemed **unlikely** in the run up to the decision about the 2012 Olympic Games that London would win. The **probability** that Paris would be chosen was always very high. It was just that the other contenders had **little chance** of success when the final presentations were given.

Probability of an Event Not Happening

Mutually exclusive events are events that can't happen at the same time.

If two outcomes of an event are mutually exclusive, then:

P (outcome will happen) $=$ 1 $-$ P (outcome won't happen)

or

P (outcome will not happen) $=$ 1 $-$ P (outcome will happen)

Example

The probability that Sasoon is late is 0.31. What is the probability that he isn't late?

P (not late) = 1 – P (late)
$$= 1 - 0.31$$
$$= 0.69$$

The probability that it rains on a particular day in August is $\frac{3}{11}$. What is the probability that it does not rain in August?

P (not rain) = 1 – P (rains)
$$= 1 - \frac{3}{11}$$
$$= \frac{8}{11}$$

Probability

Possible Outcomes for Two or More Events

A **sample space diagram** can be helpful when considering the outcomes of two or more events.

Example

Two fair dice are thrown at the same time and their scores are added together. Draw a diagram to show all the possible outcomes.

1 P (score of 4)

$$= \frac{3}{36} = \frac{1}{12}$$

2 P (score of 9)

$$= \frac{4}{36} = \frac{1}{9}$$

First Dice

†	1	2	3	4	5	6
1	2	3	④	5	6	7
2	3	④	5	6	7	8
3	④	5	6	7	8	9
4	5	6	7	8	9	10
5	6	7	8	9	10	11
6	7	8	9	10	11	12

Second Dice

The Addition Law

In the **addition law**, if two or more events are mutually exclusive, the probability of A or B or C, etc. is found by adding the probabilities.

$$P (A \text{ or } B \text{ or } C...) = P (A) + P (B) + P (C) + ...$$

The Multiplication Law

The **multiplication law** is used when two events are independent whilst the outcome of the second event is not affected by the outcome of the first event.

The probability of A and B and C happening together is:

$$P (A \text{ and } B \text{ and } C) = P (A) \times P (B) \times P (C)$$

Tree Diagrams

Tree diagrams are another way of showing the possible **outcomes** of two or more **events**.

Example

A bag has 3 red and 4 blue buttons in it. A button is taken from the bag at random and its colour noted. The button is then replaced. A second button is taken from the bag and its colour noted.

Draw a tree diagram of the information.

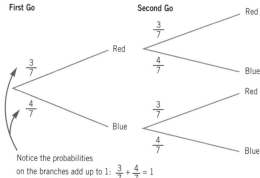

First Go   Second Go

Notice the probabilities on the branches add up to 1: $\frac{3}{7} + \frac{4}{7} = 1$

a) Find the probability of picking two red buttons:

$$\begin{aligned} P\text{ (Red and Red)} &= P\text{ (Red)} \times P\text{ (Red)} \\ &= \frac{3}{7} \times \frac{3}{7} \\ &= \frac{9}{49} \end{aligned}$$

> The multiplication law P (A and B) = P (A) × P (B)

b) Find the probability of picking one of either colour:

$$\begin{aligned} P\text{ (Red and Blue)} &= P\text{ (Red)} \times P\text{ (Blue)} \\ &= \frac{3}{7} \times \frac{4}{7} \\ &= \frac{12}{49} \end{aligned}$$

or
$$\begin{aligned} P\text{ (Blue and Red)} &= P\text{ (Blue)} \times P\text{ (Red)} \\ &= \frac{4}{7} \times \frac{3}{7} \\ &= \frac{12}{49} \end{aligned}$$

> The multiplication law P (A or B) = P (A) + P (B)

c) P (one of each colour) $= \frac{12}{49} + \frac{12}{49}$
$$= \frac{24}{49}$$

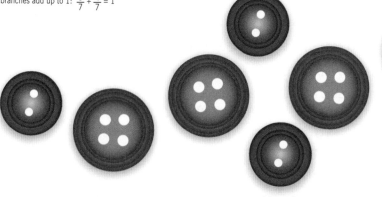

Quick Test

1. What is the probability of getting a 7 on a fair dice? **a)** 1 **b)** $\frac{1}{2}$ **c)** 0 **d)** $\frac{1}{6}$
2. The probability that it will rain is $\frac{4}{9}$. What is the probability that it will not rain?
3. If a fair coin is thrown 500 times, approximately how many heads would you expect?
4. P (A or B) = P (A) × P (B). True or false?

Probability

Skills Practice

1 A bag has 6 red, 3 blue and 2 yellow beads. A bead is taken out of the bag at random.
What is the probability of choosing the following:
a) A red bead.
b) A yellow bead.
c) Not a blue bead.
d) A red or blue bead.

2 The probability that the Bank of England base rate will go below 0.5% is 0.15. Work out the probability that the base rate will not go below 0.5%.

3 The probability that Ryan is late for school is 0.42. Work out the probability that Ryan is not late for school.

4 Rupert roles a fair 6-sided dice once. Write down the probability that the dice will show a 3 or a 4.

5 A fair dice is thrown 300 times. How many fives would you expect to appear?

6 Amy plays a game of chess. She can win or draw or lose the game.

a) The table shows the probabilities that she will win or draw the game.

Result	Win	Draw	Lose
Probability	0.4	0.3	

Work out the probability that she will lose the game.

b) If Amy plays 50 games of chess, how many would you expect her to win?

7 The tree diagram shows the outcomes of throwing two coins.

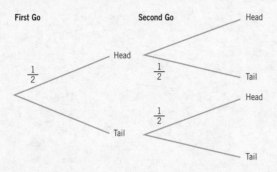

First Go

Second Go

Head

Head

$\frac{1}{2}$

$\frac{1}{2}$

Tail

Head

$\frac{1}{2}$

Tail

$\frac{1}{2}$

Tail

a) Complete the tree diagram.

b) Work out the probability of getting two heads.

c) Work out the probability of a head and a tail in any order.

8 A bag has 4 red and 5 green beads. A bead is chosen from the bag at random, its colour noted and then it is replaced. A second bead is then taken. The tree diagram shows the results.

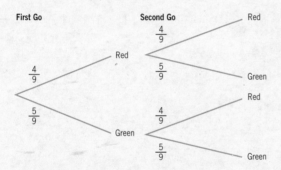

First Go

Second Go

$\frac{4}{9}$

Red

Red

$\frac{4}{9}$

$\frac{5}{9}$

Green

$\frac{5}{9}$

Red

Green

$\frac{4}{9}$

Green

$\frac{5}{9}$

Green

a) Work out the probability of getting two green beads.

b) Work out the probability of getting a bead of either colour.

ESSENTIALS

KS3
Maths Coursebook Answers
covers all three years

NUMBERS (Level 4)

Page 8 – Quick Test

1. Nine thousand, eight hundred and thirty-two

2. Highest place value

3. a) Units
   b) Round up, because the digit is greater than 5.

Page 9 – Skills Practice

1. a) 6 hundreds
   b) 6 units
   c) 6 units
   d) 6 hundreds
   e) 6 tens

2. a) 3 thousands
   b) 3 hundreds
   c) 3 tens
   d) 3 units
   e) 3 hundreds

3. a) 4638
   b) 605 209
   c) 83 039
   d) 9705
   e) 200 073

4. a) 7, 62, 93, 127, 156
   b) 37, 58, 201, 291, 1169
   c) 5, 18, 26, 37, 41, 52
   d) 26, 162, 583, 837, 1271

5. a) 70
   b) 70
   c) 280
   d) 1370

6. a) 700
   b) 1500
   c) 6300
   d) 3100

7. a) 5000
   b) 13 000
   c) 19 000
   d) 80 000

8. Round the numbers before adding them together.

9. No, the digits must line up according to place value, i.e.

   549
   23 –

10. a) $30 + 30 = 60$
    b) $600 + 900 = 1500$
    c) $80 - 20 = 60$
    d) $1000 - 600 = 400$

11. The shopping comes to roughly £8.60 so Charlie does have enough money.

12. a) 543
    b) 630
    c) 9133
    d) 486
    e) 364
    f) 1583

13. There are many possible sums that you could give. Make sure that yours has an answer of 693.

NUMBERS (Levels 5–7)

Page 13 – Quick Test

1. 20418

2. 15

3. False

4. 57

5. True

6. $2 \times 2 \times 3 \times 3$ or $2^2 \times 3^2$

7. 13104

Pages 14–15 – Skills Practice

1. 8 coaches and 22 seats left over

2. £16864

3. a) 6^5
   b) 2^6
   c) 8^4

4. a) $5 \times 5 \times 5 \times 5 \times 5 \times 5 \times 5 \times 5 \times 5$
   b) $10 \times 10 \times 10 \times 10 \times 10 \times 10 \times 10$
   c) $2 \times 2 \times 2 \times 3 \times 3 \times 3 \times 3 \times 3$

5. a) 17
   b) 6
   c) 450
   d) 67
   e) 553

6. a) 54
   b) 12
   c) 2

7. a) ± 8
   b) ± 9
   c) ± 13
   d) 25
   e) 64
   f) 9

8. a) 5×5 or 5^2
   b) $2 \times 2 \times 2 \times 2 \times 2$ or 2^5
   c) $2 \times 3 \times 3$ or 2×3^2
   d) $2 \times 2 \times 5 \times 5$ or $2^2 \times 5^2$

9. a) HCF = 2
      LCM = 420
   b) HCF = 4
      LCM = 144

10. £137.46

NUMBERS (Levels 6–8)

Page 18 – Quick Test

1. $30 \times 40 \div 6 = \frac{120}{6} = 20$

2. a) 2700
   b) 9.6
   c) 2.1

3. True

4. False

Pages 19 – Skills Practice

1. a) True
   b) False
   c) True
   d) True
   e) True
   f) False
   h) True

2. a) $900 \times 400 = 360\,000$
   b) $40 \times 20 = 800$
   c) $200 \times 2000 = 400\,000$
   d) $\frac{9000 - 10}{10} = 899$

3. a) 4^7
   b) 3^8
   c) 4^7
   d) 6^5
   e) 10^4
   f) 6^7
   g) 7^3
   h) 8^3

4. a) 6
   b) 22
   c) 8
   d) 5

5. a) $25 = 5 \times 5$
   b) $42 = 2 \times 3 \times 7$
   c) $72 = 2 \times 2 \times 2 \times 3 \times 3$

6. a) HCF = 5, LCM = 180
   b) HCF = 4, LCM = 112
   c) HCF = 4, LCM = 480

7. a) Lower 615, Upper 624
   b) Lower 3545, Upper 3554
   c) Lower 5550, Upper 5649
   d) Lower 156 500, Upper 157 499
   e) Lower 2.65, Upper 2.75

MULTIPLICATION AND DIVISION (Levels 4–5)

Page 24 – Quick Test

1. Move each digit two places to the left and put two zeros at the end.

2. Move each digit three places to the right. If a number ends in zeros, up to three zeros are lost from the end.

3. The answer given when two or more numbers are multiplied together.

4. True

5. True

6. C

7. A whole number raised to the power 3 (i.e. multiplied by itself three times).

8. True

Page 25 – Skills Practice

1. a) 630
   b) 27 000
   c) 27
   d) 59
   e) 1600

2. 1095 hours

3. a) 27 full packets
   b) 2 left over

4. a) 1, 4, 5, 20
   b) 1, 4, 25, 49, 81
   c) 1, 27
   d) 6, 12, 24
   e) 3, 5, 13, 17

5. a) 15
   b) 5
   c) 5
   d) 36
   e) 64
   f) +12 or -12

6. 12 427

7. 1638

8. 17

9. a) 26
   b) 36p

FRACTIONS (Levels 4–6)

Page 27 – Quick Test

1. False

2. D

3. Divide 16 by 4

4. C

5. True

Pages 28–29 – Skills Practice

1. a) i) Shaded = $\frac{7}{15}$

   ii) Not shaded = $\frac{8}{15}$

   b) i) Shaded = $\frac{1}{4}$

   ii) Not shaded = $\frac{3}{4}$

   c) i) Shaded = $\frac{5}{8}$

ii) Not shaded = $\frac{3}{8}$

2.

3. a) $\frac{2}{3} = \frac{8}{12}$

   b) $\frac{25}{30} = \frac{5}{6}$

   c) $\frac{9}{12} = \frac{27}{36}$

   d) $\frac{20}{32} = \frac{10}{18}$

4.

$\boxed{\frac{2}{3}} = \boxed{\frac{10}{15}}$

$\boxed{\frac{21}{27}} = \boxed{\frac{7}{9}}$

$\boxed{\frac{4}{5}} = \boxed{\frac{12}{15}}$

5. a) 1

   b) $\frac{5}{9}$

   c) $\frac{1}{10}$

   d) $\frac{7}{16}$

   e) $\frac{21}{34}$

   f) $\frac{4}{5}$

6. $\frac{1}{6}$ of the garden is the flower bed.

7. The architect has used $\frac{1}{2}$ of the playground, so $\frac{1}{2}$ of the playground is left.

8. a) 20ml
   b) 35kg
   c) £15

9. a) 700kg
   b) £72
   c) £448

10. £6

11.a) 100 minutes
   b) 150 text messages

12. $\frac{2}{3} + \frac{4}{5}$

   $= \frac{10}{15} + \frac{12}{15}$

   $= \frac{22}{15}$

   $= 1\frac{7}{15}$, not $\frac{6}{8}$ so Jessica is wrong.

DECIMALS (Levels 4–5)

Page 32 – Quick Test

1. 5 thousandths

2. True

3. B

4. 793.6

5. The number in the second decimal place.

Page 33 – Skills Practice

1. a) 3 tenths
   b) 7 hundredths
   c) 6 units
   d) 4 thousandths

2. a) 276
   b) 4.932
   c) 9630
   d) 0.2943
   e) 16 200
   f) 0.29

3. a) 518.9
   b) 260.99
   c) 114.4
   d) 42.3
   e) 171.6
   f) 45

4. a) 316.9
   b) 176.8
   c) 336.6
   d) 103.13
   e) 316.2
   f) 122

5. 4.281km

6. 0.62m

7. £7.53

8. £250.12

9. 2.41m

10.a) 6.5
   b) 7.4
   c) 5.7
   d) 4.3

11.a) 3.53
   b) 16.65
   c) 127.43
   d) 4.69
   e) 12.69
   f) 37.26
   g) 38.47
   h) 38.53
   i) 37.73

12. 1.35 metres

FRACTIONS, DECIMALS AND ESTIMATING (Levels 5–7)

Page 39 – Quick Test

1. Tenths

2. $7\frac{2}{5}$

3. b) $3\frac{5}{6}$

4. True

5. 0.719, 0.72, 0.76, 3.21, 3.255, 3.26

Pages 40–41 – Skills Practice

1. a) $1\frac{1}{21}$

b) $\frac{7}{33}$

c) $\frac{3}{10}$

d) $\frac{5}{6}$

e) $\frac{8}{9}$

f) $7\frac{6}{77}$

2. a) $\frac{4}{9}$

b) $\frac{5}{16}$

c) $\frac{16}{45}$

d) $\frac{6}{7}$

e) $\frac{3}{10}$

f) $4\frac{7}{12}$

3. a) $\frac{11}{14}$

b) $\frac{9}{11}$

c) 1

d) 2

e) 1

f) 2

4. £14000

5. 480

6. a) 4.02, 4.09, 4.26, 4.29, 4.293, 4.31
b) 8.427, 8.429, 8.475, 8.48, 8.481, 8.73
c) 6.902, 6.915, 6.92, 6.925, 6.926, 6.931

7. a) 1040
b) 76.44
c) 79.171
d) 16.3
e) 28.1
f) 12

8. a) 16.43
b) 9.37
c) 12.87
d) 3.43
e) 8.71
f) 146.93

9. a) 570

b) 1380
c) 0.631
d) 2.79
e) 0.027
f) 15700

10. a) $8 \times 4 = 32$
b) $10 \times 4 = 40$
c) $6^2 = 36$
d) $\frac{20 \times 40}{10} = \frac{800}{10} = 80$

RATIO (Level 5)

Page 43 – Skills Practice

1. A ratio is a way of comparing two or more related quantities.

2. True

3. D

4. B

5. Ratios are equivalent when they represent the same relationship.

Pages 44–45 – Skills Practice

1. a) 1 : 3
b) 2 : 3
c) 5 : 1

2. a) 1 : 2
b) 1 : 2
c) 2 : 5
d) 2 : 1
e) 15 : 7
f) 10 : 11
g) 4 : 3
h) 8 : 11
i) 5 : 11
j) 5 : 2
k) 16 : 1
l) 1 : 3

3. a) 20 : 1
b) 1 : 5
c) 2 : 1
d) 5 : 2
e) 5000 : 1
f) 4 : 1
g) 20 : 1
h) 1 : 4
i) 5 : 1

4. 1 : 4

5. 1 : 2 : 5

6. 8 : 7

7. 1 : 4

8. 25 : 8 : 5

9. 13 : 9 : 15

10. £18

11. £28.21

12. £6.75

13. 5.625 tins contain enough paint for
two coats, so Molly needs to buy 6 tins of paint.

14. a) £517.50
   b) £1414.50

15. a) 161.50 American dollars
   b) 389.50 American dollars

16. a) £126
   b) £226.80
   c) £302.40

17. a) 228 miles
   b) 418 miles

RATIO (Levels 5–6)

Page 48 – Quick Test

1. False

2. c) 2 : 3

3. £30000

4. £1.96

5. True

Page 49 – Skills Practice

1. a) 4 : 5
   b) 1 : 2
   c) 3 : 1
   d) 3 : 7
   e) 5 : 9
   f) 5 : 3

2. 50 : 20 : 36 = 25 : 10 : 18

3. $\frac{1}{7}$

4. 7.2km

5. 32 blue beads

6. £35

7. 20 marbles

8. a) €395
   b) £55

9. 700ml

FRACTIONS, DECIMALS AND RATIO (Levels 6–8)

Page 52 – Quick Test

1. True

2. £12 000

3. True

4. 6.04, 6.27, 6.37, 6.371, 6.49

Page 53 – Skills Practice

1. a) $\frac{64}{77}$
   b) $\frac{7}{15}$

c) $5\frac{13}{15}$
   d) $1\frac{7}{9}$

2. a) $\frac{6}{35}$
   b) $8\frac{1}{3}$
   c) $3\frac{27}{40}$
   d) $1\frac{4}{45}$

3. a) $1\frac{5}{7}$
   b) $2\frac{2}{3}$
   c) $\frac{49}{87}$
   d) $1\frac{19}{56}$

4. a) 6.48
   b) 17.24
   c) 25.42
   d) 9.38

5. 20

6. 7.37m, 12.04m, 12.06m, 12.39m, 12.41m, 12.63m

7. 0.0124

8. £16.72

9. 200

NEGATIVE NUMBERS (Levels 4–5)

Page 55 – Quick Test

1. True

2. False

3. B

4. False

5. C

6. B

Pages 56–57 – Skills Practice

1. a) i) 7°C
     ii) -5°C
   b) i) 2°C
     ii) -6°C
   c) i) 7°C
     ii) -9°C
   d) i) 14°C
     ii) -12°C
   e) i) 13°C
     ii) -8°C
   f) i) 10°C
     ii) -9°C

2. a) -3°C, -2°C, 0°C, 4°C, 5°C, 6°C
   b) -9°C, -7°C, -2°C, 3°C, 5°C
   c) -10°C, -5°C, 2°C, 4°C, 9°C, 12°C
   d) -6°C, -4°C, -1°C, 0°C, 7°C, 9°C
   e) -12°C, -5°C, -2°C, 7°C, 9°C, 14°C
   f) -8°C, -3°C, -1°C, 6°C, 9°C, 12°C

3. a) Glasgow
   b) 7°C

c) London
d) Glasgow

4. 2°C

5. a) -3
   b) -5
   c) 1
   d) -9
   e) -7
   f) -10
   g) -1
   h) 4
   i) 73
   j) -5
   k) -16
   l) -7

6. a) -5, -8
   b) 1, 3
   c) -10, -12

7. a) 7
   b) 7
   c) 1
   d) 3
   e) -1
   f) -16
   g) -4
   h) -5
   i) 9
   j) 9
   k) -7
   l) 6
   m) 6
   n) -5
   o) -2

8. a)
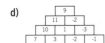

b)

c)
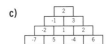

d)

e)

f)

9. a)

b)

c)

d)

e)

f)

NEGATIVE NUMBERS
(Levels 5–6)

Page 59 – Skills Practice

1. -2

2. a) -10, -6, -5, -4, -2, 0, 3, 4, 7
   b) -36, -12, -9, -7, -5, -4, 4, 6
   c) -41, -26, -13, -11, -10, -8, -3, 7

3. a) -9
   b) -3
   c) -5
   d) 4
   e) 9
   f) -2
   g) 35
   h) -38
   i) -53
   j) -1
   k) 1
   l) -10

4. a) 8
   b) 4
   c) -12
   d) 7
   e) 1
   f) -9
   g) 11
   h) -9
   i) -3
   j) -9
   k) -7
   l) 2

5. a) -21
   b) -12
   c) 20
   d) 21
   e) 5
   f) -5
   g) -50
   h) 5
   i) -42
   j) 64
   k) -2
   l) 25

6. a) -13
   b) -8
   c) 9
   d) -60
   e) 25
   f) -6
   g) 6
   h) -63

PERCENTAGES (Levels 4–5)

Page 62 – Quick Test

1. %

2. Divide by 10

3. B

4. Multiply 70 by 37 and divide by 100

5. A

6. D

Page 63 – Skills Practice

1. a) 50%
   b) 25%
   c) 10%

2. 46%

3. 73%

4. 35%

5. a) 7kg
   b) £28
   c) 15mm
   d) £144
   e) £32
   f) £27
   g) £78
   h) £52.50

6. a) 102km
   b) £576
   c) 6.24kg
   d) £0.75
   e) £97.50
   f) 75.6m
   g) £29.52
   h) 224kg

7. 42 girls

8. 420 students

9. a) £33.60
   b) £593.60

10. £9.60

PERCENTAGES (Levels 5–7)

Page 68 – Quick Test

1. Find 10% by dividing by 10 and then halve your answer to find 5%.

2. d) £48

3. b) 1.2

4. 77.5%

5. False

Page 69 – Skills Practice

1. 35

2. a) 50.4 miles
   b) £486.40
   c) 3034g
   d) 25.76cm

3. £337.84

4. 49.6%

5. 53.3̇%

6. 40.4% (1 dp)

7.

Garden furniture	60.8%
Bay tree	66.6̇%
Plant pot	277.7̇%

8. 25.3%

9. £224,640

10. 0.369, 37%, $\frac{2}{5}$, 0.409, 41%, $\frac{2}{3}$

11. £165.60

PERCENTAGES (Levels 6–8)

Page 73 – Quick Test

1. True

2. b) 1.45

3. False

4. 1.25%

Pages 74–75 – Skills Practice

1. a) £64.80
   b) £391.30
   c) 2.268kg
   d) 44.55kg

2. £438.49

3. 74.6̇%

4. 35.3%

5. 10.7% (1 d.p.)

6. £36.04

7. 68.3%

8. 50.9% (1 d.p.)

9. 26.4% (1 d.p.)

10. 90

11. £60.40

12. £874.05

13. £508.61

14. £996.06

15. £28

16. £22

17. £499

STANDARD INDEX FORM
(Levels 6–8)

Page 78 – Quick Test

1. True

2. True

3. b) 30 000

4. False

Page 79 – Skills Practice

1. a) 7.56×10^3
   b) 3×10^6
   c) 5.2×10^4
   d) 4.9×10^8
   e) 6.3×10^5
   f) 7.1×10^4
   g) 5.2×10^6
   h) 4.1×10^4
   i) 9.8×10^6

2. a) 4.6×10^{-3}
   b) 9×10^{-6}
   c) 9.7×10^{-2}
   d) 8.4×10^{-1}
   e) 9.1×10^{-6}
   f) 9.9×10^{-5}
   g) 4.76×10^{-1}
   h) 7×10^{-10}
   i) 5.55×10^{-5}

3. a) 30 000
   b) 600
   c) 320 000
   d) 72 000 000
   e) 0.000036
   f) 0.0025
   g) 0.06

h) 0.0005
i) 0.000000074

4. a) 8×10^{11}
   b) 3×10^{11}
   c) 8×10^8
   d) 2×10^3
   e) 2×10^5

5. a) 1.8×10^{15}
   b) 3.36×10^{19}
   c) 1.8×10^5
   d) 2.1×10^{-13}
   e) 2.4×10^8

NUMBER PATTERNS
(Levels 4–5)

Page 81 – Quick Test

1. Add 3 to the preceding number.

2. The Fibonacci sequence is 1, 1, 2, 3, 5, 8, ...
   Each term is the sum of the previous two terms.

3. D

4. True

5. A

6. D

Pages 82–83 – Skills Practice

1. a) i) 10, 12
      ii) Add 2 each time.
   b) i) 21, 25
      ii) Add 4 each time.
   c) i) -2, -5
      ii) Subtract 3 each time.
   d) i) 4, 2
      ii) Divide by 2 each time.
   e) i) 10, 5
      ii) Subtract 5 each time.
   f) i) 45, 54
      ii) Add 9 each time.
   g) i) 30, 20
      ii) Subtract 10 each time.
   h) i) 320, 640
      ii) Multiply by 2 each time.

2. a) 12, 15. Add 3 each time.
   b) 21, 25. Add 4 each time.
   c) 39, 36. Subtract 3 each time.
   d) 36, 31. Subtract 5 each time.
   e) 36, 30. Subtract 6 each time.
   f) 16, 25. Square numbers.
   g) 11, 16. Add 1, then 2, then 3, etc. That is, increase the difference by one each time.
   h) 24, 48. Multiply the previous term by 2.

3. a)

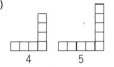

4   5

b)

Diagram	1	2	3	4	5
No. of Squares	1	3	5	7	9

c) 17 squares

d) 49 squares

4. a)

b)

Pattern	1	2	3	4
Matchsticks	3	5	7	9

c) Add 2 each time.

5. 1, 1, 2, 3, 5, 8, 13, 21, 34, 55, 89, 144, 233, 377, 610

6. a) Add 5
  b) Subtract 2
  c) Multiply by 2
  d) Divide by 3
  e) Divide by 4
  f) Multiply by 2 and add 1

7. a) i) Input 2, 4, 6, 8
    ii) 10, 20, 30, 40
    iii) Add 10 each time / The ten times table.
  b) i) Input 2, 4, 6, 8
    ii) 8, 10, 12, 14
    iii) Add 2 each time.
  c) i) Input 2, 4, 6, 8
    ii) 7, 11, 15, 19
    iii) Add 4 each time.
  d) i) Input 2, 4, 6, 8
    ii) 4, 10, 16, 22
    iii) Add 6 each time.

8. 8, 12, 16, 20, 24, 28

9. Any four different patterns,
  for example:
  1, 2, 3, 4, 5, …
  1, 2, 4, 8, 16, …
  1, 2, 3, 5, 7, …
  1, 2, 1, 2, 1, …

Page 83 – Extension

Any instance of the Fibonacci sequence occurring in nature, for example: The number of petals on flowers.

NUMBER PATTERNS AND SEQUENCES (Levels 5–6)

Page 85 – Skills Practice

1. a) i) 11, 13
    ii) Add 2 each time
  b) i) 2, 0
    ii) Subtract 2 each time

c) i) 50, 60
    ii) Add 10 each time
  d) i) 6.25, 3.125
    ii) Divide by 2 each time
  e) i) 48, 96
    ii) Multiply each preceding term by 2
  f) i) 8, 5
    ii) Subtract 3 each time

2. a)

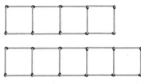

b)

Shape	1	2	3	4	5
Number of Matchsticks	4	7	10	13	16

c) 25

d) $3n + 1$

3. a) $2n$
  b) $2n + 1$
  c) $2n + 6$
  d) $2n + 3$
  e) $4n + 4$
  f) $3n + 1$

4. a) ii) 12, 20, 28
    iii) Add 8 each time
  b) ii) 5, 9, 13
    iii) Add 4 each time
  c) ii) 13, 19, 25
    iii) Add 6 each time
  d) ii) 12, 22, 32
    iii) Add 10 each time

NUMBER AND PATTERNS SEQUENCE (Levels 6–8)

Page 87 – Quick Test

1. a) $2n$
  b) $2n + 1$
  c) $2n + 2$ or $2(n + 1)$
  d) $3n + 4$
  e) $4n + 2$
  f) $10 - n$
  g) $5n - 2$

2. a) n^2
  b) $2n^2$
  c) $n^2 - 1$
  d) $n^2 - 3$
  e) $5n^2$

WORKING WITH ALGEBRA
(Levels 4–5)

Page 91 – Quick Test

1. Write the number first, then the letters in alphabetical order, i.e. $3abf$.

2. True

3. B

4. Expanding brackets

5. False (the correct answer is $6x - 12y$).

6. True

7. B

Pages 92–93 – Skills Practice

1. a) $3p$
    b) $p - 4$
    c) $3p + 6$

2. a) $t - 6$
    b) $h + 5$
    c) $p + 4$
    d) $m - 2$
    e) $x + 6$
    f) $n - r$
    g) $y - p$
    h) $x + y$
    i) $m + p$
    j) $b - k$

3. a) $6b$
    b) $\frac{a}{2}$
    c) $\frac{e}{7}$
    d) $5x$
    e) $3y$
    f) $2(5 + x)$
    g) $\frac{(x + p)}{y}$

4. a) $8a$
    b) $7b$
    c) $p + 5q$
    d) $4x + 2y$
    e) $7b$
    f) $5a + 4b$
    g) $5a + 3b$
    h) $9a + 5b$
    i) $8a$
    j) $5x + 2y$
    k) $6a - 7p$
    l) $16b$
    m) $4y - a$
    n) $6p - 7a - 3b$

5. a) $6x^2$
    b) $4b^2$
    c) $15b^2$
    d) $12y^2$
    e) $6a^2$
    f) $10a^2$
    g) $27p^2$
    h) $2a^3$
    i) $10a^3$
    j) $30a^3$

6. a) $5x - 5$
    b) $6x + 30$
    c) $6x + 12$
    d) $x^2 - 6x$
    e) $3x + 3$
    f) $5x - 20$
    g) $2x - 12$
    h) $x^2 + 5x$
    i) $5x - 30$
    j) $14x + 7$
    k) $x^2 - x$
    l) $9x - 18$
    m) $35 - 14x$
    n) $3x^2 - 6x$
    o) $12 - 24x$
    p) $15 - 30x$
    q) $2x^2 - 10x$

7. a) 4
    b) 15
    c) 30
    d) 11
    e) 7
    f) 13
    g) 32
    h) 0
    i) 19
    j) 9
    k) 36
    l) 42
    m) 12
    n) 15

8. £1.40

9. a) $d = p - q$
    b) $d = 30 - 2$
       $= 28°C$

WORKING WITH ALGEBRA
(Levels 5–6)

Page 98 – Quick Test

1. $5abd$, alphabetical order, number first and no multiplication sign.

2. d) $2a + b$

3. True

4. False

5. 42

Page 99 – Skills Practice

1. a) $4a$
    b) $11a - b$
    c) $x + 9y$

d) $12y$

e) $11c - 7d$

f) $5xy - xy^2$

2. a) $8a^2$

b) $18ab$

c) $15de$

d) $6b^2$

e) $14a^2$

f) $54p^2$

g) $30a^2b$

h) $6a^3$

3. a) $5x - 5$

b) $3x + 6y$

c) $6x - 12$

d) $x^2 + 3x$

e) $5x - 15 + 2x - 2 = 7x - 17$

f) $12x - 48 - 3x - 3 = 9x - 45$

4. a) $5(3x - 1)$

b) $10(2y + 1)$

c) $3(x - 3y)$

d) $x(x + 2)$

e) $2y(7 - y)$

f) $3(3y + 4)$

5. a) 19

b) 10

c) 20

d) 9

e) 35

f) 28

6. a) $3x$

b) $x - 5$

c) $\frac{x}{2}$

WORKING WITH ALGEBRA (Levels 6–8)

Page 104 – Quick Test

1. False

2. b) x^{12}

3. True

4. $x^2 - 4x - 12$

5. False

Page 105 – Skills Practice

1. a) x^9

b) $12x^3$

c) $2x^3$

d) x^{20}

e) $10x^5$

f) $6x^2$

g) $8x^6$

h) 1

2. a) $14x - 7$

b) $3x + 8$

c) $3x^2 - 5x$

d) $2x^2 + 12x$

e) $x^2 + 2x - 3$

f) $x^2 - 9x + 14$

g) $x^2 + 10x + 24$

h) $x^2 - 3x - 10$

3. a) $7x - 32$

b) $11x - 33$

c) $14x - 32$

4. a) $4(4x - 3)$

b) $10(2x + 1)$

c) $3x(x + 2)$

d) $12x(1 - 2x)$

e) $(x + 2)(x + 6)$

f) $(x + 1)(x + 1)$

g) $(x - 2)(x - 5)$

h) $(x + 1)(x - 4)$

5. a) 19.2

b) -4.1

c) -11.05

6. $t = \sqrt{a^2 - d}$

EQUATIONS (Levels 5–6)

Page 107 – Quick Test

1. Subtract 6 from both sides of the equation.

2. Add 2 to both sides of the equation.

3. Divide both sides of the equation by 5.

4. True

5. C

Pages 108–109 – Skills Practice

1. a) $x = 4$

b) $x = 6$

c) $x = -3$

d) $x = 12$

e) $x = 3$

f) $x = 21$

g) $x = -1$

h) $x = -2$

i) $x = -5$

j) $x = -2$

k) $x = -3$

l) $x = 4$

m) $x = -5$

n) $x = 9$

2. a) $x = 13$

b) $x = 9$

c) $x = 16$

d) $x = 36$

e) $x = 39$

f) $x = 18$

g) $x = 18$

h) $x = 16$

i) $x = 17.6$

j) $x = 24.5$

k) $x = 11$

l) $x = 29$
m) $x = 39$
n) $x = 21$

3. a) $x = 2$
   b) $x = 3$
   c) $x = 2$
   d) $x = 3$
   e) $x = 9$
   f) $x = 8$
   g) $x = 32$
   h) $x = 8$
   i) $x = 11$
   j) $x = 2\frac{4}{7}$
   k) $x = 4\frac{4}{5}$
   l) $x = 12$
   m) $x = 4\frac{1}{3}$
   n) $x = 3\frac{1}{2}$

4. a) $x = 18$
   b) $x = 20$
   c) $x = 90$
   d) $x = 15$
   e) $x = 14$
   f) $x = 36$

5. a) $x = 9$
   b) $x = 7$
   c) $x = 10$
   d) $x = 22$
   e) $x = 15$
   f) $x = 12\frac{6}{7}$

6. a) $x = 2$
   b) $x = 11$
   c) $x = 4$
   d) $x = 8$
   e) $x = 19$
   f) $x = 9$
   g) $x = 16$
   h) $x = 6$
   i) $x = 32$
   j) $x = 30$
   k) $x = 6$
   l) $x = 2$
   m) $x = 4$
   n) $x = 13$

7. a) $x = 5$
   b) $x = 3$
   c) $x = 4$
   d) $x = 3$
   e) $x = 3$
   f) $x = 5$
   g) $x = 1$
   h) $x = 2$
   i) $x = 1$
   j) $x = 4$
   k) $x = 8$

l) $x = 2$
m) $x = 2\frac{2}{3}$
n) $x = 4\frac{1}{2}$
o) $x = 11\frac{1}{3}$

8. a) $x = 1\frac{1}{5}$
   b) $x = 2\frac{2}{3}$
   c) $x = 11\frac{1}{5}$

9. a) $9x = 288$
      $x = \frac{288}{9}$
      $x = 32$p
   b) $3x + 7 = 49$
      $3x = 49 - 7$
      $3x = 42$
      $x = \frac{42}{3}$
      $x = 14$

10.
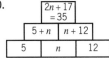

Since $2n + 17 = 35$
$2n = 35 - 17$
$2n = 18$
$n = 9$

EQUATIONS AND INEQUALITIES (Level 6)

Page 113 – Quick Test

1. True

2. b) 9

3. False

4. c) -10

5. a) $-3 < -1$
   b) $7 < 9$
   c) $6 > -6$
   d) $-5 < 4$

6. False.

Pages 114–115 – Skills Practice

1. a) $x = 8$
   b) $x = 4$
   c) $x = 10$
   d) $x = 8$
   e) $x = 8$
   f) $x = 4$
   g) $x = 30$
   h) $x = 12$
   i) $x = 1$
   j) $x = 4$
   k) $x = -5$
   l) $x = -15$

2. a) $x = 2$
   b) $x = 4$
   c) $x = 4$
   d) $x = 8$
   e) $x = 2$
   f) $x = 5$
   g) $x = 4$
   h) $x = 7.5$
   i) $x = 2$
   j) $s = 8\frac{2}{3}$

   k) $x = 1\frac{1}{4}$
   l) $x = 11$

3. a) $x = \frac{4}{3}$

   b) $x = 2.5$
   c) $x = 9\frac{4}{5}$

4. a) $x = 2$
   b) $x = 9$
   c) $x = 1$
   d) $x = 3$
   e) $x = 8$
   f) $x = -3$
   g) $x = -3$
   h) $x = -\frac{9}{5} = -1\frac{4}{5}$

5. a) $x = 5$
   b) $x = 9$
   c) $x = 3$
   d) $x = 2$
   e) $x = 9$
   f) $x = 10$
   g) $x = -\frac{3}{4}$

   h) $x = -4$

6. $x = 2.76$

7. a) $5 < 9$
   b) $7 < 13$
   c) $15 > 8$
   d) $9 > 4$
   e) $7 < 17$

8. $6x + 16 = 40$
   $6x = 24$
   $x = 4$
   Length = 13cm
   Width = 7cm

9. $2n + 13 = 26$
   $2n = 13$
   $n = 6.5$

EQUATIONS AND INEQUALITIES (Levels 6–8)

Page 120 – Quick Test

1. d) 2

2. b) 3.5

3. True

4. a) 2.75

Page 121 – Skills Practice

1. a) $x = 9$
   b) $x = 1.5$
   c) $x = 28$
   d) $x = 4$
   e) $x = 3$
   f) $x = 9$

2. a) $x = 4$
   b) $x = \frac{-5}{3}$
   c) $x = 4$
   d) $x = -20$
   e) $x = -1\frac{3}{8}$
   f) $x = -11$

3. a) $x = 3$, $y = 2$
   b) $x = 1$, $y = -1$
   c) $x = 2$, $y = -2$

4. a) $x \le 11$

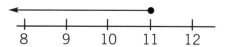

   b) $x > 2$

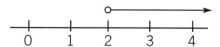

   c) $x \le 3$

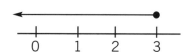

   d) $3 < x \le 6$

5. $x = 1.6$ (1 d.p.)

6. $b = 5$

COORDINATES AND GRAPHS (Levels 4–6)

Page 123 – Quick Test

1. You read horizontally first and then vertically.

2. False

3. a) True
   b) D
   c) (-2, -4)

Pages 124–125 – Skills Practice

1. a) i) Monkeys
   ii) Giraffes
   iii) Lions
   iv) Car park
   v) Café
   vi) Elephants
   b) i) (9, 3)
   ii) (2, 7)
   iii) (4, 3)

2. a) i) Shops
   ii) Café
   iii) Church
   iv) Hotel
   v) Fire station
   b) i) (-7, 6)
   ii) (-7, 3)
   iii) (0, -2)
   iv) (0, -6)
   v) (5, 2)

3. a) $x = 3$
   b) $y = 5$
   c) $x = -6$
   d) $y = -3$

4. a) 17.5 centimetres
   b) 6 inches
   c) 2.5 centimetres
   d) 4 inches

5. a)

Weight of chicken (kg)	0.5	1.0	1.5	2.0
Cooking time (minutes)	50	80	110	140

b)

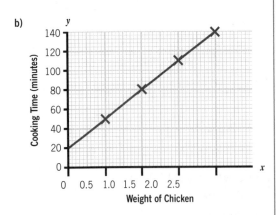

c) Approximately 96 minutes.

GRAPHS (Levels 5–6)

Page 132 – Quick Test

1. Read across first then upwards or downwards.

2. True

3. False, $y = 2x$ is steeper

4. b) (0,-4)

Page 133 – Skills Practice

1. a) i) $y = 3x$

x	-3	0	3
y	-9	0	9

(ii) $y = x - 5$

x	-2	0	2
y	-7	-5	-3

(iii) $y = 2x + 1$

x	-2	0	2
y	-3	1	5

b)

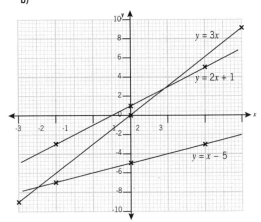

c) i) $y = 3x$
   ii) $y = x - 5$
   iii) (0,1)

GRAPHS (Levels 6–8)

Page 138 – Quick Test

1. False

2. True

3. True

4. d) (4, 13)

1. a) i) and ii)

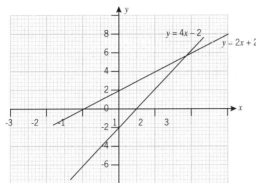

b) (2 , 6)
   c) 4

2. a) Gradient = 2
   b) (0 , 2)
   c) $y = 2x - 2$

3. a)

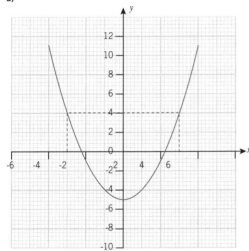

   b) $y = 0$
   c) $x = 3$ or $x = -3$

SHAPES (Levels 4–6)

Page 142 – Quick Test

1. Lines that meet at right angles to each other.

2. Two sides are equal in length and base angles are equal.

3. True

4. 12

5. 5

1. a)

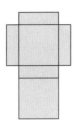

   b) Any suitable net, for example:

   c) 8

2. a)

   b) Any suitable net,
      for example:

3. a) Any suitable net,
      for example:

   b) 5 faces
   c) 8 edges
   d) 5 vertices

4. a) 1
   b) 3
   c) 1

5. a) Order 2
   b) Order 3
   c) Order 1

6. a) Parallelogram
   b) Kite

MEASURES AND MEASUREMENT (Levels 4–5)

Page 147 – Quick Test

1. True

2. D

3. True

4. False

5. B

6. C

Pages 148–149 – Skills Practice

1. a) Centimetres
   b) Kilometres
   c) Millimetres
   d) Grams
   e) Tonnes
   f) Grams

2. a) 6.2kg
   b) 720mm
   c) 61 000cm
   d) 5000kg
   e) 300cl
   f) 6200m
   g) 16 300g
   h) 72.5cm
   i) 9.6cl
   j) 5.2cm
   k) 8.6cl
   l) 3.6kg
   m) 0.525kg
   n) 1.06l
   o) 7.2km
   p) 6300g
   q) 0.56m
   r) 7200ml
   s) 2700g

3. 8 times

4. a) 1507cm
   b) 15.07m

5. 1m 62cm, 1m 640mm,
   3m 25cm, 562cm, 5700mm

6. Yes, it can all go in the lift at once (the total weight is 283kg).

7. a) 0720
   b) 1915
   c) 2036
   d) 1025

8. a) 9.16am
   b) 10.18pm
   c) 5.32pm
   d) 4.25am

9. a) 47 minutes
   b) 54 minutes
   c) 35 minutes
   d) 126 minutes
   e) 132 minutes
   f) 79 minutes
   g) 4 minutes
   h) 56 minutes

10. 8.25am

11. 105 minutes (or 1 hour 45 minutes).

12. 12.5 miles

13. 14.4 litres

SHAPES AND MEASURE
(Levels 5–6)

Page 154 – Quick Test

1. 6 faces

2. 9 edges

3. d) 7.7 pounds

4. True

Page 155 – Skills Practice

1. A – Diameter
   B – Radius
   C – Tangent
   D – Circumference
   E – Arc

2.

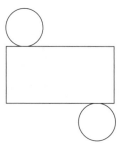

3. Triangle drawn accurately with lengths
   ±2mm

4. 550m

5. 30cm

SHAPES AND SOLIDS
(Levels 6–8)

Page 158 – Quick Test

1. True

2. (0, 3, 0)

3. False

4. True

Page 159 – Skills Practice

1.

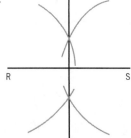

2.

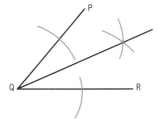

3.

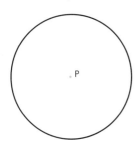

4. P (0, 2, 0)
Q (0, 1, 7)
R (4, 1, 7)
S (1, 2, 6)
T (0, 1, 6)

ANGLES (Level 5)

Page 163 – Quick Test

1. An angle greater than 180°.

2. True

3. 180°

4. 143°

5. 55°

Pages 164–165 – Skills Practice

1. a) i) Acute
     ii) 60°
   b) i) Reflex
     ii) 340°
   c) i) Obtuse
     ii) 140°
   d) i) Obtuse
     ii) 150°
   e) i) Right angle
     ii) 90°
   f) i) Acute
     ii) 65°

2. a) $a = 30°$
   b) $b = 36°$
   c) $c = 100°$

3. a) $a = 100°$
   b) $a = 155°$
   c) $a = 105°$
   d) $a = 120°$
   e) $a = 130°$, $b = 50°$, $c = 130°$
   f) $a = 56°$

4. a) $a = 60°$
   b) $a = 59°$
   c) $a = 38°$
   d) $a = 63°$
   e) $a = 70°$, $b = 55°$
   f) $a = 49°$
   g) $a = 122°$

5. a) $a = 124°$, $b = 55°$
   b) $a = 60°$, $b = 44°$
   c) $a = 82°$
   d) $a = 46°$
   e) $a = 78°$, $b = 85°$

6. Any question that gives an answer of 63°, for example: A triangle has one angle measuring 42°, another angle measuring 75°, what is the size of the third angle?

7. a)–b) Accurate diagrams constructed using the given measurements.
   Lengths should be drawn correctly to within ±1mm.
   Angles should be drawn correctly to within ±1°.

ANGLES (Levels 5–6)

Page 170 – Quick Test

1. 180°

2. False

3. True

4. 50°

5. c) pentagon

Page 171 – Skills Practice

1. a) $a = 75°$
   b) $b = 157°$
   c) $a = 63°$
      $b = 117°$
      $c = 63°$
   d) $a = 112°$
   e) $a = 52°$
   f) $a = 84°$
   g) $a = 59°$
   h) $a = 57°$
      $b = 54°$
      $c = 126°$

2. i) Interior = 135°
   ii) Exterior = 45°

3. a) 230°
   b) 050°

ANGLES AND COMPOUND MEASURES (Levels 6–8)

Page 175 – Quick Test

1. 47°

2. False

3. 175 miles

4. 72mph

Page 176–177 – Skills Practice

1. a) $a = 68°$
   $b = 68°$
   $c = 68°$
   $d = 112°$
   b) $a = 55°$
   $b = 75°$
   c) $a = 52°$
   $b = 76°$
   d) $a = 98°$
   e) $a = 89°$
   $b = 91°$
   $c = 91°$
   $d = 91°$
   f) $a = 113°$

2. Exterior angle = 45°
   Interior angle = 135°

3. 30°

4. a) i) 065°
   ii) 245°
   b) i) 135°
   ii) 315°
   c) i) 327°
   ii) 147°

5. a) i) 320°
   ii) 140°
   b) i) 143°
   ii) 323°
   c) i) 233°
   ii) 053°

6. 170km

7. $0.09\dot{3}\,kg/m^3$

8. 112.5km/h

9. 7.8g

PERIMETER, AREA AND VOLUME (Levels 4–6)

Page 181 – Quick Test

1. The distance around the outside edge of a shape.

2. A

3. C

4. False

5. D

Pages 182–183 – Skills Practice

1. a) 10cm
   b) 22cm
   c) 16cm

2. a) $6cm^2$
   b) $19cm^2$
   c) $11cm^2$

3. Any shape with a perimeter of 20cm, for example: An 8×2 rectangle.

4. Approximately $14cm^2$

5. a) $12cm^2$
   b) $36cm^2$
   c) $42cm^2$
   d) $100cm^2$
   e) $28cm^2$
   f) $82.96cm^2$

6. a) 156cm
   b) $1512cm^2$

7. a) $20cm^2$
   b) $27cm^2$
   c) $8.7cm^2$
   d) $42cm^2$
   e) $45cm^2$
   f) $12.24cm^2$

8. $8\,200m^2$

9. a) $24cm^3$
   b) $40cm^3$
   c) $40cm^3$
   d) $350cm^3$
   e) $288cm^3$

PERIMETER, AREA AND VOLUME (Levels 5–6)

Page 188 – Quick Test

1. True

2. 5cm

3. 2cm

4. 3cm

5. False

Page 189 – Skills Practice

1. a) $24.5cm^2$
   b) $64.26cm^2$
   c) $161.85cm^2$
   d) $205cm^2$
   e) $132.75cm^2$
   f) $631.2cm^2$

2. a) (i) 53.38cm
   (ii) $226.87cm^2$
   b) (i) 45.22cm
   (ii) $162.78cm^2$
   c) (i) 401.92cm
   (ii) $12861.44cm^2$

3. $245.31cm^2$

4. Volume = $992cm^3$
   Surface area = $667.2cm^2$

AREA AND VOLUME
(Levels 6–8)

Page 192 – Quick Test

1. True

2. 69.12cm (2 d.p.)

3. True

Page 193 – Skills Practice

1. 165cm^2

2. 7.96cm (2 d.p.)

3. a) 67.5cm^3
   b) 240cm^3
   c) 1592.79cm^3

4. a) 114cm^2
   b) 288cm^2
   c) 755.55cm^2

5. Volume = 150cm^3
   Surface Area = 218cm^2

6. a) 60 000cm^2
   b) 5 000 000cm^3
   c) 160 000cm^2
   d) 40 000mm^3

TRANSFORMATIONS (Level 6)

Page 196 – Quick Test

1. Translation, reflection, rotation and enlargement.

2. True

3. False

4. True

Page 197 – Skills Practice

1.

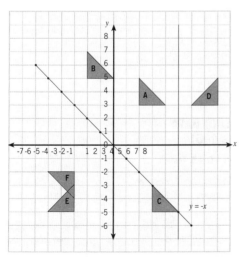

2.

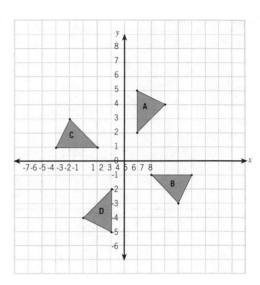

3.

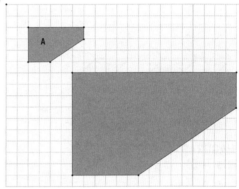

TRANSFORMATIONS
(Levels 6–8)

Page 200 – Quick Test

1. True

2. True

3. False

4.

Page 201 – Skills Practice

1. a) – d)

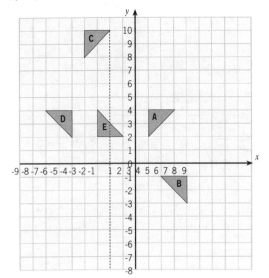

2.

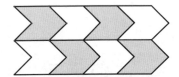

3. a) No – since all three lengths must be the same.
   b) Yes – since two angles and a side are equal.

PYTHAGORAS' THEOREM
(Levels 7–8)

Page 204 – Quick Test

1. True

2. It is always opposite the right angle.

3. d) 5 cm

4. True

Page 205 – Skills Practice

1. a) 8.1cm
   b) 19.2m
   c) 11.7m
   d) 37.5m
   e) 76.9m
   f) 55.2m
   g) 9.6m
   h) 31.3m

2. a) 14.7m
   b) 15.7m
   c) 34.4m
   d) 9.7m
   e) 24.4m
   f) 10.5m
   g) 6.5m
   h) 27cm

3. 15cm

4. 20.3cm

SIMILARITY
(Levels 6–8)

Page 207 – Skills Practice

1. a) 9.6cm
   b) 20.2cm
   c) 5.1cm
   d) 6.6cm
   e) 10.3cm

2. a) Similar
   b) Similar
   c) Not similar
   d) Similar
   e) Not similar

TRIGONOMETRY
(Levels 6–8)

Page 210 – Quick Test

1. b) Opposite

2. True

3. Sine

4. 6m

Page 211 – Skills Practice

1. a) 10.04m
   b) 17.79m
   c) 21.43m
   d) 18.54m
   e) 19.56m
   f) 7.8m

2. a) 36.9°
   b) 36.9°
   c) 37.7°
   d) 43.8°
   e) 41.8°
   f) 30.96° = 31.0° (3 s.f.)

3. 35.7m

4. 33.7°

HANDLING DATA
(Levels 4–6)

Page 215 – Quick Test

1. a) By questionnaire / survey.
   b) Primary
   c) Discrete
   d) A tally chart. The data is unlikely to cover a wide range of values, so this is a better choice than a frequency table
   e) Pictogram, bar chart or bar line graph.

2. A tally chart records each piece of data as an individual mark, while a frequency table records the total number of data items as a number.

3. **a)** The newsagent sells at least 250 cards every month, with large peaks in November, December and February. There are smaller peaks in March, April and June.

b) The peaks on the graph correspond to occasions when lots of people might buy cards – Valentine's Day in February and Christmas in November/December. There were also smaller rises in March, April and June, which could be due to Mother's Day, Easter and Father's Day.

Pages 216–217 – Skills Practice

1.

Type of Book	Tally	Frequency
Fiction		
Non-fiction		
Horror		
Autobiography		
Other		

2. The first two options overlap. Those who receive £1 could tick both boxes.

3. **a)**

Sport	Tally	Frequency
Swimming	卌 I	6
Squash	卌	5
Badminton	III	3
Yoga	卌 I	6

b)

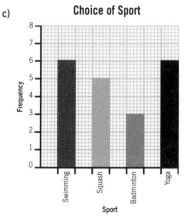

Key 🛉 = 1 person

c)

d) Swimming and yoga.

4. **a)** Coffee

b) 140

c) **Any suitable answer, for example:** The flavour of the soup might not have appealed to customers.

5. **a)** 10

b) 2

c) **Any suitable answer,**
for example: Most students might live close to school or the school might have a healthy lifestyle policy.

6. **a)** **Any suitable answer,**
for example: The weather was hot and sunny or the café might have only opened for half of the day.

b) **Any suitable answer,**
for example: The weather was cold or the café had more customers because more people go out on a weekend.

HANDLING DATA (Level 6)

Page 222 – Quick Test

1. False

2. How many hours per day do you watch television?

3. True

4. Positive, negative and zero

5. **a)** Zero correlation.

b) Positive correlation.

c) Positive correlation.

d) Negative correlation.

e) Positive correlation.

Page 223 – Skills Practice

1. What type of books do you read? Choose from this list:

Fiction ☐
Non-fiction ☐
Crime ☐
Other ☐

2. Angles: Vanilla 45°, Strawberry 120°, Chocolate 90°, Mint 105°

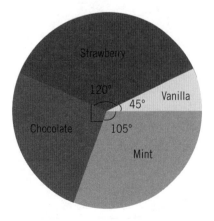

3.

	Walk	Car	Coach	Total
Boys	5	11	26	42
Girls	12	12	19	43
Total	17	23	45	85

Stem	Leaf
4. 2	5 5 6 7
3	2 7 8 9
4	1 1 6
5	8 8 9
6	2 5

Key 4|1 = 41 seconds

HANDLING DATA
(Levels 6–8)

Page 226 – Quick Test

1. True

2. Negative correlation

3. True

Page 227 – Skills Practice

1. Her results will be biased as most of the people she will ask will use the leisure centre. Her sample also needs to include people who may not use the leisure centre. Also, on a Tuesday morning she will bias her sample towards people who don't work.

2.

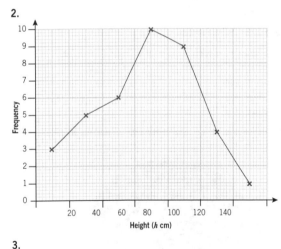

3.

AVERAGES
(Level 5)

Page 230 – Quick Test

1. The mode is the number that occurs most often.

2. False (the correct answer is 8).

3. B

4. C

5.

Mean	=	Sum of a set of values / The number of values in the set

6. True

Page 231 – Skills Practice

1. a) 6.2
   b) 7
   c) 7
   d) 6

2. a) 6
   b) 5.5
   c) 3
   d) 8

3. a) 5.06
   b) 4.75
   c) 4.7
   d) 6.7

4. 7K got the highest mean mark. There was also less spread in their data, so 7K did the best in general.
   7M, however, did have some students who scored higher than the highest scoring student in 7K.

5. Mean = 2.4 experiments (to 1 d.p.)

6. a) 1.25
   b) 1
   c) 3

AVERAGES
(Levels 5–6)

Page 234 – Quick Test

1. True

2. Highest value – lowest value

3. b) 10

Page 235 – Skills Practice

1. a) Mean = 5.25
   b) Median = 5
   c) Mode = 5
   d) Range = 8

2. The averages for Paulo:
   Mean: 1.429
   Mode: 2
   Median: 2
   Range: 3

The averages for Cesc:
Mean: 1.571
Mode: 1
Median: 1
Range: 2

Nigel should choose Cesc. Cesc's mean score is higher than Paulo's and his range is smaller, so he is more consistent.

3. a) Mode = 3 Merits
   b) Range = 5 Merits
   c) Mean = 3.42 (2 dp) Merits
   d) Median = 3 Merits

4. a) 3.5 seconds
   b) 30.9 seconds
   c) 31.4 seconds

AVERAGES (Levels 6–8)

Page 237 – Quick Test

1. a) 1.214

   b) False

   c) True

   d) False

Page 238–239 – Skills Practice

1. a) 1.3̇ minutes
   b) 0 minutes
   c) 0 minutes
   d) 6 minutes

2. a) 140.1cm
   b) $135 \leqslant h < 140$
   c) $135 \leqslant h < 140$

3. a) 52.67kg
   b) $50 \leqslant w < 60$
   c) $50 \leqslant w < 60$

4. a) $40 < t \leqslant 60$
   b) 42.3̇ minutes

CUMULATIVE FREQUENCY GRAPHS (Levels 7–8)

Page 242 – Quick Test

1. a) Class T
   b) 67 marks
   c) False
   d) False

Page 243 – Skills Practice

1. a)

Distance (d km)	Frequency	Cumulative Frequency
$0 \leqslant d < 5$	8	8
$5 \leqslant d < 10$	22	30
$10 \leqslant d < 15$	25	55
$15 \leqslant d < 20$	18	73
$20 \leqslant d < 25$	14	87
$25 \leqslant d < 30$	3	90

b)

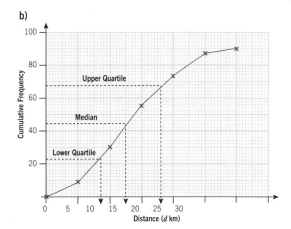

c) Approximately 12.5km
d) Approximately 9.6km
e)

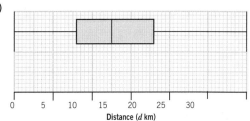

PROBABILITY (Level 5)

Page 246 – Quick Test

1. Probability is the chance that something will happen.

2. a) C
   b) A
   c) B

3. True

4. True

Page 247 – Skills Practice

1. a) Impossible
   b) Certain
   c) Impossible
   d) Possible

2.

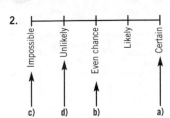

3. Any suitable outcomes, for example:
A – A person has five heads.
B – Winning the lottery jackpot.
C – Getting a head when a coin is thrown.
D – The Sun rises in the East.

4. a) Red, Yellow, Pink, Black, Blue, Green
b) Red, Pink, Blue, Green, Orange

5. a) $\frac{3}{9} = \frac{1}{3}$
b) 0
c) $\frac{4}{9}$

6. a) $\frac{2}{11}$
b) $\frac{4}{11}$
c) $\frac{1}{11}$
d) 0

PROBABILITY (Levels 5–6)

Page 250 – Quick Test

1. The likelihood that something will happen.

2. False

3. $\frac{2}{9}$

4. True

Page 251 – Skills Practice

1. a) $\frac{3}{9} = \frac{1}{3}$
b) $\frac{4}{9}$
c) $\frac{2}{9}$
d) 0

2. 77%

3. 0.9

4. $\frac{3}{5}$

5. Geography, History
Geography, German
Geography, ICT
French, History
French, German
French, ICT
Technology, History
Technology, German
Technology, ICT

6.

	Dice 2					
	1	2	3	4	5	6
1	2	3	4	5	6	7
2	3	4	5	6	7	8
3	4	5	6	7	8	9
4	5	6	**7**	**8**	**9**	**10**
5	6	**7**	**8**	**9**	**10**	**11**
6	**7**	**8**	**9**	**10**	**11**	**12**

(Dice 1 labels the rows)

a) $\frac{2}{36} = \frac{1}{18}$

b) $\frac{3}{36} = \frac{1}{6}$

c) $\frac{1}{36}$

d) 0

PROBABILITY (Levels 6–8)

Page 255 – Quick Test

1. c) 0

2. $\frac{5}{9}$

3. 250

4. False

Page 256–257 – Skills Practice

1. a) $\frac{6}{11}$
b) $\frac{2}{11}$
c) $\frac{8}{11}$
d) $\frac{9}{11}$

2. 0.85

3. 0.58

4. $\frac{1}{3}$ or $\frac{2}{6}$

5. 50 times

6. a) 0.3
b) 20

7. a)

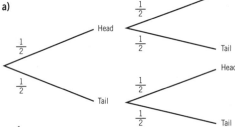

b) $\frac{1}{4}$
c) $\frac{1}{2}$

8. a) $\frac{25}{81}$
b) $\frac{40}{81}$

Notes

Notes

Index

ndex

ACKNOWLEDGEMENTS

p.15 ©iStockphoto.com
p.26 ©iStockphoto.com / Kim Freitas
p.26 ©iStockphoto.com / Kim Freitas
p.29 ©iStockphoto.com / Dawn Hudson
p.32 ©iStockphoto.com / Jolande Gerritsen
p.41 ©iStockphoto.com / Stephen Sweet
p.42 ©iStockphoto.com / Joshua Blake
p.43 ©iStockphoto.com / Aleksander Volodin
p.46 ©iStockphoto.com
p.60 ©iStockphoto.com / Kim Freitas
p.63 ©iStockphoto.com / Yulia Polishchuk
p.76 ©iStockphoto.com
p.89 ©iStockphoto.com / Justin Welzien
p.91 ©iStockphoto.com / Will Evans
p.92 ©iStockphoto.com / Kathy Kifer
p.99 ©iStockphoto.com / Jolande Gerritsen

p.140 ©iStockphoto.com / Christian Jaberg
p.144 ©iStockphoto.com / Mark Stay
p.146 ©iStockphoto.com / Stephen Sweet
p.146 ©iStockphoto.com / Russell Tate
p.149 ©iStockphoto.com
p.152 ©iStockphoto.com / Kim Freitas
p.154 ©iStockphoto.com / Mark Stay
p.160 ©iStockphoto.com
p.178 ©iStockphoto.com / Helle Bro Clemmensen
p.210 ©iStockphoto.com
p.217 ©iStockphoto.com / Lisa McDonald
p.236 ©iStockphoto.com / Kim Freitas
p.238 ©iStockphoto.com / Rodrigo Eustachio

All other images ©2009 Jupiterimages
Corporation, and Lonsdale.